Bring Science Alive!®
Weather and Climate

Co-Chief Executive Officer
Bert Bower

Co-Chief Executive Officer
Amy Larson

Chief Operating Officer
Ellen Hardy

Director of Product Development
Maria Favata

Strategic Product Manager
Nathan Wellborne

Managing Editor
Ariel Stein

Senior Science Editor
Rebecca Ou

Senior Strategic Editor
Kim Merlino

***Weather and Climate* Lead Editor**
Suzanne Lyons

Science Content Developers
Karin Akre
Tanya Dewey
Mantissa Johnston
Abigail Pillitteri
Clay Walton
Jennifer Yeh

Editors
Helene Engler
Sally Isaacs
Lauren Kent
Marlene Martzke
Tylar Pendgraft
Alex White
Ginger Wu

Writers
Sarah Martin
Linda Blumenthal
Sabre Duren
Rebecca Mikulec
Laura Prescott
Molly Wetterschneider

Illustrator/Graphic Artists
Andrew Dakhil
Martha Iserman
Aki Ruiz

Production and Design
Jodi Forrest
Jen Valenzuela
Michelle Vella

Web and Print Designer
Sarah Osentowski

Video Developer
Dominic Mercurio

Director of Operations
Marsha Ifurung

Investigation UX Testing
Davin Kunovsky

Software
Morris Thai
Christopher Ching
Robert Julius
Gabriel Redig

Software Quality Assurance
Mrudula Sarode

Art Direction
Julia Foug

Teachers' Curriculum Institute
PO Box 1327
Rancho Cordova, CA 95741

Customer Service: 800-497-6138
www.teachtci.com

ISBN 978-1-58371-076-0

1 2 3 4 5 6 7 8 9 10 -WC- 23 22 21 20 19 18

Manufactured by Webcrafters, Inc., Madison, WI
United States of America, March 2018, Job # 134706

Welcome to *Bring Science Alive!*

Welcome to *Bring Science Alive! Weather and Climate.* We've created this program to help you understand the science and engineering ideas in the Next Generation Science Standards (NGSS). As you begin the program, you will investigate weather patterns related to rainfall, temperature, and humidity. Identifying these patterns will help you understand climate, which is the average weather in a place over many years. Then you will use your newfound knowledge to make sense of the alarming, and often-times controversial, topic of climate change. This is a lot of science to learn, but we have many engaging investigations to inspire you.

You're going to have fun throughout this program. You'll build your own weather instruments to measure your local weather. You'll design a model, using balloons, syringes, and plastic tubes, that shows how differences in air pressure cause wind. You will visit eight locations on Earth to gather evidence of climate change and use that evidence to make predictions. And you'll use your engineering skills in the mythical land of "Weatherlandia" to develop plans for lessening the impact of a changing climate.

By the time you finish this program, you'll have a deep appreciation for what causes the weather. A sudden cold front, a blast of wind, or a heavy downpour will make more sense than ever before. And you'll be able to connect those events to the larger patterns of weather and climate around Earth.

Be prepared to become an avid weather watcher!

Bert Bower
TCI Co-CEO and Founder

How to Read the Table of Contents

The table of contents is your guide to *Bring Science Alive! Weather and Climate*. In addition to showing parts of your Student Text, it shows the exciting science and engineering investigations you will be doing in class.

Each unit has a fun and interesting phenomenon or problem that will give you a focus for learning.

The lesson title identifies the science topic.

An essential question prepares you for inquiry—and for using evidence to explain how the natural world works.

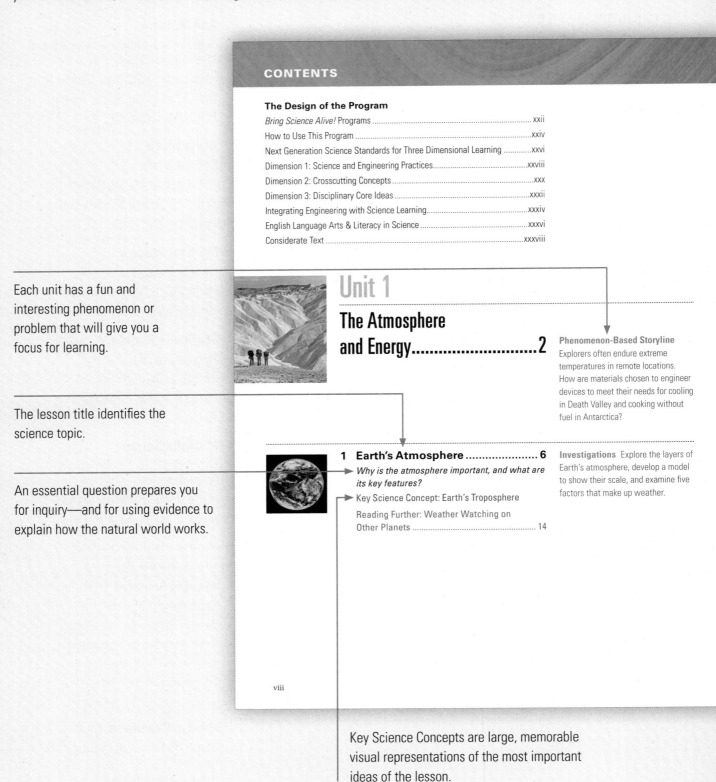

CONTENTS

Unit 1

The Atmosphere and Energy 2

Phenomenon-Based Storyline
Explorers often endure extreme temperatures in remote locations. How are materials chosen to engineer devices to meet their needs for cooling in Death Valley and cooking without fuel in Antarctica?

Investigations Explore the layers of Earth's atmosphere, develop a model to show their scale, and examine five factors that make up weather.

viii

Key Science Concepts are large, memorable visual representations of the most important ideas of the lesson.

Engineering Design will help prepare you for success in solving engineering-focused investigations. Look for the symbol with three circles to see how engineering design is integrated into the lesson.

Investigations integrate:

- science and engineering practices,
- crosscutting concepts,
- and disciplinary core ideas.

Engineering Challenge investigations invite you to apply science concepts and the engineering design process to solving relevant and engaging problems.

Reading Further features are fun, interesting articles that promote literacy and help you engage with the lesson content in more depth.

A Performance Assessment related to the unit's storyline inspires you to use science and engineering practices, crosscutting concepts, and disciplinary core ideas.

 Engineering Design will help prepare you for success in solving engineering-focused investigations. Look for this symbol to see how engineering design is integrated into the lesson.

CONTENTS

The Design of the Program

Unit 1

The Atmosphere and Energy..............2

Phenomenon-Based Storyline
Explorers often endure extreme temperatures in remote locations. How are materials chosen to engineer devices to meet their needs for cooling in Death Valley and cooking without fuel in Antarctica?

Why is the atmosphere important, and what are its key features?

Key Science Concept: Earth's Troposphere

Investigations Explore the layers of Earth's atmosphere, develop a model to show their scale, and examine five factors that make up weather.

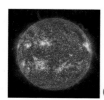
 Engineering Design will help prepare you for success in solving engineering-focused investigations. Look for this symbol to see how engineering design is integrated into the lesson.

Unit 2

Weather

Phenomenon-Based Storyline
People's lives and property are at risk when severe weather strikes. How can monitoring atmospheric conditions, improving forecasts, and issuing weather warnings save lives?

You cannot see it but you can feel it—what is wind, and what makes it blow?

Key Science Concept: Sea and Land Breezes

Engineering Design: Designing Hang Gliders to Ride the Wind

Investigations Use a model to describe how differences in air pressure cause wind. Build your own barometer and collect air pressure data.

How does water affect weather as it cycles through the Earth system?

Key Science Concept: Energy and the Water Cycle

Engineering Design: Cleaning Wastewater with Plants

Investigations Build and test a device for measuring humidity. Develop a model that shows the role of water in shaping the weather.

How do giant masses of air that move around the world change weather?

Key Science Concept: Relating Air Masses, Fronts, and Pressure Systems

Investigations Collect and analyze weather data to answer questions and make predictions about how interactions between air masses change the weather.

Investigations Explore the probabilities of different severe weather phenomena by analyzing and interpreting weather maps and weather data.

Performance Assessment
Develop an action plan for a severe weather event, including providing advanced warning, preparation plans, and mitigation of its effects.

Unit 3

Phenomenon-Based Storyline
A rise in average global temperature may result in major impacts to Earth. What specific problems can you identify that are associated with climate change?

Investigations Compare weather and climate, and develop and use a model to describe the uneven heating of Earth's surface.

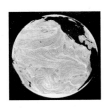

Investigations Use models to explore how global wind patterns are caused by the uneven heating of Earth's surface and Earth's rotation.

Investigations Develop and use models that describe the global circulation of ocean water and how it affects climate in different ways.

Investigations Use models to explain how local climates are determined by the ground surface, topography, vegetation, and urban structures.

Engineering Challenge Choose a microclimate to model, define the design problem, and then build and test your model to see how microclimates work.

Investigations Ask questions about, and explore the evidence for, changes in Earth's climate over its history. Then examine the evidence of recent climate change.

Investigations Identify and clarify the evidence for how a changing climate is causing rising sea levels and changes in ecosystems and weather patterns.

Performance Assessment
Work with a team to develop a device or an action plan designed to mitigate a specific problem associated with rapid climate change.

Key Science Concepts

Key Science Concepts are visually exciting infographics that synthesize, summarize, and explain with enhanced features in the online subscriptions.

Figures

Figures have been crafted with care by *Bring Science Alive!* scientific illustrators and are discussed in the text.

Primary Sources

Bring Science Alive! Programs

Bring Science Alive! is a collection of nine middle school science programs that are 100 percent aligned to NGSS. These programs can be organized into three year-long courses for either integrated-science or discipline-specific learning progressions. Programs are well coordinated to crosscutting concepts such as patterns, energy and matter, and structure and function. Science and engineering practices are integrated with disciplinary core ideas and crosscutting concepts in engaging and challenging investigations.

Weather and Climate

Investigate the atmosphere and energy transfer, the water cycle, air pressure and air masses, weather prediction, climate factors and patterns, and Earth's changing climate.

Planet Earth

Construct explanations about Earth's natural resources, the rock and water cycles, rock layers, fossils, geologic time, plate tectonics, and natural hazards using varied time scales.

Space

Model cause and effect relationships involving Earth's rotation, revolution, and tilted axis; lunar phases and eclipses, the solar system, galaxies, and the universe.

Bring Science Alive! integrates Science and Engineering Practices, Crosscutting Concepts, and Disciplinary Core Ideas to result in Three Dimensional Learning.

Cells and Genetics

Use evidence to explore traits, survival, and reproduction; the structure and functions of body systems and cells; genes and inheritance of traits, mutations, and engineering and genetics.

Ecosystems

Model interdependency in ecosystems, photosynthesis and cellular respiration, energy flow and cycling of matter, biodiversity, and explore the human impacts on ecosystems and biodiversity.

Adaptations

Identify cause and effect relationships between Earth's history and the fossil record, natural selection and changes in species, genes and patterns of inheritance; and humans, evolution, and heredity.

Matter

Apply the concepts of conservation of matter and energy transfer to model atoms, molecules, particle motion, state changes, and chemical reactions; and explore engineering solutions involving chemical reactions.

Forces and Energy

Solve engineering problems and plan investigations about forces, Newton's Laws of Motion; kinetic and potential energy; thermal energy, heat, and the thermal properties of matter.

Waves

Explore mechanical waves and their properties by looking at patterns in data, waves in different mediums, the wave model of light, properties of light waves, and technologies using waves to transfer information.

How to Use this Program

The components of *Bring Science Alive!* provide the tools needed for a complete learning system that integrates science and engineering practices, crosscutting concepts, and disciplinary core ideas. Designed for deep learning, *Bring Science Alive!* lessons use research-based learning strategies to reach all students.

1 Each new lesson begins with a **Lesson Guide** preview activity that teachers access through their online subscriptions. Lesson guides are the interactive guides at the heart of every TCI lesson.

2 Guided by the Lesson Guide and using the **Science Materials Kits** and their **Interactive Student Notebooks**, students conduct one or more investigations that powerfully integrate the three dimensions of NGSS. While investigating, students build understandings that they will need in order to complete the end-of-unit performance assessment.

4

The lesson concludes with students demonstrating their mastery of the science and engineering practices, crosscutting concepts, and disciplinary core ideas through a variety of paper and online **assessment tools**.

3

In their online student subscriptions, students expand their understanding by engaging with their dynamic **Student Text** and working through an **Interactive Tutorial**. Then they process what they have learned in their online **Interactive Student Notebook**.

Alternatively, students can read from the hardcover Student Edition and process their learning in a consumable Interactive Student Notebook.

Next Generation Science Standards for Three Dimensional Learning

The Next Generation Science Standards (NGSS) were written to change the way science is taught in K–12 classrooms and reflect recent advances in science, technology, and the understanding of how students learn. NGSS aims to help students prepare for college, 21st-century careers, scientific literacy needed as citizens, and competition in an increasingly global economy.

Performance Expectations

NGSS standards are called *performance expectations* and are worded to explain what students should be able to do in assessments at the completion of a unit of study. The performance expectations are built on the foundation provided by *A Framework for K-12 Science Education* (2012). Every performance expectation integrates the three dimensions described in the Framework: science and engineering practices, crosscutting concepts, and disciplinary core ideas. Also included in the performance expectations are clarification statements providing examples and other details, and assessment boundaries to guide test development. The graphic shows an example of how all the pieces result in a coherent standard to guide instruction.

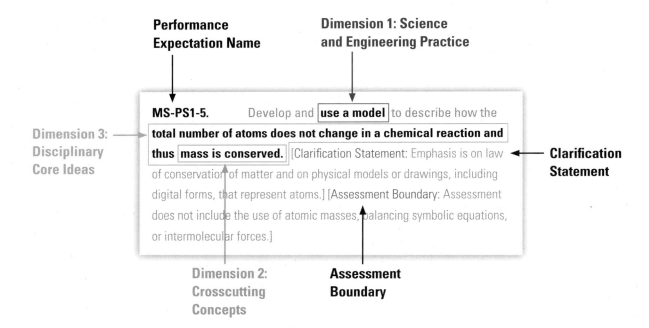

Performance Expectation Name

Dimension 1: Science and Engineering Practice

Dimension 3: Disciplinary Core Ideas

Clarification Statement

MS-PS1-5. Develop and use a model to describe how the total number of atoms does not change in a chemical reaction and thus mass is conserved. [Clarification Statement: Emphasis is on law of conservation of matter and on physical models or drawings, including digital forms, that represent atoms.] [Assessment Boundary: Assessment does not include the use of atomic masses, balancing symbolic equations, or intermolecular forces.]

Dimension 2: Crosscutting Concepts

Assessment Boundary

Dimension 1: Science and Engineering Practices

Science and Engineering Practices, such as developing and using models, describe what actual scientists and engineers do. Students develop the ability to use these practices through investigating the natural and designed worlds. While engaged in practices, students develop understandings described by the disciplinary core ideas and crosscutting concepts. The eight practices involve ways of thinking about investigations and engineering problems, the integration of mathematics, and social interactions. Without any particular order implied, these eight practices help define what has been called "scientific inquiry" and "engineering processes."

Bring Science Alive! investigations guide students to develop and reflect on their use of science and engineering practices.

Dimension 2: Crosscutting Concepts

Crosscutting Concepts, such as patterns and cause and effect, are the themes that organize students' understanding of science and engineering in the same way that scientists and engineers do. They can also be thought of as lenses all students should use as they explore and describe phenomena related to physical, earth and space, and life sciences. These "big picture" concepts are important in helping students make connections across all disciplines of science and engineering.

Each lesson focuses on a crosscutting concept that is explained in the lesson introduction and developed through the lesson.

Dimension 3: Disciplinary Core Ideas

Disciplinary Core Ideas are focused statements of content specific to the physical, earth and space, life sciences, or engineering. There are a limited number of core ideas, avoiding "mile wide, inch deep" curricula. The purpose of limiting the number of science concepts is to allow students the time they need for learning science and engineering practices through investigations. NGSS core ideas assume that students have mastered the content of previous grades and are ready for more advanced learning.

Students learn disciplinary core ideas by collecting evidence and building arguments through investigations, research, reading, and using multimedia tools.

Science and Engineering Practices | Dimension 1

The Next Generation Science Standards (NGSS) emphasize learning by investigating the natural world through the practices of scientific inquiry. Being able to use science understandings and practices allows students to investigate further questions about the natural world and solve meaningful engineering problems. NGSS identifies eight practices of science and engineering. Each lesson of *Bring Science Alive!* provides scaffolded instruction and reflection of one or more of these practices.

Asking Questions and Defining Problems

Science often begins by asking meaningful questions that can be answered by explanations supported by evidence. Similarly, engineering may begin with a question but always involves defining a problem that can be solved by carefully-tested solutions. Students learn to ask supporting questions that clarify and move them forward in investigations and solving engineering problems.

Developing and Using Models

Science and engineering use models to represent very large, very small, or very complicated systems. Using models helps scientists and engineers develop questions and explanations, gather data and make predictions, and communicate ideas to others. Students learn to develop, interpret, and modify models to describe scientific phenomena and test their engineering solutions.

Planning and Carrying Out Investigations

Scientific investigations are planned and carried out to describe a phenomena, test a hypothesis, or model how the world works. They are also used to test engineering solutions. Students design investigations that generate data for evidence to support their claims and learn how to be systematic in their methods so that they can obtain the most precise results.

Analyzing and Interpreting Data

All the data in the world is meaningless unless it can be presented in a form that reveals patterns and relationships and allows results to be communicated. Students analyze and interpret data by organizing their data into tables and graphs to identify overall trends and specific patterns.

Using Mathematics and Computational Thinking

Scientists and engineers use mathematics to represent physical variables and their relationships and to make quantitative descriptions and predictions. Students use mathematics aligned to the Common Core State Standards to analyze data for patterns and answer scientific questions. They also use mathematics to test and compare scientific arguments and engineering solutions.

Constructing Explanations and Designing Solutions

The goal of scientific inquiry is to construct explanations for why things happen. Likewise, the goal of engineering is to design solutions to people's problems. Students engage in constructing explanations when they make sense of the data they collect during investigations and when they propose solutions to engineering problems.

Engaging in Argument from Evidence

Argument is a process for comparing different explanations and solutions, and determining which is best. Reasoning and argument based on evidence are important for identifying the best explanation or the best solution to a design problem. Students engage in critical discussions to practice listening to, comparing, and evaluating competing explanations and solutions.

Obtaining, Evaluating, and Communicating Information

Researching, reading, interpreting, and producing scientific and technical text is an important part of science and engineering. Students learn to recognize key ideas, identify bias, distinguish observations from inferences, arguments from explanations, and claims from evidence. They communicate their findings orally, in writing, and through extended discussions.

The Next Generation Science Standards (NGSS) underscore the importance of making connections between the life, earth, physical sciences, and engineering. The seven crosscutting concepts are designed to do just this. While the seven overarching concepts are the same from kindergarten through twelfth grade, the details increase in complexity as students progress. *Bring Science Alive!* develops crosscutting concepts in conjunction with appropriate disciplinary core ideas and science and engineering practices throughout the Student Text, Lesson Guide activities and investigations, and assessments.

Patterns

Middle school students relate macroscopic patterns to microscopic structures, identify relationships that show patterns in rates of change, analyze numerical data on graphs and charts for patterns, and identify patterns that lead to understanding cause-and-effect relationships.

Cause and Effect

Through investigations and discussion, students come to appreciate that a phenomenon may have more than one cause, that the likelihood of certain types of outcomes must be expressed in terms of probability, and that by recognizing cause-and-effect relationships they can make predictions in science and engineering. They also discover how relationships can be causal or correlational but that not all correlational relationships are causal.

Scale, Proportion, and Quantity

Phenomena involving time, space, or energy can be observed at different scales. The function of a system may change, depending on the scale at which it is observed. Students learn that some natural systems are either too large

or too small to be directly observed, but they can explored using models of various scales. Mathematical reasoning becomes increasingly important to understanding and communicating scientific ideas as students learn that certain relationships can be represented as expressions or equations and that proportional relationships are useful for describing relationships between many scientific quantities.

Systems and System Models

The concept of a system as an organized group of parts is essential in all science disciplines and, certainly, for designing, building, and testing solutions to engineering problems. Throughout their investigations, students use the concept of systems to show how parts interact both within and outside a system, as well as how systems have sub-systems. Models are essential for understanding inputs and outputs and that energy and matter flow through many systems.

Energy and Matter

Energy and matter flow into, out of, and within both natural systems and designed systems. Students learn to track energy flow through both natural and designed systems. They use that understanding to describe the role energy plays in cycling of matter, and in describing the many forms energy takes as it is transferred from one part of a system to another.

Structure and Function

This crosscutting concept is closely related to systems and system models. Students learn to analyze the functions of all parts of a system by examining their shapes, properties, and their relationships to each other. Designing and building structures for particular functions also requires consideration of the parts' shapes and the materials from which they are made.

Stability and Change

Like structure and function, stability and change is a concept that directly supports the understanding of systems. Students' explanations of stability and change in systems include how changes to one part affect other parts of the system, how change can be gradual or sudden, and how equilibrium is maintained through feedback mechanisms.

Disciplinary Core Ideas | Dimension 3

The Next Generation Science Standards include a limited number of compelling scientific and engineering ideas to ensure that K–12 students learn and engage in the practices of science and engineering. Every *Bring Science Alive!* lesson allows students to build understanding of the disciplinary core ideas through the uses of these practices and the crosscutting concepts.

Core Idea ESS1: Earth's Place in the Universe

Planet Earth is part of a vast universe that has developed over a huge expanse of time and can be understood using observation, physics, and chemistry. Middle school students learn how gravitational forces hold the solar system together; explain patterns that result in lunar phases, eclipses, and seasons; and explore Earth's history by understanding rock strata and the fossil record.

Core Idea ESS2: Earth's Systems

Earth is made up of a set of dynamic systems whose interactions and processes determine how Earth changes over time. Students study the effects of energy flows and the cycling of matter in many of these systems, such as plate tectonics, the water cycle, weather systems, and changes due to weathering and erosion.

Core Idea ESS3: Earth and Human Activity

Humans depend on, are affected by, and cause changes to Earth's systems. Students learn how many natural resources are limited in quantity or distribution, the causes of natural hazards and likelihood that they will occur, and how humans impact the biosphere and can design solutions to lessen their impacts.

Core Idea LS1: From Molecules to Organisms: Structures and Processes

The functioning of all organisms is closely related to the structures that make them up, on scales ranging from individual molecules to whole body systems. Middle school students study structures such as cells, tissue, organs, and organ systems; and functions like behaviors, photosynthesis, cellular respiration, and sensory responses.

Core Idea LS2: Ecosystems: Interactions, Energy, and Dynamics

Ecosystems are dynamic systems in which organisms interact with one another and nonliving resources. They can be described by the flow of energy and cycling of matter. Students study patterns of interdependency; producers, consumers, and decomposers; and the effects of disruptions to ecosystems.

Core Idea LS3: Heredity: Inheritance and Variation of Traits

Heredity is the mechanism by which traits are passed via genes from parents to offspring. Middle school students learn that

genes control the production of proteins that affect traits, how sexual reproduction results in variation in inherited genetic information, and about the effects of mutations on traits.

Core Idea LS4: Biological Evolution: Unity and Diversity

Biological evolution explains both the similarities and differences among species and their history on Earth. Students learn how the fossil record and embryological development indicate that species are related, how natural and artificial selection result in changes to species over time, and how changes in biodiversity can affect humans.

Core Idea PS1: Matter and Its Interactions

The existence of atoms is fundamental to understanding the characteristics and behavior of matter. Middle school students apply the concepts of atoms and molecules to explain the existence of different substances, properties of matter, changes in state, and conservation of matter in chemical reactions.

Core Idea PS2: Motion and Stability: Forces and Interactions

Forces are a tool for describing the interactions between objects and for explaining and predicting the effects of those interactions. In middle school, students begin to quantitatively describe the effects of forces and learn to describe forces that act at a distance using fields.

Core Idea PS3: Energy

Energy is a tool for explaining and predicting interactions between objects. In middle school, students learn that systems often involve kinetic and potential energy. Energy concepts are extended to explain more complex interactions, such as those involved in chemical reactions, living things, and Earth systems.

Core Idea PS4: Waves and Their Applications in Technologies for Information Transfer

Waves are repeating patterns of motion that transfer energy from place to place without overall displacement of matter. Students use properties, such as wavelength, frequency, and amplitude, to understand the behaviors of wave-like phenomena, including light, sound, and water waves. Scientists and engineers also use wave properties to encode information as digitized signals for communication.

Core Idea ETS1: Engineering Design

Engineers solve problems using a design process involving specific practices and knowledge. Students in the middle grades learn the importance of defining criteria and constraints with precision, testing solutions, and using test results to improve solutions iteratively to achieve optimal designs.

Integrating Engineering with Science Learning

The Next Generation Science Standards describe engineering as a process similar to, and just as important as, scientific inquiry. The four engineering design performance expectations for middle school require students to understand how to define criteria and constraints, evaluate competing design solutions, analyze data to combine several designs, and develop models to test and refine proposed designs.

Student Text

In *Bring Science Alive!* student texts, engineering design is well integrated with the scientific core ideas of the lesson, including all the same support as other parts of the lesson: interactive tutorials, vocabulary development, and assessments.

Engineering design sections are identified by the symbol with three circles.

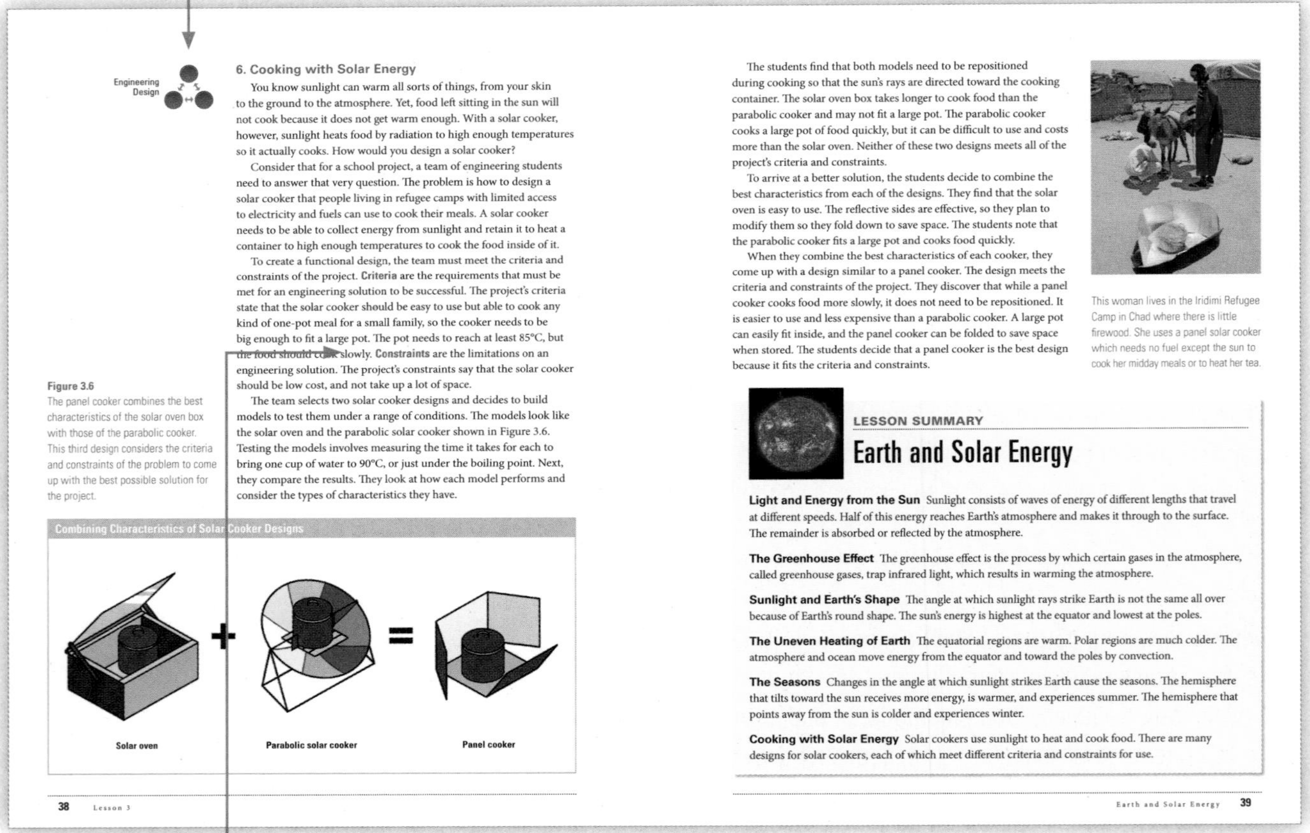

Engineering Design

6. Cooking with Solar Energy

You know sunlight can warm all sorts of things, from your skin to the ground to the atmosphere. Yet, food left sitting in the sun will not cook because it does not get warm enough. With a solar cooker, however, sunlight heats food by radiation to high enough temperatures so it actually cooks. How would you design a solar cooker?

Consider that for a school project, a team of engineering students need to answer that very question. The problem is how to design a solar cooker that people living in refugee camps with limited access to electricity and fuels can use to cook their meals. A solar cooker needs to be able to collect energy from sunlight and retain it to heat a container to high enough temperatures to cook the food inside of it.

To create a functional design, the team must meet the criteria and constraints of the project. **Criteria** are the requirements that must be met for an engineering solution to be successful. The project's criteria state that the solar cooker should be easy to use but able to cook any kind of one-pot meal for a small family, so the cooker needs to be big enough to fit a large pot. The pot needs to reach at least 85°C, but the food should cook slowly. **Constraints** are the limitations on an engineering solution. The project's constraints say that the solar cooker should be low cost, and not take up a lot of space.

The team selects two solar cooker designs and decides to build models to test them under a range of conditions. The models look like the solar oven and the parabolic solar cooker shown in Figure 3.6. Testing the models involves measuring the time it takes for each to bring one cup of water to 90°C, or just under the boiling point. Next, they compare the results. They look at how each model performs and consider the types of characteristics they have.

The students find that both models need to be repositioned during cooking so that the sun's rays are directed toward the cooking container. The solar oven box takes longer to cook food than the parabolic cooker and may not fit a large pot. The parabolic cooker cooks a large pot of food quickly, but it can be difficult to use and costs more than the solar oven. Neither of these two designs meets all of the project's criteria and constraints.

To arrive at a better solution, the students decide to combine the best characteristics from each of the designs. They find that the solar oven is easy to use. The reflective sides are effective, so they plan to modify them so they fold down to save space. The students note that the parabolic cooker fits a large pot and cooks food quickly.

When they combine the best characteristics of each cooker, they come up with a design similar to a panel cooker. The design meets the criteria and constraints of the project. They discover that while a panel cooker cooks food more slowly, it does not need to be repositioned. It is easier to use and less expensive than a parabolic cooker. A large pot can easily fit inside, and the panel cooker can be folded to save space when stored. The students decide that a panel cooker is the best design because it fits the criteria and constraints.

This woman lives in the Iridimi Refugee Camp in Chad where there is little firewood. She uses a panel solar cooker which needs no fuel except the sun to cook her midday meals or to heat her tea.

Figure 3.6
The panel cooker combines the best characteristics of the solar oven box with those of the parabolic cooker. This third design considers the criteria and constraints of the problem to come up with the best possible solution for the project.

Combining Characteristics of Solar Cooker Designs

Solar oven + Parabolic solar cooker = Panel cooker

LESSON SUMMARY
Earth and Solar Energy

Light and Energy from the Sun Sunlight consists of waves of energy of different lengths that travel at different speeds. Half of this energy reaches Earth's atmosphere and makes it through to the surface. The remainder is absorbed or reflected by the atmosphere.

The Greenhouse Effect The greenhouse effect is the process by which certain gases in the atmosphere, called greenhouse gases, trap infrared light, which results in warming the atmosphere.

Sunlight and Earth's Shape The angle at which sunlight rays strike Earth is not the same all over because of Earth's round shape. The sun's energy is highest at the equator and lowest at the poles.

The Uneven Heating of Earth The equatorial regions are warm. Polar regions are much colder. The atmosphere and ocean move energy from the equator and toward the poles by convection.

The Seasons Changes in the angle at which sunlight strikes Earth cause the seasons. The hemisphere that tilts toward the sun receives more energy, is warmer, and experiences summer. The hemisphere that points away from the sun is colder and experiences winter.

Cooking with Solar Energy Solar cookers use sunlight to heat and cook food. There are many designs for solar cookers, each of which meet different criteria and constraints for use.

Engineering vocabulary is developed in the same ways as science vocabulary.

Look for this Engineering Design symbol throughout *Bring Science Alive!*

Engineering Design

Investigations

In *Bring Science Alive!*'s engineering challenges, students use science and engineering practices to solve fun, interesting problems that have the potential to help answer scientific questions, improve lives, protect the environment, entertain, and delight.

The consistent engineering design process in *Bring Science Alive!*'s engineering challenges provides a clear road map for approaching design problems. Using it, students will decide when to define the problem, develop possible solutions, and optimize their designs.

Each engineering challenge focuses on one or two easy-to-learn engineering skills. By the time they complete the program, students will have a full set of tools for tackling any design problem.

English Language Arts & Literacy in Science

Bring Science Alive! is aligned with the Common Core State Standards for English Language Arts & Literacy (CCELA). Literacy instruction is built into the online Student Text, Interactive Student Notebook, and the Lesson Guides. The following six key points are from the grades 6–8 CCELA Standards for Literacy in History/Social Studies, Science, and Technical Subjects. They are particularly important in science instruction.

Reading Standards for Literacy

✓ **Main Ideas and Details**
Identifying key ideas and details applies to reading science text, following multistep procedures for experiments, and using scientific tools and other technology.

When using the *Bring Science Alive!* online text, students have the option to see the main idea of each section highlighted. Additionally, every lesson includes one or more multistep investigations that students must follow to carry out science experiments, analyze data, and solve engineering problems.

✓ **Craft and Structure** In the middle grades, mastering new vocabulary includes understanding the meaning of scientific and mathematical symbols as well as domain-specific terms, words, and phrases.

Learning of scientific symbols and mathematical representations is scaffolded in *Bring Science Alive!* First, the concept is presented in words and phrases. Next, symbols are shown alongside these words and phrases. Finally, the symbolic notation is shown on its own.

✓ **Integration of Knowledge and Ideas** Students should be able to integrate their learning on a topic using experiments, multimedia materials, and the text.

Each *Bring Science Alive!* lesson concludes with a processing task that requires students to demonstrate their understanding of science and engineering practices, crosscutting concepts, and disciplinary core ideas as a result of carrying out investigations, manipulating simulations, and reading the text.

Writing Standards for Literacy

✔ **Purposes for Writing** The writing standards stress the use of certain conventions of good writing, including the use of previews, supporting details, appropriate transitions, domain-specific vocabulary, and an objective tone.

Bring Science Alive! students write for different purposes, including to explain scientific concepts and to record investigation procedures and results so that others can replicate and test them. Students are asked to construct written arguments to persuade others to accept an engineering design solution. They also write accounts of their investigations using precise language, scientific vocabulary, and minimal bias.

✔ **Production and Distribution of Writing** Routine writing of clear and coherent content that is appropriate to its purpose is central throughout the writing standards.

Bring Science Alive! includes regular writing opportunities in the Lesson Guides and Interactive Student Notebook. Writing, peer review, and editing are essential tools in guiding students to develop arguments and explanations that result in three dimensional learning.

✔ **Research to Build and Present Knowledge** Short research projects, using a variety of print and digital sources appropriately, should be carried out to answer broad questions that generate more specific questions.

Students build research skills using print and digital sources, including the Internet. Unit problems require students to gather and assess relevant information and to integrate this information with what they learn during hands-on investigations.

Considerate Text

Literacy is fundamental for success in science. *Bring Science Alive!* is both engaging and helps students read text that is more complex and at a higher level than other text they read. That's because our writers wrote it as "considerate text," which is another way to say that it makes readers want to read it. Considerate text is well written and well-organized. Here are some ways this Student Text is considerate of all levels of readers.

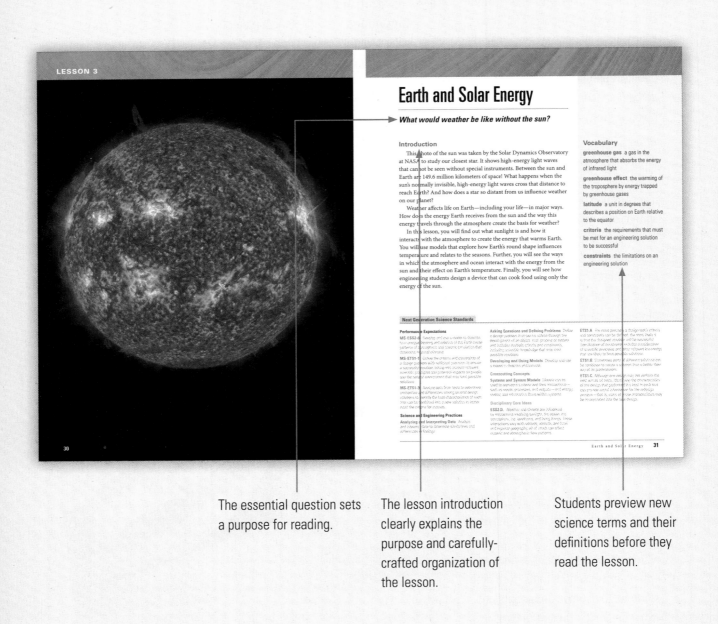

The essential question sets a purpose for reading.

The lesson introduction clearly explains the purpose and carefully-crafted organization of the lesson.

Students preview new science terms and their definitions before they read the lesson.

Short sections, each with an informative title, make it easier for readers to understand and remember the main ideas.

The paragraph that begins each section orients and engages the reader.

Scientific illustrations are carefully labeled and titled.

1. Light and Energy from the Sun

You have learned that the sun is the source of weather on Earth as its energy drives the Earth system. What would it be like if there was no sun? Would it be night all the time? What would temperatures be like for life on this planet without it?

You may guess that without sunlight, Earth would get cold very fast! However, only a small amount of sunlight reaches Earth's surface. Why is that? Of the portion of sunlight that reaches Earth's atmosphere, only about half reaches Earth's surface. The remainder of the energy is absorbed or reflected by the atmosphere. The few specific parts of the electromagnetic spectrum that make it through to Earth's surface are infrared and visible light and a very small amount of ultraviolet light, as seen in Figure 3.1.

Sunlight is made up of waves of energy of different lengths. Shorter wavelengths carry more energy than longer wavelengths. The waves of sunlight most important to weather are ultraviolet light, visible light, and infrared light because they comprise nearly all of the solar energy spectrum.

Ultraviolet light has more energy and a shorter wavelength than visible light. Although human eyes cannot detect ultraviolet (UV) light, the camera that took the photo of the sun you saw at the beginning of this lesson can. However, most UV light does not reach Earth's surface. The ozone layer, a layer of particles in the stratosphere, blocks much of the incoming UV light.

Visible light is the form of light you can see that permits you to view the world around you. Visible light has less energy than ultraviolet light and includes every color of the rainbow.

Infrared light has a longer wavelength and even less energy than visible light. It is another form of light you cannot see with your eyes, but when your skin absorbs infrared light, it feels warm. Some infrared light reaches Earth's surface, and some is absorbed by the atmosphere.

Figure 3.1
Sunlight carries energy from the sun to Earth. Sunlight is made of several kinds of light that carry different amounts of energy, including ultraviolet, visible, and infrared.

Three Components of Solar Energy

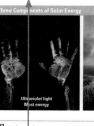
Ultraviolet light
Most energy

Visible light
Intermediate energy

Infrared light
Least energy

How the Greenhouse Effect Works

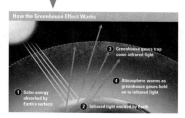
1 Solar energy absorbed by Earth's surface
2 Infrared light emitted by Earth
3 Greenhouse gases trap some infrared light
4 Atmosphere warms as greenhouse gases hold on to infrared light

Figure 3.2
Earth's surface is warmed by the visible light that it absorbs. Earth then gives off lower-energy infrared light, some of which is absorbed by greenhouse gases in the atmosphere. The absorbed infrared light warms up the atmosphere.

2. The Greenhouse Effect

Earth is sometimes called a "Goldilocks planet" because its temperature is not too hot, not too cold, but just right to support life. Is it the amount of sunlight that Earth receives that makes this planet so supportive of life? Or are there other features that produce its life-supporting temperature?

The amount of sunlight that Earth receives sets the stage for life, but there are other reasons that Earth's temperature is so hospitable to living things. After all, the planet Mars receives sunlight as well, but Mars is much colder than Earth. Besides the sunlight, it is the chemical composition—the kinds of gases—in Earth's atmosphere that sets this planet's temperature range.

Most of the sunlight that penetrates the atmosphere and actually reaches Earth's surface is in the form of visible light. In addition to all visible light, the atmosphere lets some UV and infrared light pass through and absorbs some of the infrared. Why does the atmosphere behave differently with different wavelengths of light? Look at the model in Figure 3.2. Once solar radiation reaches Earth's surface, it is absorbed by the land and ocean, warming them up. The warmed surface then emits infrared light, which has longer wavelengths and less energy compared to visible light and UV light.

Greenhouse gases are gases in the atmosphere that absorb the energy of infrared light. Carbon dioxide, methane, and water vapor are all greenhouse gases. They trap infrared light in the atmosphere. Thus, the energy carried by the infrared light away from Earth's surface largely remains in the atmosphere. As this energy is retained, atmospheric temperature increases. This is the greenhouse effect. The greenhouse effect is the warming of the atmosphere, specifically Earth's troposphere, by energy trapped by greenhouse gases. The greenhouse effect warms up the atmosphere, which in turn warms up the surface of Earth—its land and water.

The greenhouse effect is thought to be named after a gardener's greenhouse. In an actual greenhouse, warm air is simply contained by plastic or glass walls. However, the processes involved in the greenhouse effect are much more complicated.

Captions reinforce the main idea of the section and provide supporting details.

Important new science and engineering vocabulary is in bold type, defined in the same sentence, and used throughout the rest of the text.

Single-column text makes the lesson easier to read.

The Atmosphere and Energy

OVERVIEW

Death Valley, California, is a desert of extreme conditions. As these three adventurers get ready to cross it, what should they know about the weather there to prepare for their trek? In this unit, you will learn about thermal energy, the factors that make up weather, and the sun's input to the Earth system. You will model Earth's atmosphere and investigate how heat moves through substances. Then, you will apply what you have learned to explain how explorers in Antarctica and hikers crossing Death Valley deal with extreme weather conditions.

UNIT 1

Performance Expectations

MS-ESS2-6. Develop and use a model to describe how unequal heating and rotation of the Earth cause patterns of atmospheric and oceanic circulation that determine regional climates.

MS-PS3-3. Apply scientific principles to design, construct, and test a device that either minimizes or maximizes thermal energy transfer.

MS-PS3-4. Plan an investigation to determine the relationships among the energy transferred, the type of matter, the mass, and the change in the average kinetic energy of the particles as measured by the temperature of the sample.

MS-PS3-5. Construct, use, and present arguments to support the claim that when the kinetic energy of an object changes, energy is transferred to or from the object.

MS-ETS1-1. Define the criteria and constraints of a design problem with sufficient precision to ensure a successful solution, taking into account relevant scientific principles and potential impacts on people and the natural environment that may limit possible solutions.

MS-ETS1-3. Analyze data from tests to determine similarities and differences among several design solutions to identify the best characteristics of each that can be combined into a new solution to better meet the criteria for success.

Science and Engineering Practices

Asking Questions and Defining Problems Define a design problem that can be solved through the development of an object, tool, process or system and includes multiple criteria and constraints, including scientific knowledge that may limit possible solutions.

Developing and Using Models Develop and use a model to describe phenomena.

Planning and Carrying Out Investigations Plan an investigation individually and collaboratively, and in the design: identify independent and dependent variables and controls, what tools are needed to do the gathering, how measurements will be recorded, and how many data are needed to support a claim.

Analyzing and Interpreting Data Analyze and interpret data to determine similarities and differences in findings.

Constructing Explanations and Designing Solutions Apply scientific ideas or principles to design, construct, and test a design of an object, tool, process or system.

Engaging in Argument from Evidence Construct, use, and present oral and written arguments supported by empirical evidence and scientific reasoning to support or refute an explanation or a model for a phenomenon.

Connections to Nature of Science: Scientific Knowledge is Based on Empirical Evidence Science knowledge is based upon logical and conceptual connections between evidence and explanations.

Crosscutting Concepts

Scale, Proportion, and Quantity Proportional relationships (e.g., speed as the ratio of distance traveled to time taken) among different types of quantities provide information about the magnitude of properties and processes.

Systems and System Models Models can be used to represent systems and their interactions—such as inputs, processes, and outputs—and energy, matter, and information flows within systems.

Energy and Matter • Energy may take different forms (e.g., energy in fields, thermal energy, energy of motion). • The transfer of energy can be tracked as energy flows through a designed or natural system.

Disciplinary Core Ideas

ESS2.D: Weather and Climate Weather and climate are influenced by interactions involving sunlight, the ocean, the atmosphere, ice, landforms, and living things. These interactions vary with latitude, altitude, and local and regional geography, all of which can affect oceanic and atmospheric flow patterns.

PS3.A: Definition of Energy Temperature is a measure of the average kinetic energy of particles of matter. The relationship between the temperature and the total energy of a system depends on the types, states, and amounts of matter present.

PS3.B: Conservation of Energy and Energy Transfer • When the motion energy of an object changes, there is inevitably some other change in energy at the same time. • The amount of energy transfer needed to change the temperature of a matter sample by a given amount depends on the nature of the matter, the size of the sample, and the environment. • Energy is spontaneously transferred out of hotter regions or objects and into colder ones.

ETS1.A: Defining and Delimiting Engineering Problems The more precisely a design task's criteria and constraints can be defined, the more likely it is that the designed solution will be successful. Specification of constraints includes consideration of scientific principles and other relevant knowledge that are likely to limit possible solutions.

ETS1.B: Developing Possible Solutions Sometimes parts of different solutions can be combined to create a solution that is better than any of its predecessors.

ETS1.C: Optimizing the Design Solution Although one design may not perform the best across all tests, identifying the characteristics of the design that performed the best in each test can provide useful information for the redesign process—that is, some of those characteristics may be incorporated into the new design.

Connect Your Learning

Today may be hot and sunny. Tomorrow may be rainy and cold. It may be clear where you are, yet foggy less than a mile away. What kind of weather are you prepared for? As you consider weather phenomena and their impacts on almost every aspect of your daily life, you will learn that the key to understanding weather is the idea of energy transfer.

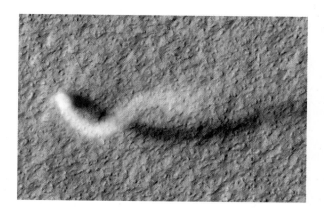

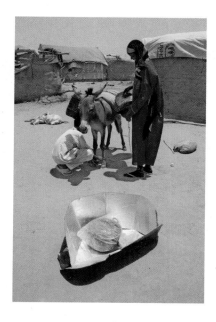

The Atmosphere and Energy

A large whirling column of dust rises from the surface—of Mars! Earth is not the only planet that experiences weather. What is weather like on other planets? How much different from Earth could it be?

Using no fuel, a solar cooker heats dinner for a family. The sun's energy powers Earth's major systems and can be channeled into applications that humans use daily. In what ways do you rely on the sun?

A heavy snowfall challenges pedestrians as they walk. Precipitation, air temperature, and wind are likely on their minds. What other elements of weather also affect you every day?

Earth's Atmosphere

Why is the atmosphere important, and what are its key features?

Introduction

When you look at Earth from space, what features do you see? What do you notice about the blue ocean, the brown land surface, and the green plants? What about the white clouds floating above the water and land? Surrounding the clouds there seems to be nothing at all. After all, you can see through the spaces between the clouds at Earth's surface. If it is not empty space, what is it?

Clouds are part of a layer of Earth as important as the solid land and liquid water. Earth's atmosphere is like a blanket surrounding our planet that is mostly made of invisible gases, tiny solid particles, and liquid droplets too. Although much of it is invisible from space except where clouds are located, the atmosphere is important because it contains the gases that living things need to survive and because it is where weather occurs. What weather might be occurring under those clouds, and how might that weather change?

Earth is a system, with all of its parts affecting one another. Changes to the ocean, to the land, and even among living things can all affect the atmosphere and the weather. The atmosphere, and therefore the weather, is dynamic and complex because of Earth's many interacting parts. Models can be used to represent systems such as these to understand their complex interactions.

This lesson is about the Earth system, especially the atmosphere. You will begin with a look at how the major parts of this system work together by viewing a model. Then, you will focus on the atmosphere and learn about the basic elements of weather.

Vocabulary

system a group of interacting parts, with each piece influencing the behavior of the whole

biosphere the parts of Earth in which organisms are able to live, along with all of Earth's living things

geosphere all of the rock, sand, and soil on Earth including at Earth's surface and deep underground

hydrosphere all of the water on Earth including ice, liquid water in the ocean, rivers, and lakes, and water vapor

atmosphere the envelope of air that surrounds the solid Earth, including gases and aerosols

weather the condition of the atmosphere and its phenomena in a certain place at a specific time

aerosol tiny liquid and solid particles suspended in the atmosphere

troposphere the relatively thin layer of the atmosphere that is closest to Earth's surface and the layer where weather occurs

stratosphere the layer of the atmosphere above the troposphere

Next Generation Science Standards

Performance Expectations
MS-ESS2-6. Develop and use a model to describe how unequal heating and rotation of the Earth cause patterns of atmospheric and oceanic circulation that determine regional climates.

Science and Engineering Practices
Developing and Using Models Develop and use a model to describe phenomena.

Crosscutting Concepts
Systems and System Models Models can be used to represent systems and their interactions—such as inputs, processes, and outputs—and energy, matter, and information flows within systems.

Disciplinary Core Ideas
ESS2.D. Weather and Climate Weather and climate are influenced by interactions involving sunlight, the ocean, the atmosphere, ice, landforms, and living things. These interactions vary with latitude, altitude, and local and regional geography, all of which can affect oceanic and atmospheric flow patterns.

1. Weather in the Earth System

Your city or town is made up of many parts that work together—buildings, vehicles, and people, to name a few. Although each part has its function, it does not make a city on its own. Like a city, planet Earth has many parts. What are the parts that work together to make Earth?

Earth is an example of a system. A **system** is a group of interacting parts, with each piece influencing the behavior of the whole. Systems come in many sizes and forms, such as the solar system, the city you live in, and even your body. Earth is a large and complex system with many elements, parts, and processes going on within it, from the tiniest human cell to the tallest mountain peak.

A system model is a simplified representation of a system. Scientists model the Earth system by dividing it into four parts—the land, water, living things, and air, or the *spheres* shown in Figure 1.1. Scientists use the Earth system model to explain the complex processes and relationships within and between each sphere. For example, they can use the model to determine how a volcanic eruption affects weather by showing interactions between the spheres.

The spheres of the Earth system are called the *biosphere, geosphere, hydrosphere,* and *atmosphere*. Earth's **biosphere** is the parts of Earth in which organisms are able to live, along with all of Earth's living things. You are part of the biosphere as are trees in the rainforest, squid in the ocean, and termites underground.

Figure 1.1

The biosphere, atmosphere, geosphere, and hydrosphere work together to make up the Earth system. Plants and animals are part of the biosphere, air is part of the atmosphere, rocks and soil are part of the geosphere, and water in clouds and the ocean are part of the hydrosphere.

Earth's Spheres Interact

Biosphere

Atmosphere

The Earth System

Geosphere

Hydrosphere

Hydrosphere

The sun supplies energy to power the Earth system

Atmosphere

Biosphere

Geosphere

Weather in the atmosphere, living things in the biosphere, landforms in the geosphere, and water on Earth in the hydrosphere are constantly interacting. Energy from the sun provides much of the energy needed for these interactions.

The dirt under your shoes and the peaks of mountains are part of the same sphere. Earth's **geosphere** is all of the rock, sand, and soil on Earth including at Earth's surface and deep underground.

The **hydrosphere** is all of the water on Earth including ice, liquid water in the ocean, rivers, and lakes, and water vapor. Both liquid water and ice are present in clouds and underground. Water vapor, or water in the gas state, is present in air.

Most important to weather is the atmosphere, as seen in the photo of Earth at the beginning of this lesson. The **atmosphere** is the envelope of air that surrounds the solid Earth and includes gases and aerosols. It is made up of a layer of mixed invisible gases, tiny solid particles such as ash, and water droplets. The condition of the atmosphere and its phenomena in a certain place at a specific time is called **weather**.

Earth's spheres interact with one another just as the parts of any system do, and weather shows these interactions. Even though weather happens in the atmosphere, it affects the geosphere, biosphere, and hydrosphere. Likewise, what happens in those spheres affects the atmosphere and weather. What are some of the interactions between Earth's spheres that you notice?

All changes and interactions among Earth's spheres need energy to happen, and almost all of this energy comes from the sun. Without the sun, there would be no weather at all. The sun's enormous energy is a primary input, and how this energy is distributed across the planet is the ultimate source of weather.

Weather is the condition of the atmosphere and its observed phenomena at a certain place and time. One day it may be clear and windy enough to fly a kite, while the next day may be cloudy with almost no wind at all.

This photo of Earth, its atmosphere, and the moon was taken from the International Space Station. The atmosphere is mostly made up of a mixture of gases. It appears as a bright blue line in the photo because of the way sunlight interacts with these gases. While the atmosphere is enormous, Earth is even bigger.

2. The Composition of Earth's Atmosphere

You look out your window on a summer morning, and you see a clear sky. Then—*ACHOO!*—something solid in the air makes you sneeze. Which materials in the atmosphere might cause this to happen? How do they affect the properties of the atmosphere?

The atmosphere is a mixture of many substances, nearly all of which are invisible and have no odor, including oxygen and nitrogen gas. Air consists primarily of nitrogen (about 78 percent) and oxygen (about 21 percent), which means nitrogen and oxygen make up 99 percent of the "air" or atmosphere. The remaining gases in the atmosphere include much smaller amounts of argon, carbon dioxide, and other pollutants. Air also has a small percentage of water vapor, which varies quite a lot.

Besides gases, the atmosphere contains aerosols. **Aerosols** are very tiny solid and liquid particles of matter suspended in the atmosphere. Aerosols include ash and soot, dust, sea salt, and pollen. You may not be able to see the individual particles, but the sky can look hazy or smoky like the sky in the photo if there are enough particles in the air. Both natural processes and human activity put aerosols into the atmosphere.

The atmosphere's aerosols come from the geosphere, biosphere, and hydrosphere. For example, pollen that is given off by plants will enter the atmosphere and may make you sneeze. This is an example of materials flowing from the biosphere into the atmosphere. Ash is added to the atmosphere by the geosphere when volcanoes erupt.

The biosphere is the source of much of the oxygen gas in the atmosphere. Animals, including people, must breathe in oxygen and exhale carbon dioxide in order to live. Most of this vital oxygen is given off by plants and certain other organisms that perform photo-synthesis. Photosynthesis is the process by which organisms use the sun's energy to turn carbon dioxide and water into food they can use. Photosynthesis produces oxygen as a byproduct, thus adding oxygen to the atmosphere that animals need to live.

The atmosphere contains tiny solid and liquid particles called aerosols. On a clear day, there are fewer aerosols in the air. When there are more aerosols present, the air looks hazy. Both photos are of Seoul, South Korea.

3. The Structure of Earth's Atmosphere

Up in the night sky, a "shooting star," or *meteor*, may burn up as it passes through the atmosphere. How does the atmosphere differ between where a shooting star burns and where you stand?

The properties of the atmosphere differ in three main ways, depending on altitude. As it extends upward, its composition, the distance between its particles, and its temperature all change. These characteristics are used to divide it into layers, as shown in Figure 1.3.

The layer of the atmosphere that is closest to Earth's surface and the layer where weather occurs is called the **troposphere**. The troposphere is where people live as well. It is the thinnest of the atmospheric layers at about 10 km (6.2 mi) and can vary in thickness from 6–20 km (3.7–12.4 mi).

The layer of the atmosphere above the troposphere is called the **stratosphere**. The stratosphere has very little water vapor, but it has more ozone than any other layer. Ozone is a gas that absorbs certain harmful high-energy waves given off by the sun.

The mesosphere is the layer above the stratosphere. It is the coldest layer of the atmosphere, with a high temperature of only about –15°C (5°F). Although the particles of air in the mesosphere are farther apart than in the stratosphere, they are close enough to make meteors burn and leave blazing trails.

The thermosphere is the layer above the mesosphere and has relatively few air particles, which are very far apart but are very energetic. The temperature near the top of this layer is extremely hot—up to 2,000°C (3,632°F)! Satellites and the International Space Station orbit in the thermosphere.

The exosphere is the very top layer of the atmosphere that blends gradually into space and does not have a clear outer edge. The particles of air in the exosphere are extremely far apart.

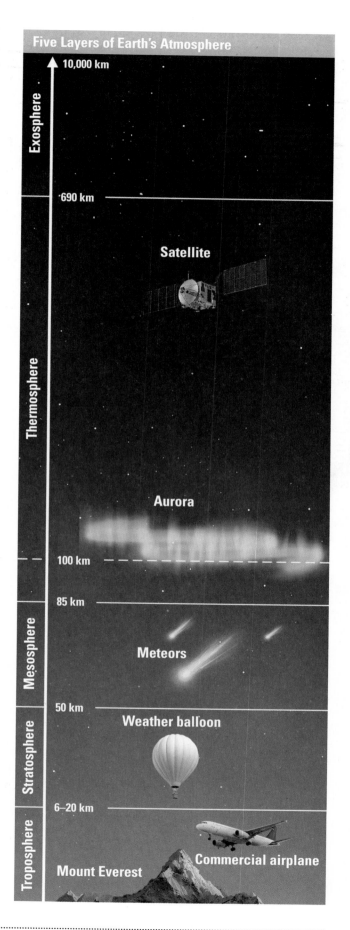

Five Layers of Earth's Atmosphere

10,000 km

Exosphere

690 km

Satellite

Thermosphere

Aurora

100 km

85 km

Mesosphere

Meteors

50 km

Stratosphere

Weather balloon

6–20 km

Troposphere

Mount Everest

Commercial airplane

Figure 1.3

Earth's atmosphere is often divided into five layers, with each layer having different characteristics. The troposphere is the thin bottom layer where humans live and weather occurs.

Earth's Troposphere

The troposphere is the thinnest layer of the atmosphere, yet it is very important to life. It is the layer that is closest to Earth's surface, so it interacts directly with the biosphere, geosphere, and hydrosphere. The troposphere is where people live and weather occurs. In the illustration, the layers are not to scale. In what ways do changes in the biosphere, geosphere, and hydrosphere affect the troposphere?

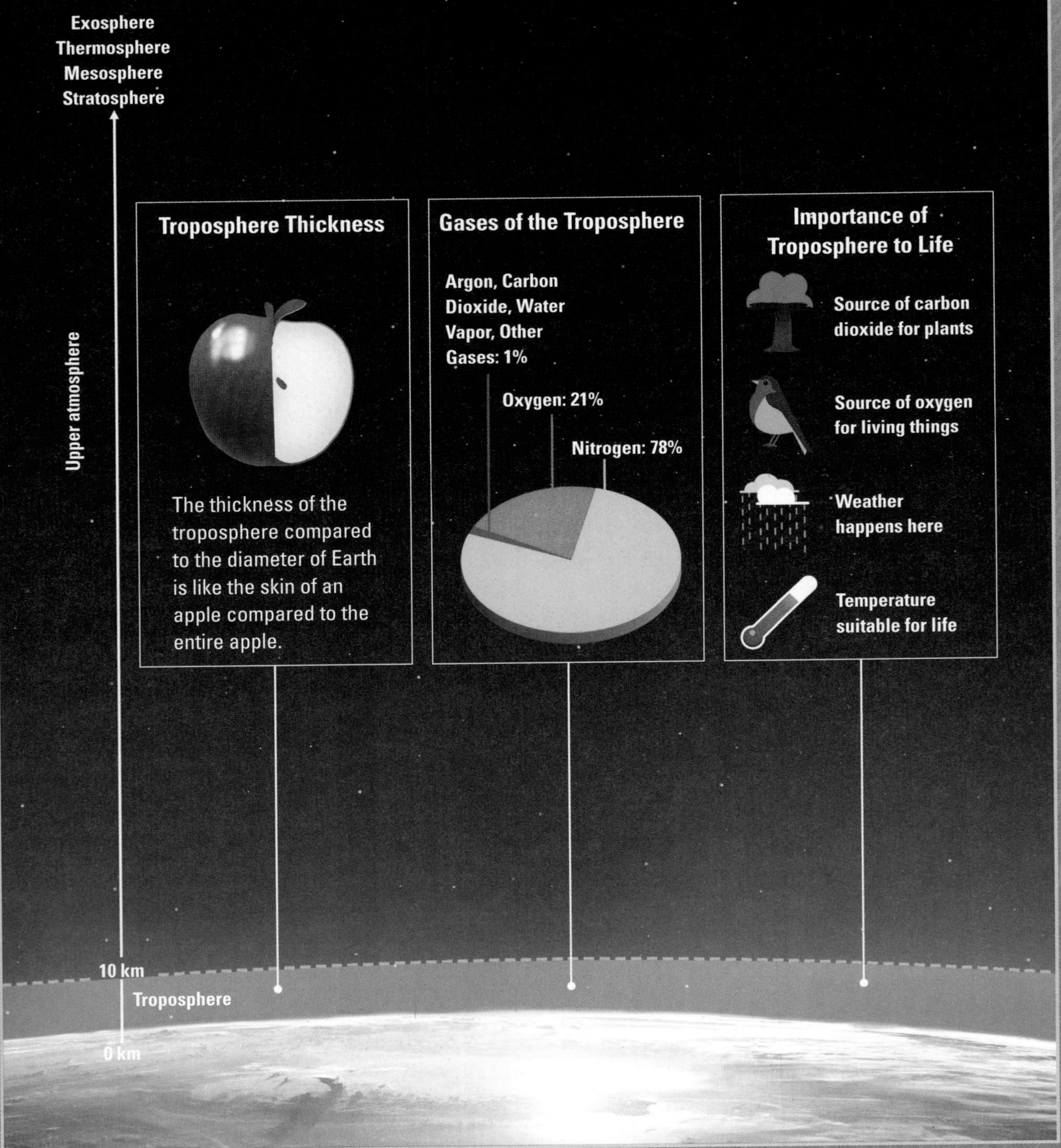

Exosphere
Thermosphere
Mesosphere
Stratosphere

Upper atmosphere

Troposphere Thickness

The thickness of the troposphere compared to the diameter of Earth is like the skin of an apple compared to the entire apple.

Gases of the Troposphere

Argon, Carbon Dioxide, Water Vapor, Other Gases: 1%

Oxygen: 21%

Nitrogen: 78%

Importance of Troposphere to Life

Source of carbon dioxide for plants

Source of oxygen for living things

Weather happens here

Temperature suitable for life

10 km

Troposphere

0 km

4. Elements of Weather

When you are getting ready for school, the state of the troposphere may determine if you need to bring a jacket. The weather around you happens in the troposphere. What conditions make up the weather?

You might say the weather is awful if a thunderstorm prevents you from playing a soccer game. People may describe the weather in many ways—windy, cloudy, sunny, clear, hot, mild, or muggy. However, scientists use measurable quantities to describe the weather. Scientists who study the conditions and phenomena in the atmosphere and predict weather are called meteorologists. The elements of weather they measure include air temperature, air pressure, wind, precipitation, and atmospheric humidity. For example, when it is raining or snowing, rain and snow are forms of precipitation. Or if you say it feels muggy outside, it is humidity that makes the air feel this way. Other elements scientists measure are important as well, including solar energy, cloud type, and cloud cover.

Weather is related to but different from climate. Weather is the state of the atmosphere at a given time and place, while climate is often defined as weather patterns in a region over a long period of time. Weather is what you dress for today, not what you expect it to be like next spring. Even if you do not enjoy the weather today, it could change tomorrow.

Brrr! These people are bundled up to face the cold, windy, and snowy weather. Air temperature, air pressure, wind, humidity, and precipitation, such as snow, are all elements scientists use to describe weather.

LESSON SUMMARY

Earth's Atmosphere

Weather in the Earth System The biosphere, geosphere, hydrosphere, and atmosphere work together to make the whole Earth system. The layer of gases and other materials that surrounds Earth is the atmosphere. Weather occurs in the atmosphere.

The Composition of Earth's Atmosphere The atmosphere is mainly a mixture of nitrogen, oxygen, and other gases. It also contains tiny solid and liquid particles that are suspended in air called aerosols.

The Structure of Earth's Atmosphere Earth's atmosphere is divided into five different layers based on composition and changes in temperature. From the ground up, the layers are the troposphere, stratosphere, mesosphere, thermosphere, and exosphere. Weather occurs in the troposphere.

Elements of Weather Meteorologists study the conditions and phenomena in the atmosphere and predict weather. The elements of weather they measure include air temperature, air pressure, wind, atmospheric humidity, precipitation, solar energy, cloud type, and cloud cover.

Weather Watching on Other Planets

Savvy travelers know to check the weather of their destination before packing for a trip. No one would want to be caught in only shorts and a T-shirt in freezing weather! If you were an astronaut traveling to another planet, what kind of weather would you prepare for?

Very Hot Venus

To have weather, a planet must have an atmosphere. Mercury doesn't have an atmosphere and consequently doesn't have any weather. Venus, however, does have an atmosphere that is thick and dense with clouds of sulfuric acid, and so it experiences very extreme weather.

The clouds on Venus act like a blanket, trapping energy and causing temperatures to reach as high as 471°C! If you could venture to Venus, and if you weren't crushed first by the weight of its atmosphere, you would need a very insulated spacesuit to protect you from the heat.

Venus's atmosphere traps energy and creates fiery temperatures. An artist drew what the weather might look like on this hot planet. In this drawing, lightning flashes out from thick, yellow, sulfuric acid clouds.

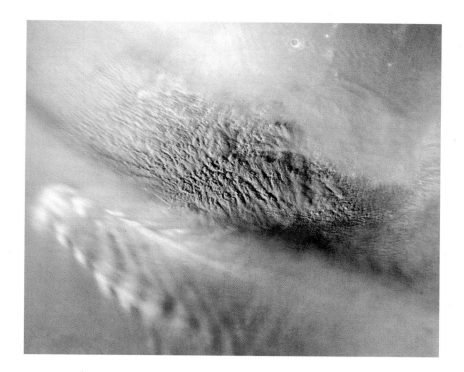

Mars has dust storms that can cover areas as large as a continent. The hazy areas of this photo are parts of a large dust storm as viewed by a spacecraft orbiting the planet.

Massive Martian Storms

You would not have to worry about a crushing atmosphere if you traveled to Mars because Mars has a very thin atmosphere. The atmosphere is so thin that its weight on Mars is less than one percent of the weight of Earth's atmosphere at sea level.

However, because Mars's atmosphere is so thin, it cannot hold energy as well as Earth's atmosphere. So, Mars's average temperature (−63°C) is much lower than Earth's average temperature (14°C). But like Earth, Mars has seasons and temperature variations. Mars's poles can be as cold as −125°C in the winter, and its equator can be as hot as 20°C in the summer.

The temperature differences on Mars cause wind, which can reach speeds of around 96 to 100 km/h, or about the speed of cars on a highway. The Martian winds regularly whip up dust from the planet's dry surface that forms dust devils reaching almost 800 m in the air. Also, several times a year, dust storms lasting for weeks cover areas as big as some continents. On rare occasions, Mars has massive dust storms that circle the entire planet.

These storms cause problems for rovers, which are remotely controlled, solar-powered research vehicles sent from Earth to explore Mars. The storms block sunlight from reaching the rovers' solar panels. The rovers depend on solar energy to run. If astronauts did go to Mars, they, too, would rely on solar energy. And if a dust storm hit while they were on the planet, they would need to have another source of energy.

A dust devil is a swirling column of air that kicks dust high into the air. This dust devil on Mars is about 800 m tall and 30 m wide.

Jupiter's atmosphere is colorful thanks to clouds, storms, and auroras. In this photo, the Great Red Spot, which is twice as wide as Earth, is in the lower right. The bright blue streaks around the planet's north pole are auroras.

Jupiter's Gigantic Weather

The four planets farthest from the sun (Jupiter, Saturn, Uranus, and Neptune) all have weather because they all have atmospheres. In fact, these planets are gas planets, which means that they are mostly made of gases and do not have a solid surface like Earth or Mars.

Jupiter is the largest gas giant (and the largest planet) in the solar system. It is so large that all the other planets in the solar system could fit inside it. Jupiter's giant size comes with giant-sized weather. Large storms swirl and can be seen moving across its colorful, cloud-covered atmosphere. Jupiter's largest and most famous storm even has a name: the Great Red Spot.

The Great Red Spot has been storming for more than 100 years—and possibly for more than 300 years! It is so large that it is twice as wide as our entire planet. Winds inside the Spot reach speeds of a little over 640 km/h, which is twice the wind speed of the most powerful hurricanes on Earth.

Jupiter also has huge, never-ending auroras that appear near its poles and are much more energetic than the ones found on Earth. Auroras are light shows produced when high-energy particles collide with gas particles, in a planet's atmosphere. The charged particles strike the gas particles, causing them to give off light. Jupiter is not the only planet that has auroras. Earth and other planets have them, too.

Solar Storm Effect on Planets

Auroras are the result of a different kind of weather—solar storms. Solar storms originate from the sun, but they are not like storms on Earth or any other planet. Storms on planets result from moving air masses in the atmosphere and stay in a planet's atmosphere. Solar storms, on the other hand, are a result of magnetic field activity within the sun's atmosphere, and some solar storms even leave the sun's atmosphere.

The two main types of solar storms are solar flares and coronal mass ejections (CMEs). Solar flares are bright flashes of electromagnetic radiation that reach the topmost layer of the sun's atmosphere. CMEs are bubbles of hot, charged particles that break off from the sun's atmosphere and travel at high speeds away from it. CMEs can reach Earth in about three to four days. Powerful CMEs can damage electrical power grids and disrupt the electrical systems of satellites, including those used for GPS and television.

CMEs are one source of charged particles that cause auroras on Earth, Jupiter, and other planets. On Earth, auroras are usually seen close to the poles. So, you don't have to be an astronaut and leave the planet to experience the effects of space weather. But you might have to travel to places near Earth's poles, in which case, you'd better pack a lot of warm clothes! ◆

Auroras are light shows produced when charged particles strike gases in a planet's atmosphere. On Earth, auroras are usually seen near the poles and can be green, purple, red, blue, or a mixture of these colors.

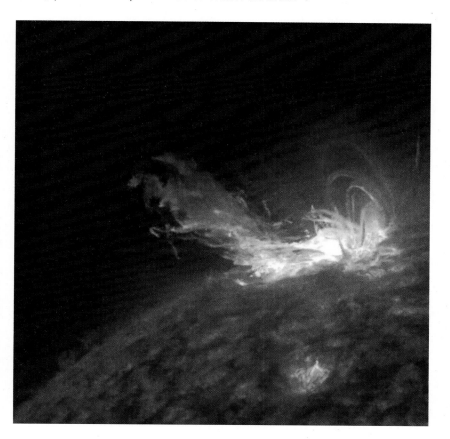

Solar storms are a kind of space weather that originates from the sun. A coronal mass ejection (CME) is a solar storm that breaks off from the sun's atmosphere and carries a bubble of charged particles off into space. In this photo, the loop coming off the sun is the start of a CME.

Taking Earth's Temperature

How do tiny, moving particles in the atmosphere cause temperature changes all around our planet?

Introduction

Brrr! One look at the mounds of ice in the photo and you know the penguins' Antarctic home near the South Pole is extremely cold. You may also know that other places on Earth can be quite different than icy Antarctica in that they may be warm and tropical or hot and dry. The sun and how it interacts with air particles plays an important role in creating these differences. How exactly does energy from the sun affect the air temperature? And how do scientists measure the temperature of locations from all over the world including remote areas in Antarctica?

This lesson will help you understand how air particles behave, and their role in energy flows in the Earth system. You will discover how the motion of the particles in all matter relates to temperature. You will find out about the tools that scientists use to measure and gather temperature data. You will also learn about thermal energy and how it functions during water changes of state. Finally, you will see how water and land temperature can affect the weather.

Vocabulary

kinetic energy the energy an object has due to its motion

temperature a measure of the average kinetic energy of the particles of a substance

proportional describes two quantities that are related by a simple ratio

heat energy transferred from a hotter object to a cooler object

conduction the transfer of energy from one part of a material to another or between two objects that are in physical contact with each other

radiation the transfer of energy by light

convection the transfer of energy caused by the circulation of matter due to differences in density

evaporation the change of state of particles from a liquid to a gas at the surface of the liquid

condensation the change of state of particles from a gas to a liquid

Next Generation Science Standards

Performance Expectations

MS-PS3-3. Apply scientific principles to design, construct, and test a device that either minimizes or maximizes thermal energy transfer.

MS-PS3-4. Plan an investigation to determine the relationships among the energy transferred, the type of matter, the mass, and the change in the average kinetic energy of the particles as measured by the temperature of the sample.

MS-PS3-5. Construct, use, and present arguments to support the claim that when the kinetic energy of an object changes, energy is transferred to or from the object.

Science and Engineering Practices

Constructing Explanations and Designing Solutions Apply scientific ideas or principles to design, construct, and test a design of an object, tool, process or system.

Planning and Carrying Out Investigations Plan an investigation individually and collaboratively, and in the design: identify independent and dependent variables and controls, what tools are needed to do the gathering, how measurements will be recorded, and how many data are needed to support a claim.

Engaging in Argument from Evidence Construct, use, and present oral and written arguments supported by empirical evidence and scientific reasoning to support or refute an explanation or a model for a phenomenon.

Scientific Knowledge is Based on Empirical Evidence

Crosscutting Concepts

Energy and Matter • Energy may take different forms (e.g. energy in fields, thermal energy, energy of motion). • The transfer of energy can be tracked as energy flows through a designed or natural system.

Scale, Proportion, and Quantity Proportional relationships (e.g., speed as the ratio of distance traveled to time taken) among different types of quantities provide information about the magnitude of properties and processes.

Disciplinary Core Ideas

PS3.A. Temperature is a measure of the average kinetic energy of particles of matter. The relationship between the temperature and the total energy of a system depends on the types, states, and amounts of matter present.

PS3.B. • When the motion energy of an object changes, there is inevitably some other change in energy at the same time. • The amount of energy transfer needed to change the temperature of a matter sample by a given amount depends on the nature of the matter, the size of the sample, and the environment. • Energy is spontaneously transferred out of hotter regions or objects and into colder ones.

Figure 2.1

All the matter that makes up Earth's atmosphere, hydrosphere, biosphere, and geosphere is made up of particles that are too small to see. These particles are always in motion, whether they make up the air, mountains, or leaves on a tree.

Moving Particles Make Up All Matter on Earth

Particles in atmosphere

Particles in rocks

Particles in trees

How warm or cold an object is depends on how fast the particles it is made of are moving. A cup of hot cocoa is warm because its particles are moving quickly, and it gets cooler as its particles slow down.

1. Earth's Matter Is Made of Moving Particles

Snow feels cold as it melts in your hands, while a slab of rock that has been sitting in the sun all day can feel hot. The same rock would feel cold if it had been covered with snow. Why do objects feel hot or cold?

All objects are made up of tiny particles that determine an object's properties, including how hot or cold it feels. Many, many particles combine together to make all objects on Earth. While the particles that make up all matter are too small to see, these particles still have mass and take up space. For example, snow or rock both have mass and take up space because they are made up of particles.

A wide variety of particles make up everything on Earth. This includes all matter found in Earth's atmosphere, hydrosphere, geosphere, and biosphere. Snow is made up of different particles than rock. Various rocks are made up of different types of particles. You and all other living things are also made up of many kinds of particles.

The particles in all matter are constantly moving as summarized in Figure 2.1, even when objects appear completely still. However, you cannot see the particles move the way you can see a snowball fly through the air because they are too small.

You may not be able to observe the particles in matter moving, but you can detect the motion in another way—by how warm or cool a material is. The warmer a particular material is, the faster its particles are moving. The particles in a cup of hot water move faster than the particles in a cup of ice water. This difference in how fast the particles are moving makes hot water hot and ice water cold.

The same is true for the air in the atmosphere. The particles of air move slower on a chilly morning than they do on a warm afternoon. The air warms up during the day because its particles move faster, and it cools down when its particles move slower.

2. Temperature Is a Measure of Particle Motion

A cup of water, the air, and the mounds of ice that surround the penguins in the photo in the beginning of the lesson can warm up or cool down as particles speed up or slow down. How does the motion of particles relate to energy?

Anything that is moving has energy. **Kinetic energy** is the energy an object has due to its motion. Objects have different amounts of kinetic energy depending primarily on how fast they are moving and how much matter they contain.

Kinetic energy also applies to particles that make up an object. How warm an object is depends on the kinetic energy of its individual particles. People usually use temperature as a way to describe how hot or cold something is. In science, **temperature** is a measure of the *average* kinetic energy of the particles in a substance because the particles in matter move at different speeds. The kinetic energy of particles increases as they speed up. Thus, the fast-moving particles in a cup of hot water have more energy than the slow-moving particles in ice. Scientists have devised instruments to measure this kinetic energy in matter. For example, Galileo is believed to have invented the first practical thermometer that could provide this measurement.

Temperature and average kinetic energy are related by a ratio. The word **proportional** describes two quantities that are related by a simple ratio. Temperature and average kinetic energy are directly proportional because temperature decreases as average kinetic energy decreases. What does the very low air temperature in Antarctica tell you about the particles in the air there? What about the high air temperature in Death Valley, California? These temperatures in Figure 2.2 tell you that most air particles in Antarctica have less kinetic energy and are moving slower than those in Death Valley.

Figure 2.2

Any moving object has kinetic energy. Temperature is a measure of the average kinetic energy of particles in matter. What does the speed of the air particles in Antarctica and in Death Valley tell you about the air temperature in those places?

Temperature Depends on the Motion of Air Particles

Eastern Antarctica

World record for lowest temperature at –93°C (–136°F)

Cold air, slower particles

Death Valley, California

World record for highest temperature at 57°C (134°F)

Hot air, faster particles

3. Why Matter Warms Up and Cools Down

Matter of all kinds can vary in temperature. You can often observe these variations with a thermometer. Why do objects warm up and cool down?

Remember that each individual moving particle in matter has kinetic energy. In order for the temperature of an object to change, the total kinetic energy of its particles must increase or decrease. Thermal energy is the *total* energy related to the motion of the many particles in an object or material.

Thus, thermal energy depends in part on an object's temperature as well as its state and mass. The thermal energy of a given object decreases as its temperature decreases. For example, the thermal energy of a ceramic mug decreases as its temperature decreases. The thermal energy of an object also depends on the mass of the object. A teapot full of boiling water has more thermal energy than a mug of boiling water. The teapot full of water has more thermal energy because it has more particles than the mug of water.

Thermal energy moves between objects that have different temperatures, as seen in Figure 2.3. **Heat** is the energy transferred from a hotter object to a cooler object. So, heat causes your hand to feel warm when you hold a mug of hot cocoa because thermal energy is being transferred from the hot water in the cocoa to the mug to your hand. Remember though, that heat is different from thermal energy and from temperature. The water in the mug has thermal energy—it does not have heat.

How are all the examples of thermal energy in Figure 2.3 similar to each other? The transfer, or flow, of thermal energy, always goes in the same direction—from higher temperature to lower temperature. Any system you can think of, even the entire Earth system, behaves in this way. Thermal energy is always transferred from warmer regions of Earth to cooler regions.

Figure 2.3

Thermal energy is the total kinetic energy of the particles in an object or material. Energy always flows from objects with higher temperatures to objects with lower temperatures. Energy stops being transferred between objects when they reach the same temperature.

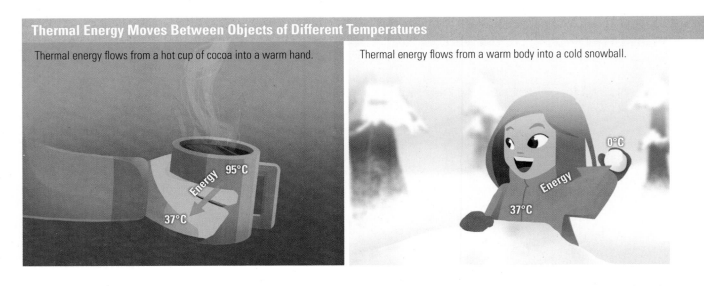

Thermal Energy Moves Between Objects of Different Temperatures

Thermal energy flows from a hot cup of cocoa into a warm hand.

Thermal energy flows from a warm body into a cold snowball.

You may think of thermal energy as the reason objects warm up. Its flow also causes objects to cool down. Consider what happens when you hold a mug of hot cocoa. Thermal energy is transferred from the mug to your hand. Your hand warms up. At the same time, energy is flowing out of the mug, causing it to cool down. Energy continues to flow from the mug to your hand until they both reach the same temperature. Then, it stops flowing between them. There is no transfer of thermal energy between objects of the same temperature.

The type of matter that makes up an object and the environment an object is in also affect how much energy is needed to change the object's temperature. More energy must be transferred to certain types of matter than others to increase temperature. For example, with the cup of hot cocoa, more energy is needed to change the temperature of its water than to change the temperature of the same mass of ceramic in the mug because water and ceramic are different kinds of matter. More energy is also needed to raise the temperature of water in a cold environment than in a warm environment. As energy is transferred to the water, it also flows from the warmer water to the colder surroundings.

This is the same for the Earth system. Energy from the sun is transferred to the ocean and atmosphere, so thermal energy flows from warmer regions to colder ones. Thus, thermal energy at the warm equator eventually flows north and south to the cooler poles. But why don't the poles eventually reach the same temperature as the equator, if energy is constantly flowing toward them?

The reason the atmosphere and ocean distribute energy from the sun around Earth is that thermal energy is transferred from warmer regions to cooler ones and never stops being transferred. The sun continually provides more energy to the regions near the equator than to polar regions. Therefore, they never reach the same temperature and the flow of energy never stops.

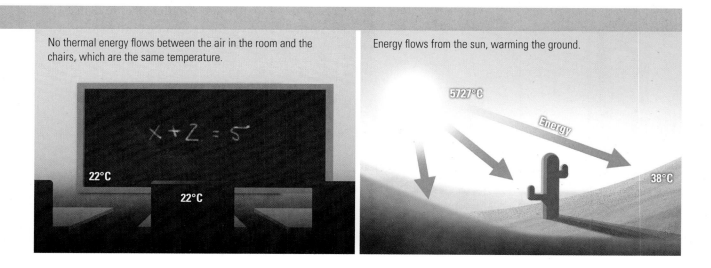

No thermal energy flows between the air in the room and the chairs, which are the same temperature.

22°C
22°C

Energy flows from the sun, warming the ground.

5727°C
Energy
38°C

4. Three Ways Energy Is Transferred

You have learned that thermal energy is transferred from warmer objects to cooler objects. Thermal energy can flow from warm water to melt ice that floats upon it. Energy flows from the sun to warm Earth. Energy flows from warm air to make fog disappear. How does energy move differently in these three cases?

Conduction is the transfer of energy from one part of a material to another or between two objects that are in physical contact with each other. For example, warmer water transfers thermal energy to colder ice. Within the ice, energy flows from warmer parts to cooler parts. Another example is when thermal energy flows from a bird to its eggs by conduction when the warmer bird touches the cooler eggs. Conduction happens when particles that make up matter bump into each other, transferring energy from fast-moving particles to slow-moving particles. Energy moves through liquids, solids, and gases in this way. Remember though, energy does not flow between two objects that are the same temperature.

Radiation is the transfer of energy by light, including visible light, infrared light, and ultraviolet light as well as other forms of energy. It is the process by which energy flows between objects that are not touching. For example, the sun transfers energy through empty space to Earth by radiation; this energy transfer does not require objects or fluids to occur. The atmosphere, water, land, and living things are warmed when they absorb sunlight.

Convection is the transfer of energy caused by the circulation of matter due to differences in density. For example, denser fog evaporates and appears to "lift" when the less dense air beneath it warms from the energy transported upward from the ground through convection. Energy moves through the atmosphere by convection when warm air flows from the equator to the poles. Warm equatorial ocean water also flows to the poles by convection.

Warmer liquid water transfers energy to ice by conduction. Energy flows from the sun to Earth by radiation. Fog evaporates when air warms from energy transported upward from convection.

Water warms up and cools down slower than land as energy is added or taken away. In the summer, daytime air temperatures above large bodies of water, such as this lake, are often cooler than over land. The land warms up faster and transfers energy to the air above it.

5. Different Substances Absorb Energy at Different Rates

Suppose you were walking along a lakeside beach. The sand underneath your bare feet is hot from the sun. *Ouch!* You hurry into the lake to cool down where the water is cold and refreshing. Both the sand and the water have been under the hot sun, so why is the sand so much warmer than the water?

Even though both the sand and the water have been absorbing thermal energy from the sun for the same amount of time, the sand warms up much faster than the water. This is because sand and water are different substances with different properties. One property of matter is how quickly a substance warms up. Different types of matter require different amounts of thermal energy to increase their temperature by the same amount. This property of matter is why people use iron or copper to make cooking pots, as these materials only require a little amount of thermal energy to heat up.

How does this property of matter affect weather? Recall when you were walking on the lakeside beach. Both sand and water have been absorbing thermal energy for the same amount of time. However, compared to land, water takes much longer to heat up, which means it also takes longer to cool down. Water changes temperature more slowly than land as energy is added or taken away. This results in a temperature difference between water, land, and the atmosphere, which affects weather. Land warms up more quickly than an ocean or lake when it absorbs energy from the sun. The warm land transfers energy to the air above it, making the air over land warmer than the air over water.

Different types of matter require different amounts of thermal energy to increase their temperature. Iron is a material that requires little thermal energy to heat up. Thus, iron is often used for cooking pots.

6. Thermal Energy and State Changes

When you put ice cubes in water, energy is transferred by conduction from the water to the ice. Eventually, the ice melts. How do the particles of matter behave when solid ice changes to liquid water?

The three common states of matter on Earth and in Earth's atmosphere are solid, liquid, and gas. The state of matter depends on the motion of particles and the attractions that hold them together. In solids, the particles are strongly attracted to each other and are locked in one place, only vibrating back and forth. In liquids, the particles are not locked. They can slide past one another, which is why liquids can flow. In gases, the particles move freely and quickly in all directions, which is why they spread out to fill any container.

In general, the thermal energy in an object depends on its state. For the same mass of a given substance, gases have more thermal energy than liquids, and liquids have more thermal energy than solids. For example, if the air temperature increases, ice melts to become liquid water, which evaporates and turns to gas, or water vapor, which becomes part of the air. The ice has the least thermal energy because its particles only vibrate back and forth. Liquid water has more thermal energy because its particles can move. Water vapor has the most thermal energy because its particles are moving quickly.

A substance's thermal energy changes when its state changes and as its energy is transferred through melting, evaporation, condensation, and freezing. **Evaporation** is the change of state of particles from liquid to gas at the surface of the liquid. **Condensation** is the change of state of particles from gas to liquid. In Figure 2.6, the environment transfers energy to ice and melts it to become liquid water, which then evaporates into water vapor. Water vapor transfers energy to its environment as it condenses and changes state from a gas to a liquid. Liquid water transfers energy to the environment as it freezes to become a solid.

Figure 2.6

Matter can exist in the solid, liquid, and gas states. When matter changes from one state to another, energy flows to or from the surrounding environment. When water transfers thermal energy to the environment, the water may freeze or condense. When the environment transfers thermal energy into water, ice may melt or water may evaporate.

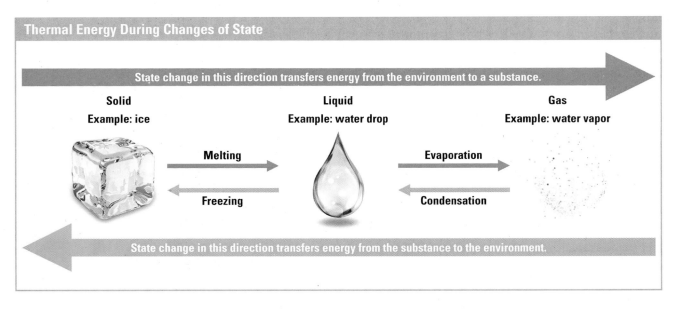

Thermal Energy During Changes of State

State change in this direction transfers energy from the environment to a substance.

Solid
Example: ice

Liquid
Example: water drop

Gas
Example: water vapor

Melting

Evaporation

Freezing

Condensation

State change in this direction transfers energy from the substance to the environment.

Thermal Energy and Changes in Temperature

Thermal energy flows from high-temperature objects, where the particles have more kinetic energy, to low-temperature objects, where the particles have less kinetic energy. As the energy flows between the objects, the hot object cools down and the cold object warms up. However, the amount that an object's temperature changes depends on the materials it is made of and how much of it there is. How do energy flow and temperature explain the way sand and water feel at the beach?

Radiation from the sun transfers energy to the sand and water, causing their temperatures to increase at different rates.

It takes more energy to increase the temperature of water than sand, so the water has a lower temperature than the sand.

Cold water

Hot sand

The average kinetic energy of the particles in the hot sand is higher than the average kinetic energy of the particles in the cold water.

When you go for a swim, conduction causes thermal energy to flow between your body and the water. Heat flows from the higher temperature object (generally your body) into the lower temperature object (the water).

7. Measuring Atmospheric Temperature

When you want to know how warm or cold it is, often you use a thermometer. Thermometers are used to measure the temperature of the air. The temperature of the air is a measure of how fast the particles of air are moving. There are different types of thermometers to measure temperature, such as liquid-in-glass and digital thermometers. You may have used a liquid-in-glass thermometer in science investigations. It is made of a tube made of thick glass, filled with a liquid such as alcohol.

How do scientists measure air temperature? You have probably seen temperature as it appears on the Fahrenheit scale. The Fahrenheit scale is usually used in the United States, so it is the one you see on your local weather report. However, most countries and scientists use the Celsius scale when measuring temperature. Celsius is based on the temperatures at which water freezes and boils. Water freezes at 0° Celsius (°C) and boils at 100°C.

To get an accurate reading, the thermometer must be located in the shade. If the sun shines on the thermometer, the sun will heat it, resulting in a higher reading than the true air temperature. Atmospheric temperature also changes with altitude, so the temperature of the air can vary depending on the height at which the thermometer is located. Most people are interested in conditions close to the ground, where the high and low air temperatures for your area's daily weather reports are measured.

Temperature for weather analysis and forecasting is usually measured at weather stations. There are thousands of weather stations located all over the world, as shown on the map in Figure 2.7. Scientists receive temperature data from these stations and can use the data to observe patterns in weather worldwide.

Figure 2.7

Weather stations are located around the world. There are thousands of them in all. They measure the temperature near the ground and ocean surface. Many of the weather stations are automated and provide weather data nonstop, all year, allowing scientists to analyze rapidly changing weather conditions for better forecasts.

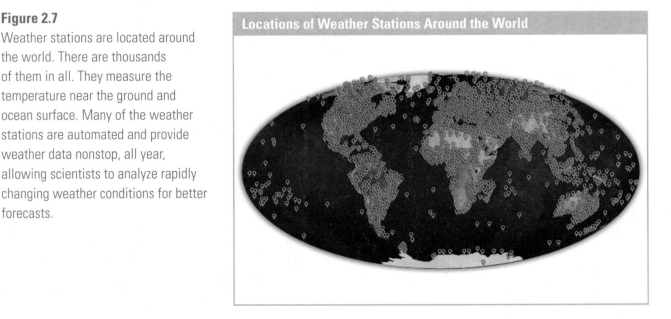

Locations of Weather Stations Around the World

Weather stations need to provide temperature data nonstop, 24 hours a day, every day of the year, and in locations all around the world, whether they are located in Eastern Antarctica, Death Valley in California, or elsewhere. These requirements are difficult for a person or a team of people to handle, even if measurements are only taken once an hour. Thus, scientists use programs such as Automated Surface Observing System (ASOS) and Automatic Weather Stations (AWS). ASOS and AWS units often include a variety of tools to measure all parts of weather, not just temperature. Both systems collect and send basic weather data, such as temperature, pressure, precipitation, humidity, and wind speed. Many ASOS units are located at airports because they also measure cloud height and visibility—important data pilots need. AWS units also operate in remote or harsh locations where it is difficult for people to work, such as Antarctica. Scientists use the data from ASOS and AWS units to record temperature and weather patterns around the world, and to compare temperatures year after year.

An Automated Surface Observing System contains sensors that collect and send data on temperature, pressure, humidity, and wind speed up to 60 times an hour. Many ASOS units are located at airports because they measure conditions that pilots need to fly, such as cloud height and visibility.

LESSON SUMMARY

Taking Earth's Temperature

Earth's Matter Is Made of Moving Particles All of the particles that make up the atmosphere, hydrosphere, geosphere, and biosphere are constantly in motion. Matter warms up as its particles move faster.

Temperature Is a Measure of Particle Motion The kinetic energy of a moving object increases as its speed increases. Temperature is the measure of the average kinetic energy of an object or material.

Why Matter Warms Up and Cools Down Thermal energy is the total kinetic energy of all the particles in an object. Heat is the thermal energy that is transferred from warmer to cooler objects.

Three Ways Energy Is Transferred Conduction is the transfer of energy through materials that are touching. Radiation is the transfer of energy by light. Moving liquids or gases transfer energy by convection as they move from one place to another.

Different Substances Absorb Energy at Different Rates Water requires more energy to heat up compared to air or land.

Thermal Energy and State Changes The state of matter—solid, liquid, or gas—depends on the motion of its particles and the attraction between them. Energy is transferred when matter melts, evaporates, condenses, or freezes.

Measuring Atmospheric Temperature Thermometers are used to measure air temperature. Data on temperature and other weather conditions are collected by weather stations around the world.

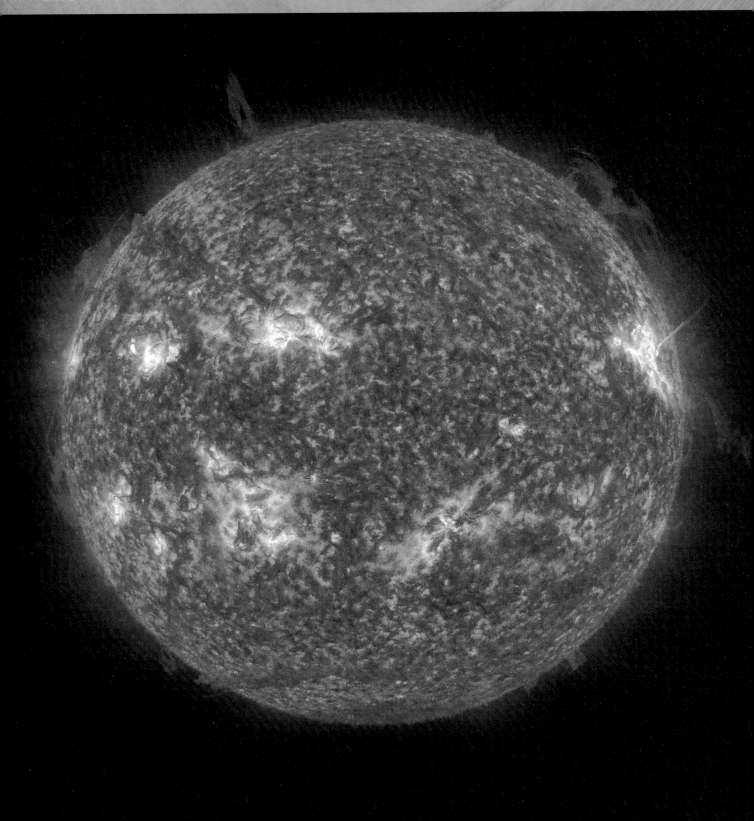

Earth and Solar Energy

What would weather be like without the sun?

Introduction

This photo of the sun was taken by the Solar Dynamics Observatory at NASA to study our closest star. It shows high-energy light waves that cannot be seen without special instruments. Between the sun and Earth are 149.6 million kilometers of space! What happens when the sun's normally invisible, high-energy light waves cross that distance to reach Earth? And how does a star so distant from us influence weather on our planet?

Weather affects life on Earth—including your life—in major ways. How does the energy Earth receives from the sun and the way this energy travels through the atmosphere create the basis for weather?

In this lesson, you will find out what sunlight is and how it interacts with the atmosphere to create the energy that warms Earth. You will use models that explore how Earth's round shape influences temperature and relates to the seasons. Further, you will see the ways in which the atmosphere and ocean interact with the energy from the sun and their effect on Earth's temperature. Finally, you will see how engineering students design a device that can cook food using only the energy of the sun.

Vocabulary

greenhouse gas a gas in the atmosphere that absorbs the energy of infrared light

greenhouse effect the warming of the troposphere by energy trapped by greenhouse gases

latitude a unit in degrees that describes a position on Earth relative to the equator

criteria the requirements that must be met for an engineering solution to be successful

constraints the limitations on an engineering solution

Next Generation Science Standards

Performance Expectations

MS-ESS2-6. Develop and use a model to describe how unequal heating and rotation of the Earth cause patterns of atmospheric and oceanic circulation that determine regional climates.

MS-ETS1-1. Define the criteria and constraints of a design problem with sufficient precision to ensure a successful solution, taking into account relevant scientific principles and potential impacts on people and the natural environment that may limit possible solutions.

MS-ETS1-3. Analyze data from tests to determine similarities and differences among several design solutions to identify the best characteristics of each that can be combined into a new solution to better meet the criteria for success.

Science and Engineering Practices

Analyzing and Interpreting Data Analyze and interpret data to determine similarities and differences in findings.

Asking Questions and Defining Problems Define a design problem that can be solved through the development of an object, tool, process or system and includes multiple criteria and constraints, including scientific knowledge that may limit possible solutions.

Developing and Using Models Develop and use a model to describe phenomena.

Crosscutting Concepts

Systems and System Models Models can be used to represent systems and their interactions—such as inputs, processes, and outputs—and energy, matter, and information flows within systems.

Disciplinary Core Ideas

ESS2.D. Weather and climate are influenced by interactions involving sunlight, the ocean, the atmosphere, ice, landforms, and living things. These interactions vary with latitude, altitude, and local and regional geography, all of which can affect oceanic and atmospheric flow patterns.

ETS1.A The more precisely a design task's criteria and constraints can be defined, the more likely it is that the designed solution will be successful. Specification of constraints includes consideration of scientific principles and other relevant knowledge that are likely to limit possible solutions.

ETS1.B. Sometimes parts of different solutions can be combined to create a solution that is better than any of its predecessors.

ETS1.C. Although one design may not perform the best across all tests, identifying the characteristics of the design that performed the best in each test can provide useful information for the redesign process—that is, some of those characteristics may be incorporated into the new design.

1. Light and Energy from the Sun

You have learned that the sun is the source of weather on Earth as its energy drives the Earth system. What would it be like if there was no sun? Would it be night all the time? What would temperatures be like for life on this planet without it?

You may guess that without sunlight, Earth would get cold very fast! However, only a small amount of sunlight reaches Earth's surface. Why is that? Of the portion of sunlight that reaches Earth's atmosphere, only about half reaches Earth's surface. The remainder of the energy is absorbed or reflected by the atmosphere. The few specific parts of the electromagnetic spectrum that make it through to Earth's surface are infrared and visible light and a very small amount of ultraviolet light, as seen in Figure 3.1.

Sunlight is made up of waves of energy of different lengths. Shorter wavelengths carry more energy than longer wavelengths. The waves of sunlight most important to weather are ultraviolet light, visible light, and infrared light because they comprise nearly all of the solar energy spectrum.

Ultraviolet light has more energy and a shorter wavelength than visible light. Although human eyes cannot detect ultraviolet (UV) light, the camera that took the photo of the sun you saw at the beginning of this lesson can. However, most UV light does not reach Earth's surface. The *ozone layer*, a layer of particles in the stratosphere, blocks much of the incoming UV light.

Visible light is the form of light you can see that permits you to view the world around you. Visible light has less energy than ultraviolet light and includes every color of the rainbow.

Infrared light has a longer wavelength and even less energy than visible light. It is another form of light you cannot see with your eyes, but when your skin absorbs infrared light, it feels warm. Some infrared light reaches Earth's surface, and some is absorbed by the atmosphere.

Figure 3.1

Sunlight carries energy from the sun to Earth. Sunlight is made of several kinds of light that carry different amounts of energy, including ultraviolet, visible, and infrared.

Three Components of Solar Energy

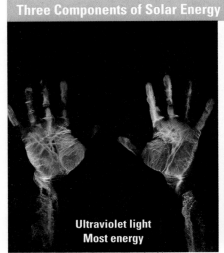

Ultraviolet light
Most energy

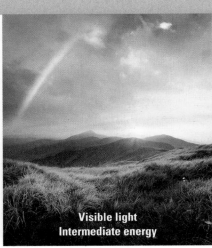

Visible light
Intermediate energy

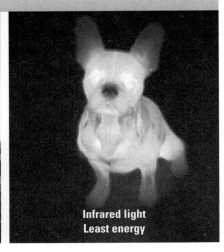

Infrared light
Least energy

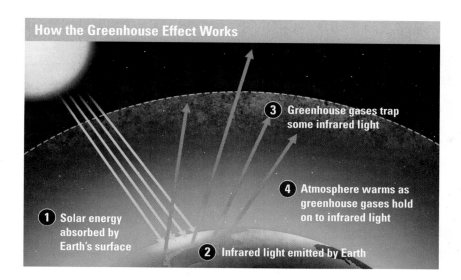

How the Greenhouse Effect Works

3 Greenhouse gases trap some infrared light

4 Atmosphere warms as greenhouse gases hold on to infrared light

1 Solar energy absorbed by Earth's surface

2 Infrared light emitted by Earth

Figure 3.2

Earth's surface is warmed by the visible light that it absorbs. Earth then gives off lower-energy infrared light, some of which is absorbed by greenhouse gases in the atmosphere. The absorbed infrared light warms up the atmosphere.

2. The Greenhouse Effect

Earth is sometimes called a "Goldilocks planet" because its temperature is not too hot, not too cold, but just right to support life. Is it the amount of sunlight that Earth receives that makes this planet so supportive of life? Or are there other features that produce its life-supporting temperature?

The amount of sunlight that Earth receives sets the stage for life, but there are other reasons that Earth's temperature is so hospitable to living things. After all, the planet Mars receives sunlight as well, but Mars is much colder than Earth. Besides the sunlight, it is the chemical composition—the kinds of gases—in Earth's atmosphere that sets this planet's temperature range.

Most of the sunlight that penetrates the atmosphere and actually reaches Earth's surface is in the form of visible light. In addition to all visible light, the atmosphere lets some UV and infrared light pass through and absorbs some of the infrared. Why does the atmosphere behave differently with different wavelengths of light? Look at the model in Figure 3.2. Once solar radiation reaches Earth's surface, it is absorbed by the land and ocean, warming them up. The warmed surface then emits infrared light, which has longer wavelengths and less energy compared to visible light and UV light.

Greenhouse gases are gases in the atmosphere that absorb the energy of infrared light. Carbon dioxide, methane, and water vapor are all greenhouse gases. They trap infrared light in the atmosphere. Thus, the energy carried by the infrared light away from Earth's surface largely remains in the atmosphere. As this energy is retained, atmospheric temperature increases. This is the greenhouse effect. The **greenhouse effect** is the warming of the atmosphere, specifically Earth's troposphere, by energy trapped by greenhouse gases. The greenhouse effect warms up the atmosphere, which in turn warms up the surface of Earth—its land and water.

The greenhouse effect is thought to be named after a gardener's greenhouse. In an actual greenhouse, warm air is simply contained by plastic or glass walls. However, the processes involved in the greenhouse effect are much more complicated.

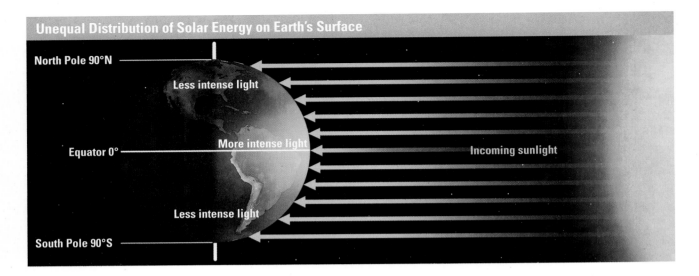

Unequal Distribution of Solar Energy on Earth's Surface

North Pole 90°N

Less intense light

Equator 0°

More intense light

Incoming sunlight

Less intense light

South Pole 90°S

Figure 3.3

The amount of sunlight during the day depends on the angle at which the sun's rays strike Earth's curved surface. The light is less concentrated at different latitudes.

This model represents the varying intensities of sunlight as it hits Earth's surface.

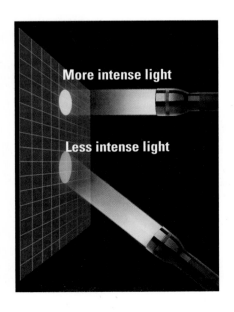

More intense light

Less intense light

3. Sunlight and Earth's Shape

If you want to vacation in a warm location, do you head far north or far south toward the poles, or head toward the equator? The answer is that you travel closer to the equator—but why is it warmer there?

While sunlight warms Earth, it does not warm all locations the same amount. Sunlight travels away from the sun in straight lines called *rays*. These rays travel parallel to each other through space. However, they do not strike Earth's surface at the same angle. The reason is that Earth is curved like a ball. Near the equator, the rays meet Earth straight on, perpendicular, at a right angle. As the surface of Earth curves toward the north and south poles, the angles at which the rays of sunlight strike Earth are nonperpendicular. Therefore, the light is less concentrated at different latitudes.

Latitude is a unit measured in degrees that describes a position on Earth relative to the equator. You can find the latitude of your city by looking at a map or globe. Latitude lines on a globe are parallel to the equator. The equator is at 0° latitude. The North Pole is at 90° North latitude. The South Pole is at 90° South latitude. Locations between the equator and the poles have latitudes between 0° and 90°.

Figure 3.3 shows how a location's latitude affects the amount of sunlight it receives. Regions near the equator, at latitude near 0°, receive the most sunlight and energy because this is where rays of sunlight strike Earth most directly. Regions at higher latitudes north and south of the equator receive less direct rays of sunlight and energy from the sun compared to the middle latitudes. Similarly, the energy from the sun is spread over a larger area near the poles compared to the equator, since those rays strike the poles at a low, slanted angle.

The model using a flashlight shining on a grid shows how this happens and why the angle of the sun's rays matters. The flashlight's beam is spread out over a larger area of the grid when the light hits it at a low, slanted angle, resulting in less intense light.

4. The Uneven Heating of Earth

If you walk into a cabin in the woods on a cold, snowy day, and there is a woodstove inside, you know you will warm up if someone lights the stove. Why will you warm up?

Thermal energy does not stay in one place—it travels. It flows from locations of high temperature to low temperature, as we see in countless examples every day. Once there is a fire in the stove, energy will flow from the stove into the room and your body, warming you.

Similarly, the sun's energy does not stay in one place. Since latitudes near the equatorial regions are warmer than the polar regions, energy travels from the equator and toward the poles, through motion in the atmosphere and oceans. If not for this pattern of the flow of energy away from the equator toward the poles, the temperature differences between places of high and low latitude would be much more extreme than they are. The poles would be so cold, and the equator would be so hot, that it would be difficult for living things to survive in those places.

However, the atmosphere is not consistent and its properties constantly change with time and location. The imbalance of energy between the equator and poles, and the resulting flow of energy away from the lower latitudes toward the higher ones, sets up a process that underlies all weather on Earth. Figure 3.4 is a model that shows this redistribution of energy from equator to poles.

How does energy move from low to high latitudes? The atmosphere behaves like a fluid, much like the ocean. As the atmosphere and ocean move, energy moves with them by convection. Thus, the atmosphere and ocean are the principal carriers of energy around Earth. As the ocean and atmosphere move energy around, the temperature changes that they bring affect the weather, as well as land and living things. Earth is a system, so all parts affect one another.

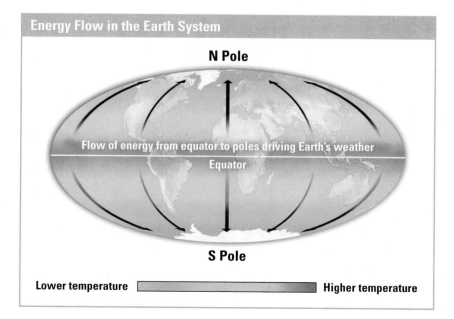

Energy Flow in the Earth System

N Pole

Flow of energy from equator to poles driving Earth's weather

Equator

S Pole

Lower temperature ————————————— Higher temperature

Figure 3.4

The lower latitudes near the equator get hotter because they receive more energy than the higher latitudes near the poles. The atmosphere and oceans help to distribute this energy from the equatorial regions towards the polar regions by convection.

5. The Seasons

Your home has the same latitude whether it is summer or winter. Yet, the weather in most places is warmer in the summer than in the winter. Why does temperature vary in seasonal patterns?

Changes in the angle at which sunlight strikes Earth causes the seasons. As Earth completes its orbit, the angle of Earth's axis stays the same. The axis is tilted at an angle of 23.5° with respect to Earth's yearly orbit around the sun. However, the part of Earth that is tilted toward the sun changes throughout the year.

When the half of Earth north of the equator, the Northern Hemisphere, tilts toward the sun in June, as Figure 3.5 shows, rays hit the Northern Hemisphere more directly—in some locations at 90°. Thus, this hemisphere receives more sunlight and energy from the sun at this time and temperatures are warmer and days are longer than they are south of the equator. When this occurs, it is summer in the Northern Hemisphere.

At the same time, the Southern Hemisphere tilts away from the sun and experiences the opposite effect. Thus, the Southern Hemisphere receives less energy at this time than it does at other times of the year, resulting in shorter days and colder weather. When the Northern Hemisphere experiences summer, the Southern Hemisphere experiences winter. The reverse phenomenon happens in December when the Northern Hemisphere tilts away from the sun.

Figure 3.5

The part of Earth that is tilted toward the sun changes the angle at which sunlight strikes Earth throughout the year, creating the seasons. Note how the angle of the axis stays the same as Earth completes its orbit.

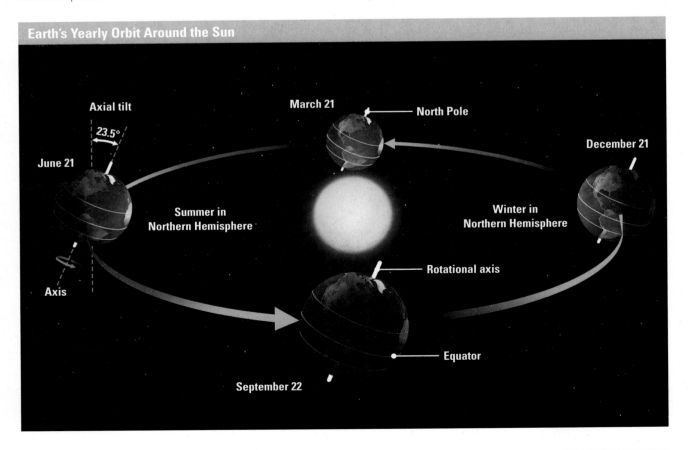

Earth's Yearly Orbit Around the Sun

How the Sun Heats Earth

The sun is vital to making life possible on Earth as well as creating weather. The hospitable temperatures on this "Goldilocks planet" are the result of a complex system of interactions involving sunlight, the atmosphere, the ocean, landforms, and living things. Look at the three ways the sun's energy influences temperature. How does each of these ways affect your daily life?

The Natural Greenhouse Effect Keeps Earth Warm

The gases that make up the atmosphere allow visible light from the sun to pass through, heating Earth's surface. Earth loses some of the energy by emitting infrared radiation to space. The atmosphere absorbs some of the infrared radiation, capturing the energy and preventing Earth from cooling down.

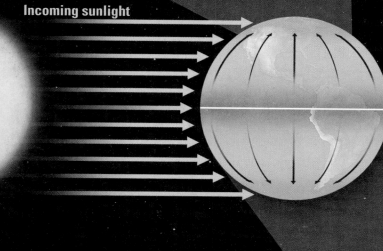

Incoming sunlight

Convection Distributes Energy on Earth

Sunlight strikes latitudes near the equator most directly, causing them to heat up most. Convection in the oceans and atmosphere transfer energy from the equatorial regions towards the cooler polar regions.

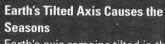

Earth's Tilted Axis Causes the Seasons

Earth's axis remains tilted in the same direction as it orbits the sun. As a result, the part of Earth that receives the most direct sunlight, and therefore the most energy, changes throughout the year. This results in seasonal changes in temperature.

6. Cooking with Solar Energy

You know sunlight can warm all sorts of things, from your skin to the ground to the atmosphere. Yet, food left sitting in the sun will not cook because it does not get warm enough. With a solar cooker, however, sunlight heats food by radiation to high enough temperatures so it actually cooks. How would you design a solar cooker?

Consider that for a school project, a team of engineering students need to answer that very question. The problem is how to design a solar cooker that people living in refugee camps with limited access to electricity and fuels can use to cook their meals. A solar cooker needs to be able to collect energy from sunlight and retain it to heat a container to high enough temperatures to cook the food inside of it.

To create a functional design, the team must meet the criteria and constraints of the project. **Criteria** are the requirements that must be met for an engineering solution to be successful. The project's criteria state that the solar cooker should be easy to use but able to cook any kind of one-pot meal for a small family, so the cooker needs to be big enough to fit a large pot. The pot needs to reach at least 85°C, but the food should cook slowly. **Constraints** are the limitations on an engineering solution. The project's constraints say that the solar cooker should be low cost, and not take up a lot of space.

The team selects two solar cooker designs and decides to build models to test them under a range of conditions. The models look like the solar oven and the parabolic solar cooker shown in Figure 3.6. Testing the models involves measuring the time it takes for each to bring one cup of water to 90°C, or just under the boiling point. Next, they compare the results. They look at how each model performs and consider the types of characteristics they have.

Figure 3.6

The panel cooker combines the best characteristics of the solar oven box with those of the parabolic cooker. This third design considers the criteria and constraints of the problem to come up with the best possible solution for the project.

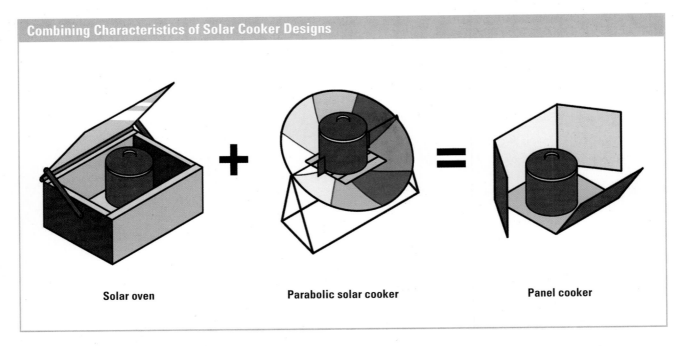

Combining Characteristics of Solar Cooker Designs

Solar oven + Parabolic solar cooker = Panel cooker

The students find that both models need to be repositioned during cooking so that the sun's rays are directed toward the cooking container. The solar oven box takes longer to cook food than the parabolic cooker and may not fit a large pot. The parabolic cooker cooks a large pot of food quickly, but it can be difficult to use and costs more than the solar oven. Neither of these two designs meets all of the project's criteria and constraints.

To arrive at a better solution, the students decide to combine the best characteristics from each of the designs. They find that the solar oven is easy to use. The reflective sides are effective, so they plan to modify them so they fold down to save space. The students note that the parabolic cooker fits a large pot and cooks food quickly.

When they combine the best characteristics of each cooker, they come up with a design similar to a panel cooker. The design meets the criteria and constraints of the project. They discover that while a panel cooker cooks food more slowly, it does not need to be repositioned. It is easier to use and less expensive than a parabolic cooker. A large pot can easily fit inside, and the panel cooker can be folded to save space when stored. The students decide that a panel cooker is the best design because it fits the criteria and constraints.

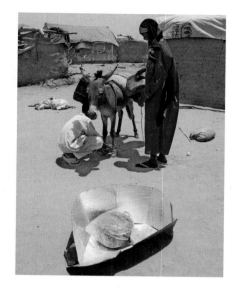

This woman lives in the Iridimi Refugee Camp in Chad where there is little firewood. She uses a panel solar cooker which needs no fuel except the sun to cook her midday meals or to heat her tea.

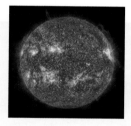

LESSON SUMMARY

Earth and Solar Energy

Light and Energy from the Sun Sunlight consists of waves of energy of different lengths that travel at different speeds. Half of this energy reaches Earth's atmosphere and makes it through to the surface. The remainder is absorbed or reflected by the atmosphere.

The Greenhouse Effect The greenhouse effect is the process by which certain gases in the atmosphere, called greenhouse gases, trap infrared light, which results in warming the atmosphere.

Sunlight and Earth's Shape The angle at which sunlight rays strike Earth is not the same all over because of Earth's round shape. The sun's energy is highest at the equator and lowest at the poles.

The Uneven Heating of Earth The equatorial regions are warm. Polar regions are much colder. The atmosphere and ocean move energy from the equator and toward the poles by convection.

The Seasons Changes in the angle at which sunlight strikes Earth cause the seasons. The hemisphere that tilts toward the sun receives more energy, is warmer, and experiences summer. The hemisphere that points away from the sun is colder and experiences winter.

Cooking with Solar Energy Solar cookers use sunlight to heat and cook food. There are many designs for solar cookers, each of which meet different criteria and constraints for use.

The Goldilocks Zone

In the children's story *Goldilocks and the Three Bears*, a girl goes into the bears' house and snoops around. At one point, she eats the bears' porridge and finds that Papa Bear's porridge is too hot, Mama Bear's is too cold, and Baby Bear's is *just right*. This story is not based on scientific fact—bears don't eat porridge! Yet, astronomers often refer to the story. *What does Goldilocks have to do astronomy?*

The Goldilocks zone is the area around a star in which the temperatures are just right for liquid water to exist on its planets' surfaces. Earth is covered with water and is in the sun's Goldilocks zone.

When astronomers talk about Goldilocks, they aren't talking about the girl who broke into a house owned by bears. Instead, they talk about something called the *Goldilocks zone*. In space, planets (like Earth) orbit around stars (like the sun). The Goldilocks zone is a region around a star in which the temperatures are *just right* for liquid water to exist on the surfaces of planets within the zone. A star's Goldilocks zone can cover an area that is millions of kilometers wide, and although that sounds like a large area, the Goldilocks zone of any star is tiny compared to the vastness of space.

Water exists in the liquid state in only a narrow range of temperatures: from 0°C to 100°C. Below that range, water is a solid (ice), and above that range, water is a gas (water vapor). Why are scientists so interested in whether a planet can have liquid water?

Liquid water is essential to all life on Earth, and scientists think that liquid water may also be essential to life on any planet. If a planet has liquid water on it, it may be habitable, which means that it could support life. In fact, a star's Goldilocks zone is also called the star's *habitable zone*.

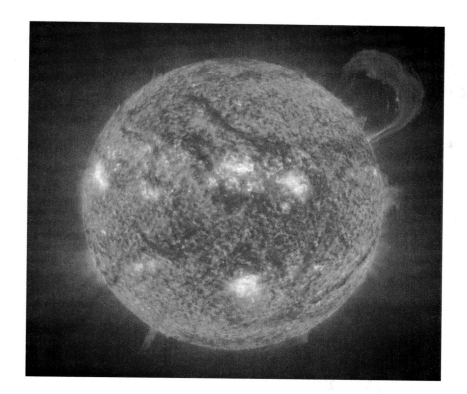

The sun is the star in the center of our solar system. It gives off energy that warms Earth, allowing liquid water to exist on Earth's surface. This energy is also converted into food energy that allows plants and animals to live.

Under the Sun

Liquid water and life exist on Earth, so Earth must be in the habitable zone of a star. That star is, of course, the sun. The sun, like all stars, is a large body of matter that is so hot that it glows, giving off light and other forms of electromagnetic radiation.

Stars get their energy from fusion reactions that happen deep within the stars. During a fusion reaction, particles of matter combine to form new particles, and some of the original matter is converted into thermal energy. This energy heats the star and also travels away from the star in all directions.

The sun's energy provides many benefits to Earth. Waves carrying energy from the sun travel nearly 150 million kilometers to reach our planet. Energy from the sun warms Earth—which allows liquid water to exist—and is converted into food energy by plants through photosynthesis. This food energy allows plants and animals to live.

Scientists also hypothesize that the sun may have had a role in the development of life on Earth in the first place. Billions of years ago, the sun may have had huge solar storms that sent high-energy, charged particles into space. When these charged particles reached Earth, they caused changes in Earth's atmosphere and possibly provided the energy needed to form complex molecules such as DNA. So, the sun may have provided an original source of energy to life that it keeps alive today!

Light from the sun travels through space to Earth. The sun may have had a role in the development of life on Earth and continues to keep it alive today.

The greenhouse effect keeps Earth at the right temperature for liquid water to exist on Earth's surface.

In this image, Earth and Mars are Goldilocks planets, but Mercury and Venus are not. The green area is not to scale and offers an estimate of the sun's Goldilocks zone.

What If Earth Were Closer to the Sun?

What would happen if Earth were not in the sun's Goldilocks zone? Scientists used computer modeling to find out what would happen if Earth were closer to the sun. The results show that life would cease to exist on Earth because if Earth were closer to the sun, it would experience a runaway greenhouse effect.

The greenhouse effect is a process that helps keep Earth's atmosphere warm. Light energy from the sun hits Earth, and some of it is trapped by greenhouse gases in the atmosphere. For now, the greenhouse effect is a good thing because it keeps Earth's temperatures just right for liquid water and life.

But if Earth were a little closer to the sun, it would receive more light energy, which would warm the atmosphere to higher temperatures. The higher temperatures would cause more of Earth's water to evaporate and become water vapor in the atmosphere. Water vapor is a greenhouse gas. So, with more water vapor in the atmosphere, the greenhouse effect would be stronger. That would lead to higher temperatures, more water evaporation, a stronger greenhouse effect . . . and so on. This cycle of increasing temperatures leading to a stronger greenhouse effect is called a runaway greenhouse effect.

A runaway greenhouse effect on Earth would mean that all the water on Earth would evaporate and the temperatures would be much too high for life as we know it. A runaway greenhouse effect is happening on the planet Venus, which is not in the sun's Goldilocks zone. Venus has no liquid water and has temperatures as high as 460°C!

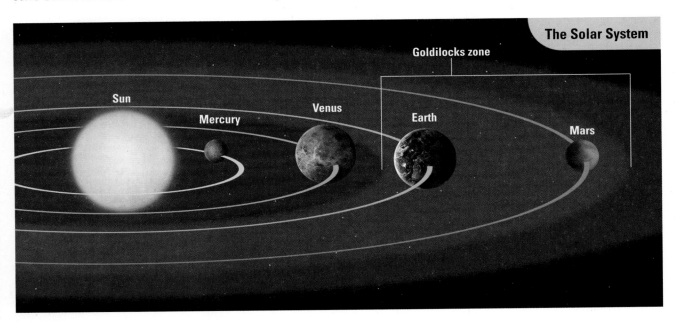

The Solar System

Goldilocks zone

Sun

Mercury

Venus

Earth

Mars

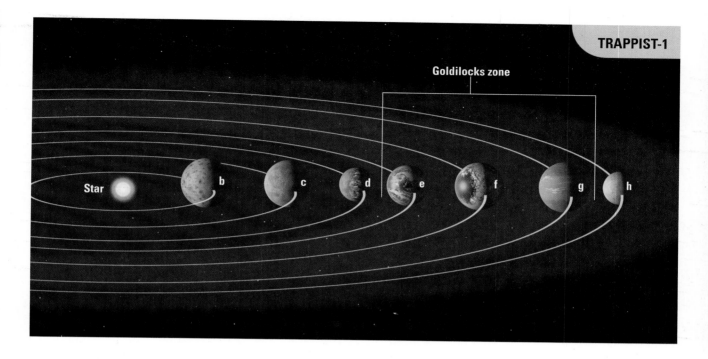

TRAPPIST-1

Goldilocks zone

Star   b   c   d   e   f   g   h

The Search for Life

Why are scientists bothering to find out what would happen if Earth were closer to the sun? Earth is not going to change its orbit! Scientists model various changes in the Earth-sun system because they are trying to figure out just how big the sun's—or any star's—Goldilocks zone is. The diagram on the previous page is only an estimate of the sun's Goldilocks zone. Some calculations of the zone show that it is narrower and does not include Mars.

Scientists are interested in finding the Goldilocks zone around various stars because they hope to find life on other planets. So far, scientists have found thousands of planets outside of the solar system. That number is too large to check each one for signs of life. So, scientists use Goldilocks zones to focus their observations.

For now, scientists are most interested in rocky planets in Goldilocks zones. A rocky planet is a planet that has a hard surface like Earth does. Such planets are interesting because they may have life that formed in a similar way to how life on Earth formed.

In February 2017, NASA announced that they found a star system that has seven Earth-sized planets orbiting it. At least three of the planets are in the star's Goldilocks zone, and potentially all could have water. The star system is named TRAPPIST-1 and has the largest number of habitable-zone planets ever found around a star. Scientists consider the TRAPPIST-1 planets to be some of the best candidates for finding liquid water outside of our solar system. Perhaps one of the planets will even be *just right* for life! ◆

The TRAPPIST-1 system has the rockiest planets ever found orbiting a star outside of our solar system. In this image, three of the planets are in the Goldilocks zone, though all of them have a possibility of having liquid water.

UNIT 2

Weather

OVERVIEW

Ominous clouds loom on the horizon. Will it be a heavy storm or fair weather? If you had to predict which it would be, what factors would you consider? In this unit, you will see which factors influence weather. You will understand the role of the water cycle in weather and the Earth system. You will also discover the tools scientists use to forecast weather and build your own devices to measure and interpret weather data. Then, using your knowledge of atmospheric conditions and forecasting, you will issue a severe weather warning.

Phenomenon-Based Storyline
People's lives and property are at risk when severe weather strikes. How can monitoring atmospheric conditions, improving forecasts, and issuing weather warnings save lives?

Investigations Use a model to describe how differences in air pressure cause wind. Build your own barometer and collect air pressure data.

Investigations Build and test a device for measuring humidity. Develop a model that shows the role of water in shaping the weather.

Investigations Collect and analyze weather data to answer questions and make predictions about how interactions between air masses change the weather.

Investigations Explore the probabilities of different severe weather phenomena by analyzing and interpreting weather maps and weather data.

Performance Assessment Develop an action plan for a severe weather event, including providing advanced warning, preparation plans, and mitigation of its effects.

UNIT 2

Performance Expectations

MS-ESS2-4. Develop a model to describe the cycling of water through Earth's systems driven by energy from the sun and the force of gravity.

MS-ESS2-5. Collect data to provide evidence for how the motions and complex interactions of air masses results in changes in weather conditions.

MS-ESS2-6. Develop and use a model to describe how unequal heating and rotation of the Earth cause patterns of atmospheric and oceanic circulation that determine regional climates.

MS-ESS3-2. Analyze and interpret data on natural hazards to forecast future catastrophic events and inform the development of technologies to mitigate their effects.

MS-ETS1-2. Evaluate competing design solutions using a systematic process to determine how well they meet the criteria and constraints of the problem.

MS-ETS1-4. Develop a model to generate data for iterative testing and modification of a proposed object, tool, or process such that an optimal design can be achieved.

Science and Engineering Practices

Developing and Using Models
• Develop a model to describe unobservable mechanisms. • Develop and use a model to describe phenomena. • Develop a model to generate data to test ideas about designed systems, including those representing inputs and outputs.

Planning and Carrying Out Investigations
Collect data to produce data to serve as the basis for evidence to answer scientific questions or test design solutions under a range of conditions.

Analyzing and Interpreting Data
Analyze and interpret data to determine similarities and differences in findings.

Engaging in Argument from Evidence
Evaluate competing design solutions based on jointly developed and agreed-upon design criteria.

Crosscutting Concepts

Patterns
Graphs, charts, and images can be used to identify patterns in data.

Cause and Effect
Cause and effect relationships may be used to predict phenomena in natural or designed systems.

Systems and System Models
Models can be used to represent systems and their interactions—such as inputs, processes, and outputs—and energy, matter, and information flows within systems.

Energy and Matter
Within a natural or designed system, the transfer of energy drives the motion and/or cycling of matter.

Influence of Science, Engineering, and Technology on Society and the Natural World
The uses of technologies and limitations on their use are driven by individual or societal needs, desires, and values; by the findings of scientific research; and by differences in such factors as climate, natural resources, and economic conditions. Thus technology use varies from region to region and over time.

Disciplinary Core Ideas

ESS2.C: The Roles of Water in Earth's Surface Processes
• Water continually cycles among land, ocean, and atmosphere via transpiration, evaporation, condensation and crystallization, and precipitation, as well as downhill flows on land. • Global movements of water and its changes in form are propelled by sunlight and gravity. • The complex patterns of the changes and the movement of water in the atmosphere, determined by winds, landforms, and ocean temperatures and currents, are major determinants of local weather patterns.

ESS2.D: Weather and Climate
• Weather and climate are influenced by interactions involving sunlight, the ocean, the atmosphere, ice, landforms, and living things. These interactions vary with latitude, altitude, and local and regional geography, all of which can affect oceanic and atmospheric flow patterns. • Because these patterns are so complex, weather can only be predicted probabilistically.

ESS3.B: Natural Hazards
Mapping the history of natural hazards in a region, combined with an understanding of related geologic forces can help forecast the locations and likelihoods of future events.

ETS1.B: Developing Possible Solutions
• A solution needs to be tested, and then modified on the basis of the test results, in order to improve it. • There are systematic processes for evaluating solutions with respect to how well they meet the criteria and constraints of a problem. • Models of all kinds are important for testing solutions.

ETS1.C: Optimizing the Design Solution
The iterative process of testing the most promising solutions and modifying what is proposed on the basis of the test results leads to greater refinement and ultimately to an optimal solution.

Connect Your Learning

How many times a day do you check the weather? It's likely your answer is "many," because weather affects decisions you make and what activities you do over the course of your day. Whether you check a weather app, use weather tools, or look at the sky, you are observing and interpreting ever-changing weather phenomena. How do changes to the ocean, land, and living things affect the atmosphere and, in turn, change the weather?

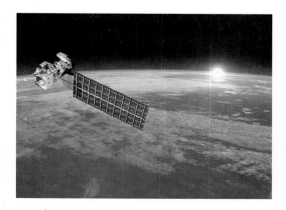

The Aqua satellite gathers and sends back data about water to scientists. The satellite, along with other weather tools, helps in forecasting weather. What tools help you to predict weather?

Lightning emerges from menacing storm clouds as severe weather moves in. People may be in danger on the ground below. What should you do during a severe weather event?

Hail can be smaller than a marble or grow as large as a softball! Hail is just one of many forms of precipitation. In what other ways have you seen how the water cycle affects weather?

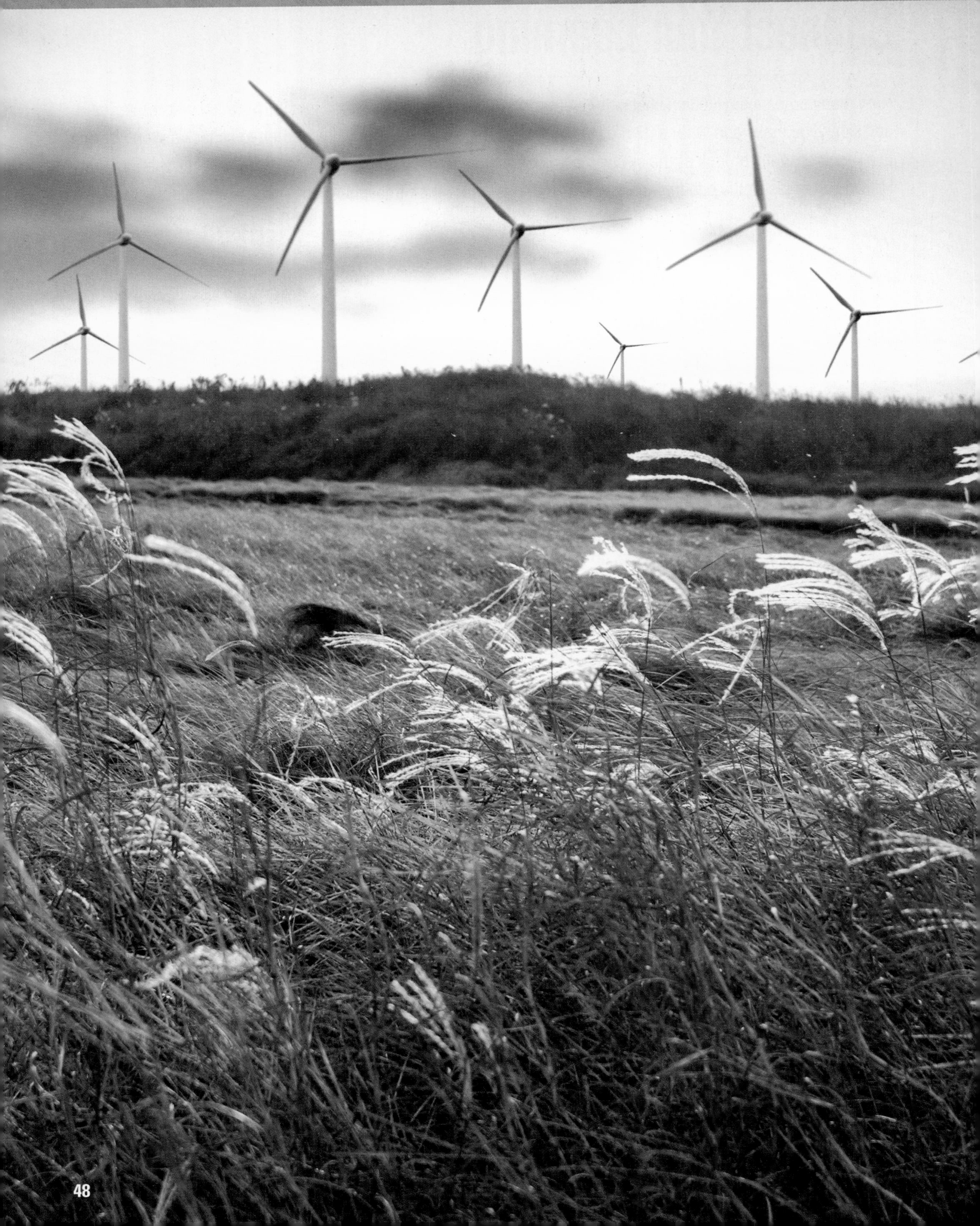

Air Pressure and Wind

You cannot see it but you can feel it—what is wind, and what makes it blow?

Introduction

On the day this photo was taken, the tall grasses were waving back and forth and the blades on the wind turbines in the distance were spinning. Of course, you know the cause is wind. But what is wind, and what causes it to blow? Why is wind strong enough to turn huge wind turbine blades one day, when it barely rustles the tall grass on other days?

Air is matter and wind is air in motion. Because air is matter, it has weight and can make objects move. When something is not heavy, people say it is "as light as air"—like the air has no weight at all. But the weight of air can be measured. The atmosphere contains an enormous amount of air and pushes down on the ground with a great force.

You have already learned about temperature, and now you will explore one of the important relationships in weather—between atmospheric pressure and wind. You will learn how atmospheric pressure varies with altitude, how it is measured, and how changes in it cause wind. You will explore how wind interacts with other parts of the Earth system and how it is involved in the flow of energy. You will conclude by finding out how engineers designed hang gliders so that people can soar on the winds.

Vocabulary

atmospheric pressure the weight of the air pushing down on an area; the force exerted over an area by all of the air above that area

density a property of matter that is equal to the amount of mass in a certain volume of matter

sea level the elevation of the land surface where the atmosphere meets the ocean

barometer a tool used to measure atmospheric pressure

wind air that is moving from a region of higher pressure to a region of lower pressure

anemometer a tool used to measure wind speed

convection cell a circulation of matter, such as air, caused by constantly rising warm matter and falling cool matter

prototype a working model of a design solution that can be used for testing and refining the design

---

Next Generation Science Standards

Performance Expectations

MS-ESS2-5. Collect data to provide evidence for how the motions and complex interactions of air masses results in changes in weather conditions.

MS-ESS2-6. Develop and use a model to describe how unequal heating and rotation of the Earth cause patterns of atmospheric and oceanic circulation that determine regional climates.

MS-ETS1-4. Develop a model to generate data for iterative testing and modification of a proposed object, tool, or process such that an optimal design can be achieved.

Science and Engineering Practices

Developing and Using Models • Develop and use a model to describe phenomena. • Develop a model to generate data to test ideas about designed systems, including those representing inputs and outputs.

Planning and Carrying Out Investigations
Collect data to produce data to serve as the basis for evidence to answer scientific questions or test design solutions under a range of conditions.

Crosscutting Concepts

Cause and Effect Cause and effect relationships may be used to predict phenomena in natural or designed systems.

Systems and System Models Models can be used to represent systems and their interactions—such as inputs, processes, and outputs—and energy, matter, and information flows within systems.

Disciplinary Core Ideas

ESS2.C. The complex patterns of the changes and the movement of water in the atmosphere, determined by winds, landforms, and ocean temperatures and currents, are major determinants of local weather patterns.

ESS2.D. Weather and climate are influenced by interactions involving sunlight, the ocean, the atmosphere, ice, landforms, and living things. These interactions vary with latitude, altitude, and local and regional geography, all of which can affect oceanic and atmospheric flow patterns.

ETS1.B. • A solution needs to be tested, and then modified on the basis of the test results, in order to improve it. • Models of all kinds are important for testing solutions.

ETS1.C. The iterative process of testing the most promising solutions and modifying what is proposed on the basis of the test results leads to greater refinement and ultimately to an optimal solution.

Although pressure within the tire increases as the tire is pumped up, air pressure outside the tire is also pushing against its outside walls—as well as on you and everything else on Earth.

1. Atmospheric Pressure

Air can affect the shape of things. How? A bike tire feels squishy when it goes flat because it does not have enough air in it. You have to pump it full of air to make it firm again. So, how does adding air to a bike tire help it keep its shape?

Pumping air into a bike tire increases the pressure inside the tire. **Pressure** is a force applied to a certain area, with force being any push or pull. The girl pushing down on the pump in the photo is exerting a force on the handle of the pump. The particles in the air also push on the inside of the tire when they bump into the sides of the tire tube. As more air is pumped into the tire, more particles bump into the tube sides, increasing the pressure of the air inside the tire.

The pressure of the air inside the tire is not the whole story behind why bike tires need to be filled with air. The air outside of the tire is also pushing against the outside walls of the tire. In fact, all of the air in the atmosphere above the tire is pressing down on the tire. Air may be very light, but there are many kilometers of air above the bike tire as well as above you. Earth's gravity pulls on all of this air, giving it weight. **Atmospheric pressure** is the weight of the air pushing down on an area and is often measured in millibars (mb). It pushes down on you, the bike, the ground under the bike, and everything else on Earth.

Pressure increases as the density of air increases. **Density** is a property of matter that is equal to the amount of mass in a certain volume of matter. For air, density depends on the number of particles that are in a given volume. You can use the model in Figure 4.1A to explain this relationship. The model on the left represents air at sea level, while the one on the right represents air at the top of Mount Whitney. Notice that there are more particles in the same volume of air at sea level than on top of the mountain. The models show that air is less dense at higher altitudes than at lower altitudes. As a result, atmospheric pressure is also lower at higher altitudes than at lower altitudes.

Figure 4.1A

These particle models, shown in the circles, compare the density of equal volumes of air at sea level and at the top of Mount Whitney in California. The air is less dense on the top of the mountain because it contains fewer particles there than at sea level.

The Density of Air Depends on Altitude

Sea level,
0 km (0 ft)

Top of Mt. Whitney,
4.4 km (14,505 ft)

The density of air in the atmosphere decreases as altitude increases because gravity pulls air downward. The density of air depends on altitude because gases are highly compressible. That means that air's volume will shrink when you press on it. In the atmosphere, air presses down on the air below it. Think of a tall stack of pancakes. The pancake on top will be the fluffiest because no other pancakes are pressing down on it. The pancake on the bottom will be a bit squished because the weight of all the other pancakes is pressing down on it. As a result, that bottom pancake will be a little bit denser than the pancakes above it.

Just like the bottom pancake, the air at the bottom of the troposphere is compressed by all the air above it. Therefore, air is more dense at sea level. **Sea level** is the elevation of the land surface where the atmosphere meets the ocean. It is the starting point for altitude measurements at 0 kilometers (km). Some places on land, such as New Orleans, Louisiana, are a few meters below sea level. Others, such as the top of Mount Whitney, California, are more than a kilometer above sea level. Therefore, the density of air in New Orleans is greater than the density of the air on top of Mount Whitney.

Atmospheric pressure decreases as altitude increases. This is because the density of air decreases the higher you go. The graph in Figure 4.1B shows this. At sea level, such as the shoreline of San Francisco, California, the atmospheric pressure is 1,013 mb. In Denver, Colorado, at about 1.6 km above sea level, atmospheric pressure is 840 mb. At the top of Mount Whitney, about 4.4 km above sea level, atmospheric pressure is about 600 mb. At 10 km above sea level—the top of the troposphere in some places—atmospheric pressure is only about 260 mb. Did you notice how much lower the density of air is at 10 km than at sea level? This explains why commercial aircraft cabins must be pressurized.

Thus, there is a cause-and-effect relationship between altitude and atmospheric pressure. A cause-and-effect relationship is a connection between events in which one event is caused by another event. When altitude increases, atmospheric pressure decreases; this relationship can help you predict how atmospheric pressure will vary from place to place in the world.

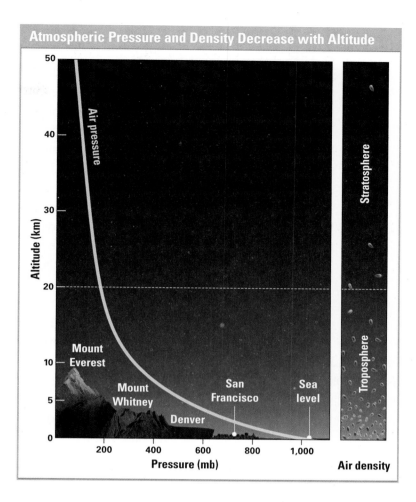

Atmospheric Pressure and Density Decrease with Altitude

Figure 4.1B
There is a cause-and-effect relationship between altitude and atmospheric pressure. The density of air decreases as altitude increases. As the density of air decreases, note how the atmospheric pressure also decreases rapidly.

2. How Atmospheric Pressure Is Measured

Beyond the thermosphere, the density of air is extremely low. There, outer space is considered a vacuum, or empty space. Scientists can make vacuums in containers at sea level, too. How was the first vacuum made?

In 1643, Italian physicist Evangelista Torricelli invented the first human-made vacuum. He removed almost all the air from a container without letting the surrounding air flow back in. Figure 4.2 shows how he did this. He filled a thin glass tube, sealed at one end, with liquid mercury. Next, he flipped the tube over into a dish of mercury. Some, but not all, of the mercury flowed out of the tube into the dish, leaving an airless space, or vacuum, at the top of the tube.

The weight of the atmosphere pushing down on the mercury in the dish keeps all the mercury from flowing out of the tube. When there is more atmospheric pressure, there is more force pushing on the surface of the mercury in the dish. So, more mercury moves up the tube and reduces the space of the vacuum. Thus, the height of mercury in the tube increases as atmospheric pressure increases and decreases as pressure decreases. Torricelli's tube of mercury was also the first **barometer,** a tool that is used to measure atmospheric pressure.

Torricelli observed that the height of the mercury in the tube changed from day to day. Atmospheric pressure at a given location depends on weather, as well as altitude. It is usually higher when air is colder because cold air is denser than hot air. Likewise, pressure is usually lower when air is warmer and therefore less dense.

Scientists today do not use mercury barometers. They mostly use digital barometers to analyze changes in atmospheric pressure to help them forecast the weather. When these changes are measured in conjunction with other factors such as temperature, cloud formation, and wind, scientists can predict approaching weather more accurately.

Figure 4.2

Evangelista Torricelli's barometer used a mercury-filled tube turned upside down in a dish of mercury to measure atmospheric pressure. As air pressure increases, more force pushes down on the mercury in the dish, causing the mercury to rise in the tube. The height of the mercury in the tube can be measured by the scale. Mercury has since been found to be harmful to handle, so scientists today typically will use aneroid or digital barometers.

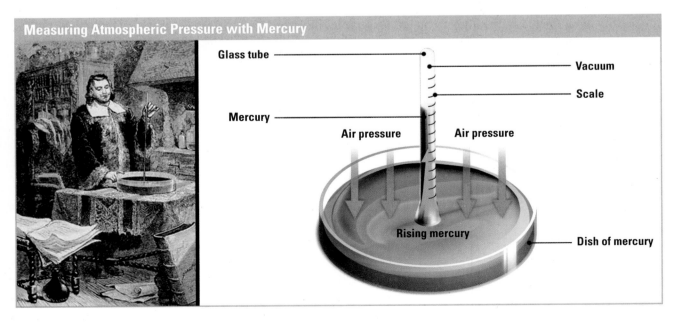

Measuring Atmospheric Pressure with Mercury

Glass tube

Vacuum

Scale

Mercury

Air pressure

Air pressure

Rising mercury

Dish of mercury

Differences in Atmospheric Pressure Cause Wind

Cold air

Warm air

Higher pressure

Wind

Lower pressure

Figure 4.3A
Wind is moving air that blows from regions of high pressure to those of low pressure. Because dense cold air flows toward less dense warm air, wind also usually blows from colder areas to warmer areas.

3. Wind

Most people do not notice changes in air pressure, especially small ones. But, they certainly notice when a strong wind whips through tree branches. How are wind and air pressure related?

The atmospheric pressures at a given altitude only vary by a relatively small amount. However, small differences in atmospheric pressure from place to place cause *wind*. **Wind** is air moving from a region of higher pressure to a region of lower pressure. Look at the model that relates wind to pressure in Figure 4.3A. The air from the higher pressure area flows to the lower pressure area. Remember, cold air is denser and has a higher pressure than warm air does. So, wind usually blows from colder regions toward warmer ones.

Wind speeds vary from day to day and even throughout the day. Some days may be very calm, with only a gentle wind rustling tall grass, while other days the wind may be so strong that you feel like you might be blown over. The gentle wind is air that is moving slowly, while the strong winds mean that the air is moving quickly.

Differences in atmospheric pressure cause wind, and increasing the difference in atmospheric pressure causes wind speed to increase. Thus, a gentle wind is caused by a small difference in pressure, and a higher wind speed is caused by a larger difference in pressure. Scientists use this cause-and-effect relationship to predict wind speeds so that they can forecast damaging high-speed winds. By determining the pressure differences across a region, they can calculate the expected wind speed.

Wind speed is often measured in units of kilometers per hour (km/h). In the United States, it is traditionally expressed in units of miles per hour (mph). An **anemometer** is a tool used to measure wind speed. The photo shows one type of anemometer, which has little cups that are pushed by the wind. The faster the cups rotate, the higher the wind speed.

Wind speed increases as the difference in pressure increases. Anemometers are instruments that measure wind speed. Wind pushes on the cups of this anemometer, making them rotate. The faster the wind speed, the faster the cups move.

The Beaufort Scale			
Beaufort Number	Wind Speed (km/h)		Effect
0	< 1		Smoke rises straight up.
1	1–5		Smoke is blown in the direction wind is going.
2	6–11		Leaves rustle. You feel wind on your face.
3	12–19	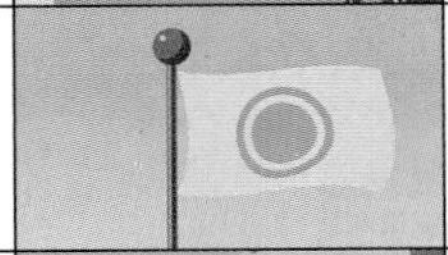	Light flags stretch out.
4	20–28		Dust is blown. Small branches move.
5	29–38		Small trees sway.
6	39–49		Large branches move.
7	50–61		Large trees move.
8	62–74	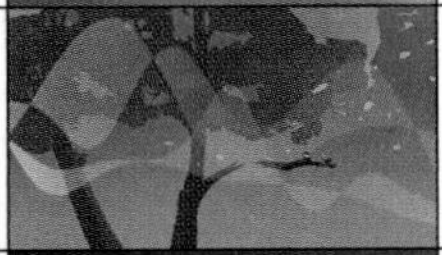	Twigs break off trees.
9	75–88		Shingles are blown off buildings.
10	89–102	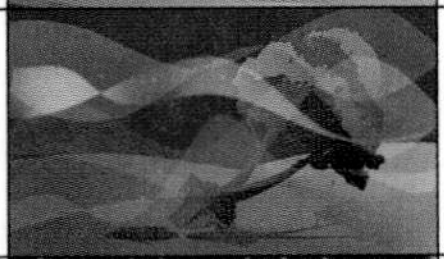	Trees are uprooted.
11	103–117		Widespread damage occurs.
12	≥118	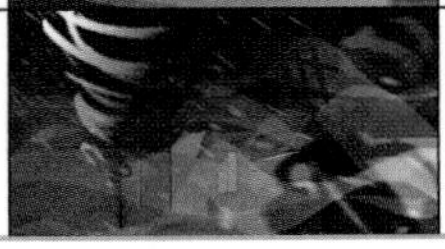	Severe hurricane damage

What effect could higher wind speeds have on the environment around you? The Beaufort Scale, shown in Figure 4.3B, describes the effect winds of different speeds have on the surroundings. This scale was originally developed in 1805 by Commander Francis Beaufort of the British Navy as a way for sailors to classify the effects of different wind speeds upon a man-of-war sailing ship while out at sea. Today, it also includes the effects of wind on land. For example, according to the Beaufort Scale, leaves will rustle at approximately 6–11 km/h, yet shingles are blown off rooftops when winds reach approximately 75–88 km/h. While this scale is not often used in forecasts anymore, it allows you to use your own observations of wind to estimate wind speed if you do not have an anemometer. You can give it a try by simply looking outside on a windy day.

In addition to its speed, wind is described by the direction from which it is blowing across Earth's surface. Winds are named after the direction they blow from. For example, a 10 km/h northwesterly wind is blowing from the northwest toward the southeast. That means the wind would be blowing in your face if you are facing the northwest. A 30 km/h easterly wind is blowing from the east toward the west three times as fast as a 10 km/h wind.

Now when you hear that a 10 km/h northwesterly wind is forecast, you know more about the weather than just the wind speed and direction. You also know that the atmospheric pressure is higher and the temperature is colder in the northwest than in the southeast because winds blow from high pressure to low pressure. And, according to the Beaufort Scale, if you hear instead that an 89 km/h wind is forecast, you know it is a good idea to stay inside if you can!

Figure 4.3B
Wind is described by its speed and the direction from which it is blowing. The Beaufort Scale classifies wind speeds based on their effects on the surroundings. This 200-year-old scale allows you to estimate wind speed without the use of an anemometer by using observation of your surroundings instead.

4. Wind in the Earth System

The Beaufort Scale is a historic scale that is not often used today. However, it is based, in part, on the effect of wind's force upon things. How else does wind affect parts of the Earth system?

Wind interacting with the biosphere is seen in animals using wind for transportation and wind spreading plant seeds and pollen. Gliding birds, such as albatrosses, depend on winds above the water to glide and soar long distances over the ocean without flapping their wings. The dandelion seed is attached to a bit of fluff, which wind carries away from the parent plant to a new place to grow. This fluff floats on the slightest of breezes, as shown in the photo.

Winds can also affect living things by making them feel cooler. *Wind chill* describes how much colder the temperature feels because of wind moving over your uncovered skin. Thermal energy transfers from your body to the air around your skin, and this air is replaced by cooler air when the wind is blowing. Because your skin is constantly transferring thermal energy to cool air, your skin temperature decreases and the air temperature feels cooler to you than it actually is. Wind chill increases as wind speed increases because higher speed winds replace air around you faster and make temperatures feel cooler. Strong winds can be dangerous on a cold day because your skin can freeze quickly.

Wind interacts with the geosphere and hydrosphere by moving materials, making waves, and increasing evaporation. It blows parts of the geosphere, such as sand and soil, from place to place. As the wind blows materials over land, it erodes rocks, hills, and mountains. As the wind blows over the ocean and other bodies of water, it transfers energy to the water and makes waves. High-speed winds can result in large waves, and it also increases how quickly water evaporates into the atmosphere.

Wind occurs in the atmosphere but affects the biosphere, geosphere, and hydrosphere in various ways. Birds use wind to glide, and winds spread the seeds of plants. Wind makes the air feel colder to the skin. Wind also moves sand, soil, and rocks, causes waves, and hastens evaporation.

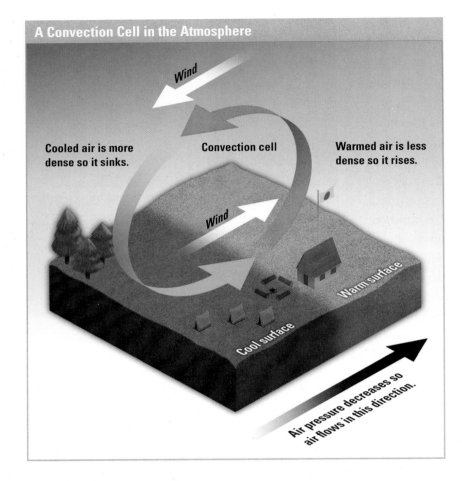

A Convection Cell in the Atmosphere

Wind

Cooled air is more dense so it sinks.

Convection cell

Warmed air is less dense so it rises.

Wind

Warm surface

Cool surface

Air pressure decreases so air flows in this direction.

Figure 4.5

A cycle of rising warm air and falling cold air forms a circulation of air in the atmosphere called a *convection cell*. Wind is the horizontal flow of air in a convection cell. The uneven heating of Earth by the sun causes convection cells by producing areas of high and low pressure.

5. Convection Cells

Moving sand and creating ocean waves are examples of the effects of wind transferring energy between the atmosphere and other parts of the Earth system. But where does wind get that energy from?

The sun is the original source of the wind's energy. Without the sun, there would be no difference in temperature, and thus, no difference in pressure. Winds occur because different parts of Earth's surface are heated unequally by sunlight. Cooler land and water cool the air above them, causing a region of higher pressure to form. Warmer parts of the land and bodies of water warm the air above them, causing a region of lower pressure to form. Air flows from the regions of high pressure to the regions of low pressure.

Areas of high and low pressure are connected by a circular pattern of air flow. A **convection cell** is a circulation of matter, such as air, caused by constantly rising warm matter and falling cold matter. Examine the movement of warm and cold air in the model of a convection cell in Figure 4.5. Notice that the circle is perpendicular to Earth's surface. The air moves in this circle because cold air is denser than warm air. The warm air over hotter surfaces rises because it is less dense than the surrounding air. At higher altitudes, the warm air cools and becomes denser. The rising air creates an area of high pressure at high altitudes. Eventually, the air becomes dense enough to sink down to the surface. At high altitudes, the pressure is low where the air is sinking and the air flows horizontally from high- to low-pressure areas. At the surface, the cooler, denser air flows in to take the place of the rising air. You already know about this horizontal flow of air—it is wind.

Some convection cells on Earth are very large, and others are smaller. Large, global convection cells transfer energy from the warm equator to the cooler, higher latitudes. These convection cells lead to global wind patterns. Smaller convection cells also transfer energy daily in the atmosphere where large bodies of water meet the land. That is why the weather at the beach may be very windy in the afternoon when the air has heated up inland.

Sea and Land Breezes

These models show the convection cells where land and large bodies of water meet. Remember, water changes temperature more slowly than land. Even though the land and nearby water receive the same amount of sunlight, the land warms up more quickly than water during the day and cools off more slowly at night. The resulting wind patterns are called *sea breezes* and *land breezes*.

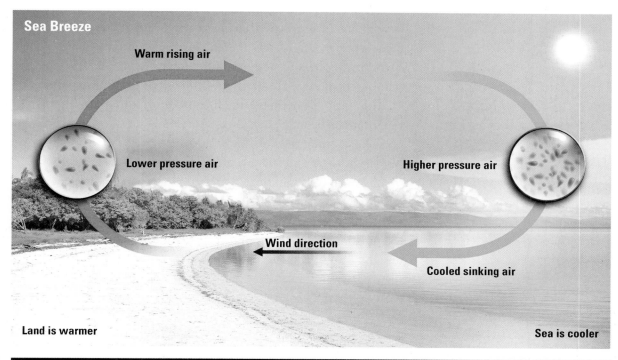

Sea Breeze

Warm rising air

Lower pressure air

Higher pressure air

Wind direction

Cooled sinking air

Land is warmer

Sea is cooler

Land Breeze

Warm rising air

Higher pressure air

Lower pressure air

Wind direction

Cooled sinking air

Land is cooler

Sea is warmer

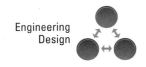

6. Designing Hang Gliders to Ride the Wind

Birds are not the only living things that can glide on air. Humans have also learned how to use wind to soar at great heights above Earth. However, they need to use technology to do it. How did engineers develop a safe design for hang gliders?

Hang gliders are different from airplanes—they do not have motors. Yet, like airplanes, they are heavier than air and are pulled to the ground. To launch hang gliders, pilots usually jump off the edge of a cliff and ride winds that blow up a hillside.

In 1891, German engineer Otto Lilienthal designed the first glider by applying his studies of the physics of bird flight. He drew detailed models of his designs, and then he made a prototype. A **prototype** is a working model of a design solution that can be used for testing and refining the design. He also built a hill to test his prototype.

After testing a design, Lilienthal modified it to try to improve it. For example, he made the wings shorter so that the glider could hold up against stronger winds. He would continue to test and improve his designs over and over again based on his test results. In an effort to maximize the flight time, he tested more than 16 different glider designs in this way. His longest flight was a short 15 seconds. His research came to an end in 1896, when he died in a fatal crash caused by a gust of wind. The crash revealed one of the limitations of his glider designs—it was difficult to control.

Otto Lilienthal was known as the "Flying Man" of Germany. He is shown here testing one of his gliders. He created multiple prototypes for his glider designs and tested them carefully. He upheld the idea that researchers should jump before they fly, suggesting they should work their way up to increasingly powerful gliders based on initial, modest successes.

Jet planes were flying across the skies before the next major advance in hang glider design. In the late 1940s, engineer Francis Rogallo designed a large flexible wing that resembled a kite, which became known as the *Rogallo wing*. Although the wing had an advantage over Lilienthal's designs in that it could be easily steered, the kite-like wing was not the end in improvements in hang glider design. Most modern hang gliders now include an A-shaped frame under the wing to support the pilot and an easy way to steer the glider. To improve the design of hang gliders, engineers need to understand winds in the atmosphere. For each improvement in glider design, engineers follow an iterative process, following a cycle of testing, modifying, retesting, and modifying again until the optimum design is reached.

Hang glider safety has improved since Lilienthal's time and continues to improve with newer designs and modifications. However, hang gliding is a dangerous sport and is not something to attempt without proper training. Pilots need months of training before gliding through the air. It is important for pilots to have a thorough understanding of wind and weather conditions before they fly.

Engineers have made many improvements to hang gliders since the first hang gliders of Lilienthal's time. However, pilots of hang gliders must continue to understand winds and be well-trained to glide safely.

LESSON SUMMARY

Air Pressure and Wind

Atmospheric Pressure Atmospheric pressure is the weight of air pressing down on a certain area. Pressure increases as the density of air increases. Thus, air is more dense and atmospheric pressure is higher at lower altitudes than at higher altitudes.

How Atmospheric Pressure Is Measured Evangelista Torricelli invented the mercury barometer. In this type of barometer, the height of mercury in a glass tube increases as atmospheric pressure increases. Atmospheric pressure changes in a given place are related to changes in the weather.

Wind Wind is air that flows from areas of high pressure to areas of low pressure. Wind speed is measured with an anemometer and increases as the difference in pressure increases. Descriptions of wind also include the direction from which the wind is blowing.

Wind in the Earth System Wind in the atmosphere interacts with the biosphere, geosphere, and hydrosphere. It transports seeds and is used by birds to glide. It also causes wind chill, erodes rocks, moves soil, produces waves, and contributes to evaporation.

Convection Cells Convection cells are circular air patterns that are formed by constantly rising warm air and sinking cooled air. They are driven by the uneven heating of Earth by energy from the sun.

Designing Hang Gliders to Ride the Wind The design of hang gliders has been improved by many engineers over decades. For each improvement, engineers followed an iterative or continual process.

Into the Death Zone

Indiana native Arnetta is visiting her friend Katie in Colorado, and the two of them decide to go hiking in the mountains with Katie's friends, Mike and Jamal. After ten minutes of walking, Arnetta exclaims, "Why am I so out of breath? I feel like I'm going to die!" Katie laughs and explains that Arnetta must not be used to the thin air on the mountain. What is "thin air," and why is it found on mountains?

"Thin air" is a term that is used to describe air that has less oxygen in it than air at or near sea level. Air is thin at high elevations, so people encounter thin air on mountains. Why air is thin at high elevations has to do with atmospheric pressure.

The weight of the atmosphere exerts a force known as atmospheric pressure. Atmospheric pressure is related to altitude. Air pressure will decrease as elevation increases. In reverse, as elevation goes down, air pressure goes up. Atmospheric pressure is also related to the density of air: as atmospheric pressure decreases, air density will decrease. Therefore, as elevation goes up, air density goes down.

Low-density air has fewer particles in a given volume than high-density air. These particles include oxygen particles that people need to breathe. So, when Arnetta is hiking on a mountain and breathes in a lungful of low-density air, she breathes in fewer oxygen particles than she was used to breathing in her home state of Indiana. Because she is taking in fewer oxygen particles, she becomes out of breath easily.

Atmospheric pressure decreases with elevation, so pressure is lower at the top of a mountain than it is at the base of the mountain. As a result, people hiking on mountains breathe lower-density air, which is also called *thin air*.

To the Top of the World

If you went for a hike in the Colorado Rocky Mountains, you might walk around at elevations of 2,000–4,000 m above sea level. Those elevations are much higher than what most people in the United States are used to, but they are not very high compared to the highest mountains on Earth.

With an elevation of 8,850 m, Mount Everest, in the Himalayas, is the highest peak in the world. The air is so thin on Mount Everest that it is dangerous for people to go there. In fact, any elevation above 7,600 m is part of the so-called *death zone*. That's a name used by mountain climbers to describe where people might die due to a lack of oxygen.

Not everyone who goes up to the death zone dies, but many can get *altitude sickness*. Altitude sickness is caused by a lack of oxygen and can have a variety of symptoms. Some symptoms are mild, such as headaches, lack of appetite, and trouble sleeping. But other symptoms are more serious, such as loss of vision or brain damage. In the worst cases of altitude sickness, a person's lungs may fill with fluid or their brain may swell, either of which can cause death. Despite these dangers, hundreds of people attempt to climb Mount Everest each year for a chance to stand at the top of the world.

Mount Everest has an elevation of 8,850 m and is the tallest mountain on Earth. The air on the mountain is so dangerously thin that mountain climbers call the area above 7,600 m the *death zone*.

The Mount Everest Base Camp is located at 5,400 m above sea level and is the first place that climbers rest on their way up the mountain. Climbers need to rest to give their bodies time to adjust to the thin air.

Almost all people who climb Mount Everest breathe oxygen from tanks to stay alive. This climber is wearing an oxygen mask to avoid altitude sickness.

Stopping for Safety

The key to surviving a trip to the death zone is patience. Mountain climbers who want to climb Mount Everest or other very tall mountains have to give their bodies time to get used to the thinning air. To do so, they must climb the mountain slowly. They can do this by going only around 15 km each day or by resting at camps no more than 300 m higher at the end of each day.

Mount Everest has five established camps that are at elevations ranging from 5,400 m to 8,000 m above sea level. Some people stop for several days at each camp on their way up Mount Everest. The stops allow people's bodies to adjust and allow them to get much-needed rest. During their stay at a camp, people actually climb up beyond the camp and then climb back down to spend the night. This practice helps them adjust to climbing at high altitudes. Climbers also wait out bad weather at the camps.

Another way that climbers can avoid the more serious effects of altitude sickness is to carry oxygen. Typically, Mount Everest climbers carry or have access to oxygen tanks to use in case of emergencies, and almost all climbers breathe oxygen from tanks at some point during their climb. The air near the top is just too thin for people to breathe, especially when they are also exerting a lot of effort to climb up the sometimes steep and always very cold mountain.

Sherpa Guides

Another key to surviving a trek up Mount Everest is the help of Sherpa guides. The Sherpa are a group of people most of whom live high in the Himalaya Mountains. Mountain-climbing Sherpa guides have been assisting climbers from Western countries since the 1920s. In fact, Tenzing Norgay was the Sherpa guide who assisted Sir Edmund Hillary. Together, they completed the first known successful trip to the top of Mount Everest in 1953. Today, Sherpa guides help climbers by carrying supplies, setting up camps, attaching climbing ropes to the side of the mountain, and looking out for the climbers' safety.

Sherpa guides are important because they are experienced climbers familiar with the area. They are also biologically adapted to living and working in the thin air. Scientists found that cells in the bodies of Sherpas were more efficient at using oxygen than the cells of people who had not lived at high altitudes for generations. They also found that the Sherpas' blood circulation did not slow down at high altitudes as other people's circulation did. Blood carries oxygen to different parts of the body, so better circulation means that oxygen can be distributed easier to muscles and other organs.

Because of their biological differences, the Sherpa are better able to function normally in thin air. If a Sherpa went hiking with Arnetta in Colorado, he might find it odd that she thinks she's going to die. After all, she's nowhere near the death zone! ◆

The Sherpa are a group of people who have lived in the Himalaya Mountains for generations. These Sherpa guides are carrying supplies up Mount Everest for climbers who are attempting to reach the top.

Water and the Weather

How does water affect weather as it cycles through the Earth system?

Introduction

In the photo, the tallest of the distant snow-capped peaks is hidden by dark, threatening clouds. However, the misty valley and its rushing stream are lit up by beams of sunlight. In this setting, how does water move from snow to the stream to the clouds? Where is water changing from a liquid to a gas or to a solid? Which processes require gravity?

Water continuously cycles through the Earth system, changing its location and its state. The snow on a mountain may melt and flow down to the stream. Water in the clouds may fall as rain and snow, while water in the stream evaporates into the atmosphere. Trillions upon trillions of water particles evaporate from Earth's surface every second. And, nearly all the energy needed for this cycling of water comes from the sun—Earth's ultimate energy source! As water makes its journey through the water cycle and changes state, it transfers energy to and from the surrounding environment.

You may not be able to see all the processes by which water moves between different parts of the Earth system. But in this lesson, you will use models of the water cycle to help you understand these mechanisms and how they affect weather. You will learn the details about how water enters and leaves the atmosphere. You will also explore how the water cycle affects the characteristics of the atmosphere. Finally, you will learn how engineers choose designs for systems to clean wastewater in a town.

Vocabulary

groundwater water located underground that fills pore spaces in soil and rock layers

water cycle the movement of water through the Earth system

transpiration the evaporation of water from the leaves of plants

absolute humidity the amount of water vapor in a given volume of air, usually expressed as grams per cubic meter (g/m³)

relative humidity the ratio, usually expressed as a percentage, of the actual amount of water vapor in air to the maximum amount of water vapor air can hold at the same temperature

dew water droplets that form on surfaces due to condensation of water vapor

dew point the temperature at which air is saturated with water vapor

crystallization the formation of a solid structure whose atoms or molecules are arranged in a repeating, three-dimensional pattern

precipitation solid or liquid water that falls from clouds to the ground

Next Generation Science Standards

Performance Expectations

MS-ESS2-4. Develop a model to describe the cycling of water through Earth's systems driven by energy from the sun and the force of gravity.

MS-ETS1-2. Evaluate competing design solutions using a systematic process to determine how well they meet the criteria and constraints of the problem.

Science and Engineering Practices

Developing and Using Models Develop a model to describe unobservable mechanisms.

Engaging in Argument from Evidence Evaluate competing design solutions based on jointly developed and agreed-upon design criteria.

Crosscutting Concepts

Energy and Matter Within a natural or designed system, the transfer of energy drives the motion and/or cycling of matter.

Disciplinary Core Ideas

ESS2.C. • Water continually cycles among land, ocean, and atmosphere via transpiration, evaporation, condensation and crystallization, and precipitation, as well as downhill flows on land. • Global movements of water and its changes in form are propelled by sunlight and gravity.

ETS1.B. There are systematic processes for evaluating solutions with respect to how well they meet the criteria and constraints of a problem.

1. Sun, Gravity, and the Water Cycle

You sweat when you exercise, but the water particles in sweat do not usually just stay on your skin. As they dry, they evaporate into the air, and days later, those same water particles may fall on someone else as rain. Where is water found in the Earth system?

The hydrosphere is unevenly distributed on Earth. About 97 percent of Earth's water is found in the ocean. The atmosphere contains only 0.001 percent of the total water on Earth. Water is also found in other places, including ice, freshwater (water that is not salty), living things, and the ground. **Groundwater** is water located underground that fills pore spaces in soil and rock layers.

The **water cycle** is the movement of water through the Earth system. It is driven by the energy from the sun and by gravity. Figure 5.1 models this cycle, including mechanisms that you cannot directly observe, such as evaporation. Water in the atmosphere, above ground, in groundwater, and in living things are all part of the water cycle.

Energy from the sun drives evaporation, causing liquid water at Earth's surface to change to water vapor that enters the atmosphere. Plants also give off water vapor through their leaves as they use energy from the sun to grow. Once in the atmosphere, water vapor may change back into liquid water from condensation.

Gravity causes the downward movement of water and pulls larger water droplets and ice crystals toward the ground as raindrops, snowflakes, or small icy balls of hail or sleet. During infiltration, water seeps into the ground. Gravity also causes water to flow downhill over the surface as runoff. Runoff and groundwater feed streams, rivers, lakes, and the ocean, and the sun provides energy for water to evaporate from any of these places into the atmosphere again.

Figure 5.1

The water cycle is the movement of water through the Earth system. It is driven by energy from the sun and by the pull of gravity. During the water cycle, water moving through bodies of water, the ground, and the atmosphere continuously cycles through the parts of the Earth system.

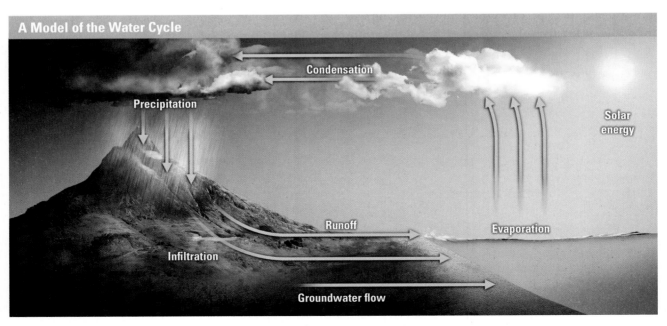

A Model of the Water Cycle

Condensation

Precipitation

Solar energy

Runoff

Evaporation

Infiltration

Groundwater flow

2. Evaporation and Transpiration

Spring rains fill the lake at the park. However, during a dry summer, you notice that its water level keeps getting lower and lower, and the ground around it dries out. Where did the lake's water go?

Most water vapor in the atmosphere comes from evaporation of liquid water at the enormous surfaces of Earth's oceans. Water in lakes, rivers, and the surface of the soil also evaporates. What happens during evaporation? Remember, water changes state from a liquid to a gas when it evaporates. Water particles in liquid water are always moving and bumping into each other, and some of these particles have more kinetic energy than others. At the surface of liquid water, some particles have enough kinetic energy to escape the liquid and become water vapor.

Water also enters the atmosphere through **transpiration**, which is the evaporation of water from the leaves of plants. The water in the leaves comes from the soil as plant roots absorb groundwater and the water travels up the stem of the plant to its leaves. Similar to the pores in your skin that allow you to sweat, plants have tiny openings on the underside of their leaves. Water vapor escapes through these pores back into the atmosphere. Thus, groundwater enters the atmosphere through plant transpiration.

Evaporation and transpiration occur more quickly on a hot day. Water evaporates faster at high temperatures because more water particles have enough energy to escape the liquid surface or leaf. Figure 5.2 shows this movement. The kinetic energy of moving water particles ultimately comes from energy from the sun. So, energy from the sun that is absorbed by water and plants drives evaporation and transpiration in the water cycle.

Figure 5.2

Most water enters the atmosphere by evaporation of water at Earth's surface. Water also evaporates from plants through their leaves by transpiration. Energy from the sun drives these processes.

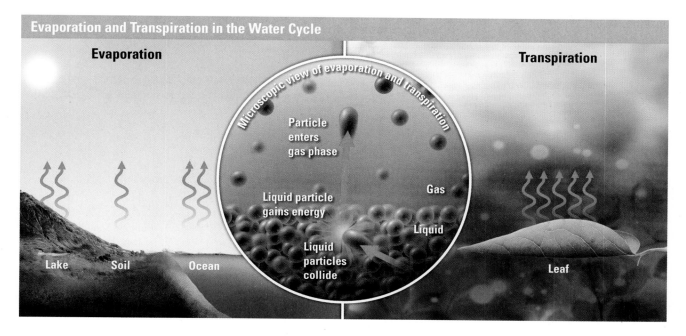

Evaporation and Transpiration in the Water Cycle

Evaporation

Transpiration

Microscopic view of evaporation and transpiration

Particle enters gas phase

Gas

Liquid particle gains energy

Liquid

Liquid particles collide

Lake   Soil   Ocean

Leaf

Places such as the Everglades near Miami, Florida (top photo), are described as humid because they have a high absolute humidity. Phoenix, Arizona, in the Sonoran Desert (bottom photo), is considered dry. Relative humidity is the ratio of the amount of water in the air to the amount of water in saturated air.

3. Humidity

Even when the temperatures in the Everglades near Miami and Phoenix in the Sonoran Desert are the same, the air may feel very different. The air often feels stickier in Miami than in Phoenix. Why?

Differences in the amount of water vapor in the atmosphere affect the way the air feels. *Humidity* is the general term used to describe the amount of water vapor in the atmosphere at a given time and place. **Absolute humidity** is the amount of water vapor in a given volume of air, usually expressed as grams per cubic meter (g/m³). A higher absolute humidity means there is more water vapor in the air. For example, the air in Miami often contains more water vapor than the air in Phoenix. Therefore, the absolute humidity is higher in Miami and the air feels muggy. The air in Phoenix feels very dry because the absolute humidity is low. You can see the difference absolute humidity makes in these two locations by comparing the photos.

The amount of water vapor that air can hold depends on its temperature. Just like when a sponge is sopping and cannot hold any more liquid, air is *saturated* when it cannot hold any more water. **Relative humidity** is the ratio of the actual amount of water vapor in the air (absolute humidity) to the maximum amount of water vapor that the air can hold at the same temperature. Figure 5.3 shows how temperature affects the amount of water vapor that air can hold before saturation. The amount of water vapor that air can hold increases as the temperature increases. When weather reports refer to humidity, values of relative humidity are expressed as a percentage. This formula shows how to calculate the relative humidity in a specific volume:

$$\text{relative humidity (\%)} = \frac{\text{amount of water vapor in air}}{\text{amount of water vapor the air can hold}} \times 100$$

So, for example, the relative humidity in Miami might be 75 percent while the relative humidity in Phoenix might be 16 percent.

Figure 5.3

The amount of water vapor that air can hold increases as temperature increases. The blue line represents the maximum amount of water vapor the air can hold at a given temperature.

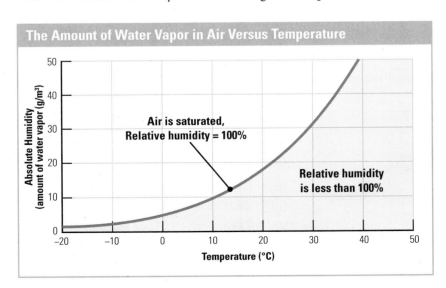

4. Dew and Condensation

You walk through the grass on a cool morning. Even though it hasn't rained and the grass was not watered by sprinklers, your shoes are all wet. Why is the grass wet in the morning?

Grass may be wet in the morning because it is covered with water droplets that formed at night. **Dew** is water droplets that form on surfaces due to condensation of water vapor. Condensation is the opposite change of state of evaporation. Water particles in water vapor come together to form drops of liquid water during condensation. Just as evaporation occurred when water absorbed energy, water releases energy during condensation.

Dew forms at the **dew point,** which is the temperature at which air is saturated with water vapor. The dew point depends on the amount of water vapor in the air, so it can vary. The dew point is higher when the amount of water vapor is greater, and lower when the air is drier. At the dew point, air is saturated, so liquid water condenses out of the air. Another way to say this is that relative humidity is 100 percent at the dew point.

Tiny water droplets, called dew, form when water vapor in the air condenses at the dew point. The dew point is the temperature at which air is saturated with water. Dew forms at night when the air temperature cools to the dew point.

Dew forms as the air cools at night. As the temperature decreases, the amount of water vapor that the air can hold also decreases. Consider a day when the dew point is 20°C. Dew does not form during the day when the temperature is greater than 20°C. During the night, the air cools to 20°C and the relative humidity reaches 100 percent. Water condenses out of the air onto blades of grass, as well as other surfaces, as liquid droplets—dew. Think about walking through dew-covered grass early in the morning. As the sun warms up the air during the morning, air can hold more water. So, the dew evaporates and becomes water vapor again, and you can walk through the grass without getting your shoes wet!

When the dew point is below 0°C, tiny ice crystals form instead of liquid water. Frost is a thin layer of ice crystals that forms on surfaces, such as grass. Frost forms at the frost point, which is the dew point when the temperature is below freezing or 0°C.

Fog is water droplets that are suspended in the air near the ground. It forms when the temperature drops below the dew point. Instead of forming dew on cool surfaces, droplets of water form in the air, making a cloud near the ground like the one in the photo at the beginning of this lesson.

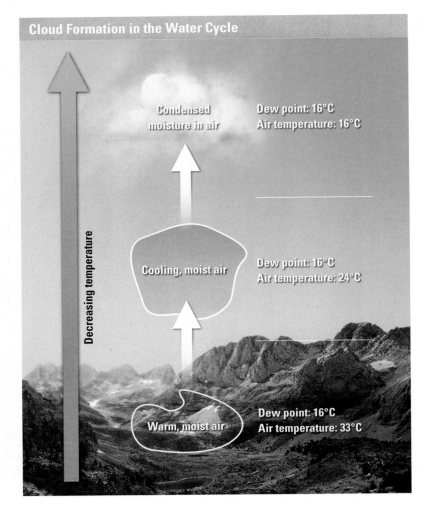

Cloud Formation in the Water Cycle

Decreasing temperature

Condensed moisture in air — Dew point: 16°C / Air temperature: 16°C

Cooling, moist air — Dew point: 16°C / Air temperature: 24°C

Warm, moist air — Dew point: 16°C / Air temperature: 33°C

Figure 5.5A

Clouds are made of water droplets or ice crystals. Water droplets form around dust, salt, or smoke particles as moist air rises and cools to the dew point, causing water vapor to condense. Clouds are an important part of the water cycle as water changes state when clouds form and clouds transport water back to Earth's surface.

5. Clouds

Even on a humid day, you cannot see the tiny particles of water vapor in the air around you, but you can see clouds in the sky. They may be the wispy clouds that appear on pleasant days and look like they were painted with a stroke of a paintbrush. Or they may look like puffy cotton balls or a thick, gray ceiling during storms. How do clouds form and why are they different?

A cloud is a collection of liquid water droplets or solid ice crystals that you can see. The water droplets or ice crystals in clouds are so tiny that they can stay in air. Gravity pulls downward on the tiny particles, but updrafts, or air that is flowing upwards, push up the particles. Gravity is not strong enough to overcome this upward push, so the water droplets and ice crystals in clouds float.

Liquid droplets that make up clouds form in a way similar to the way dew forms, in which moist air must reach the dew point. Remember that warm air cools as it rises. Look at what happens to the air in Figure 5.5A. The higher the air rises, the more it cools. When the air reaches a height where its temperature is the same as the dew point, water vapor can condense. However, water vapor needs a surface on which water particles can form droplets. In the atmosphere, droplets form around tiny particles of dust, salt, or smoke. Many, many water droplets must form to make a cloud.

Clouds that are made of ice crystals form in a slightly different way. These clouds form when the temperature is below freezing and water vapor forms crystals. **Crystallization** is the formation of solid structures, called crystals, whose atoms or molecules are arranged in a repeating, three-dimensional pattern. Water vapor crystallizes around the surface of dust particles or other ice crystals. Snowflakes form in clouds in this way. Some clouds are made of only water droplets or only ice crystals, and some are a mixture of the two.

Clouds are a part of the water cycle, even when rain or snow is not falling from them. Clouds transport water from one area to another, and the water they contain is eventually pulled to the ground again by gravity.

Figure 5.5B shows various types of clouds. Clouds are divided into three main groups based on their altitude in the sky—high, mid, and low. Each cloud group has members that have different shapes, including wispy, puffy, and sheet-like clouds.

The High Clouds The highest clouds in the sky are made of ice crystals and are usually white. Cirrocumulus clouds look like light puffs of cotton. Cirrus clouds are white, wispy clouds. Cirrostratus clouds look like a thin white sheet that covers the sky. You may see any of the high clouds when the weather is fair, but cirrostratus clouds may mean that rain or snow is on its way.

The Mid Clouds Altostratus, altocumulus, and nimbostratus clouds are found at mid-range heights between high and low clouds. Altostratus clouds form a thin gray blanket across the sky, and altocumulus clouds look like they are made of grayish-white puffs of cotton. Altocumulus clouds may indicate that a thunderstorm will occur later in the day. Nimbostratus clouds are dense, dark gray clouds that often bring steady rain or snow.

The Low Clouds Cumulus, stratocumulus, stratus, and cumulonimbus form at the lowest altitudes. Cumulus clouds look like big clusters of puffs, and stratocumulus clouds look like rolls of gray bunches bringing snow or rain. Stratus clouds appear like a low, gray ceiling over the sky and may produce light rain. Fog is a stratus cloud at ground level. Cumulonimbus clouds are very tall in height with a top flattened in the shape of an anvil. These dark clouds often bring thunderstorms, hail, and heavy rain.

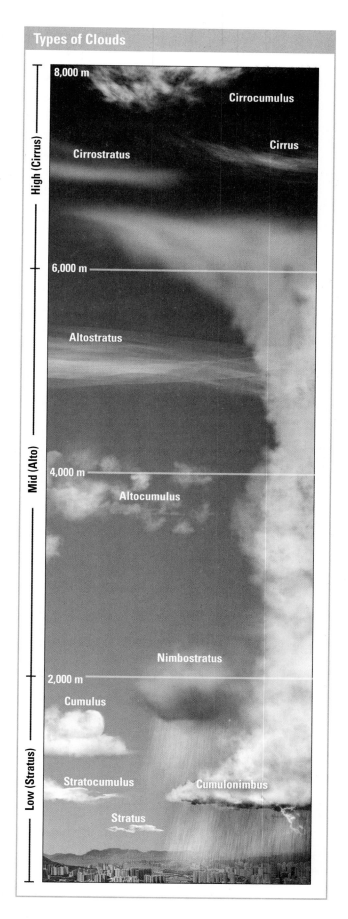

Figure 5.5B

Clouds are divided into high, mid, and low clouds based on their altitude in the atmosphere. They are also described by their shapes or if they often bring rain. Knowing the different types of clouds can help you predict the weather.

6. Precipitation

Big gray clouds appear on the horizon, and the rumble of thunder gets louder and louder. You run inside to avoid the storm coming your way. And just in time! Tiny balls of ice smack into the windows and bounce off the sidewalk. Where did these balls of ice come from?

The icy balls are hail. Like raindrops, they fall from clouds because gravity pulls on them. **Precipitation** is liquid or solid water that falls from clouds to the ground. It is the main way that water in the atmosphere makes its way back to Earth's surface.

Rain, snow, sleet, and hail are four common types of precipitation and are shown in the photos. Rain is drops of liquid water falling to the ground. Snow, hail, and sleet are solid precipitation. Snow is made of delicate six-sided ice crystals, while hail and sleet are larger ice particles.

How can you tell the difference between sleet and hail? First, the icy balls of hail are bigger than the ice pellets in sleet. Sometimes they are much bigger, getting up to the size of ping-pong balls or even softballs, which is why hail can damage plants, cars, and buildings. Second, sleet and hail fall during different types of storms. Sleet may fall during a storm when the air near the ground is cold, whereas hail may fall during a severe thunderstorm on a warm summer day.

Rain, snow, sleet, and hail are types of precipitation. While rain is liquid water, the other three types are ice. They are all an important part of the water cycle, as they are the means in which water in clouds reaches the ground.

Rain

Snow

Sleet

Hail

Before raindrops, snowflakes, or hail fall from clouds, they must become heavy enough for gravity to overcome the updrafts that are holding them aloft. Figure 5.6 represents one model of how a raindrop forms and grows in clouds. First, water droplets collide and stick together to form a small raindrop. This raindrop begins to fall through the cloud, growing into a large raindrop as it takes in smaller droplets below it. Notice the raindrop is not the shape of a teardrop. Instead, it has a flat bottom as it grows because air is pushing up on it as it falls. If the raindrop grows large enough, it will break apart into two smaller raindrops. In cold clouds with enough moisture, ice crystals continue to grow and group together in a similar way to form snowflakes that fall toward the ground.

Hailstones form when air blows tiny ice particles upward and downward many times through clouds and the particles continually grow into bigger balls of ice. The ice is pushed up by strong updrafts, so hail can grow larger than raindrops or snowflakes before it is pulled to the ground by gravity.

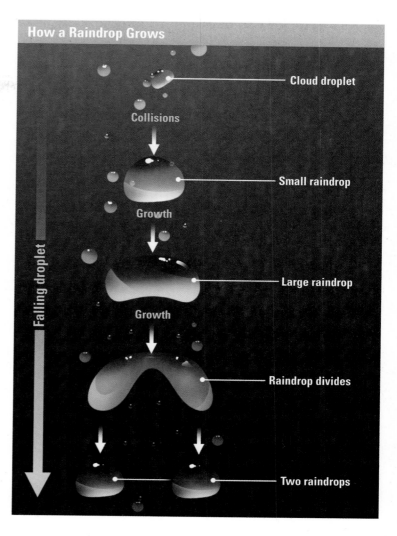

How a Raindrop Grows

Cloud droplet

Collisions

Small raindrop

Growth

Falling droplet

Large raindrop

Growth

Raindrop divides

Two raindrops

Figure 5.6

A raindrop grows as small droplets of water in a cloud collide. When the raindrop is massive enough for gravity to pull it to the ground, it falls through the cloud. It grows even more as it falls into the drops below it, and may become big enough to divide into two raindrops.

The type of precipitation that reaches the ground depends on the temperatures of the atmosphere. Snowflakes will reach the ground if they fall through air below the freezing temperature of water. But, they melt and become rain if they fall through warmer air. Rain may also freeze into sleet if the temperatures near the ground are below freezing. In this case, sleet reaches the ground.

Rain is measured using a rain gauge, which is a clear container that has an opening at the top so that rain can be collected as it falls. The gauge also has a scale on the side that is in units such as millimeters (or inches in the United States) to measure the height of precipitation that is collected. Snow sits on top of the ground, so its depth can be measured with a meter stick.

Precipitation is an important part of the water cycle. It provides freshwater for infiltration that many plants and animals use. Even snow provides freshwater as it melts to form streams that flow into lakes and rivers. Long periods without enough precipitation can lead to droughts. Too much precipitation can also be destructive, causing floods, landslides, and avalanches.

Energy and the Water Cycle

This model of the water cycle shows how water on Earth is constantly moving, changing state, and transferring energy between the land, bodies of water, and the atmosphere, by using energy from the sun. The particles of water on Earth complete this cycle eventually: spending time in the ocean, evaporating to become water vapor in the atmosphere, and condensing to form precipitation.

Energy from the sun

Condensation

Condensation

Transpiration

Living things

Evaporation

Ocean

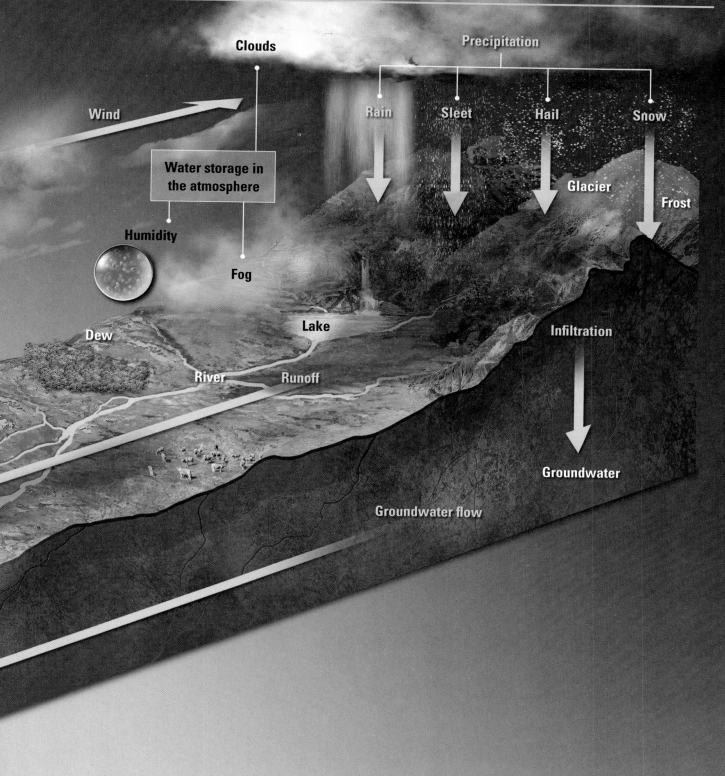

Clouds

Wind

Precipitation

Rain   Sleet   Hail   Snow

Water storage in
the atmosphere

Glacier

Frost

Humidity

Fog

Dew

Lake

Infiltration

River   Runoff

Groundwater

Groundwater flow

Which states of water become the weather that we experience? Notice that the atmosphere contains water in all three states. Invisible water vapor is stored in the atmosphere as humidity. Liquid water is stored in fog and clouds. Solid water, ice, is stored in certain high-altitude clouds. Eventually, liquid and solid water fall back to Earth due to the force of gravity, to run over or underground before returning to the ocean.

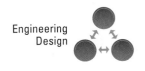

7. Engineering Design: Cleaning Wastewater with Plants

Every time you shower, wash your hands, or flush the toilet, water goes down the drain. This wastewater is part of the water cycle and eventually makes its way to lakes, rivers, and the ocean. It must be cleaned so it is safe before it enters the environment. Suppose you are an engineer helping to plan a new town. How would you choose the design that is best for treating wastewater produced by this town?

In this situation, there are two possible designs—a constructed wetland, such as the one in the photo, and a typical wastewater treatment facility. A constructed wetland is an engineered wastewater treatment system that uses plants, microorganisms, and soil to clean water as a natural wetland, such as a marsh, would. A typical wastewater treatment plant uses a series of pipes, screens, settling tanks, and filters to move wastewater through the plant. Each step purifies the water a little more until it is cleaned.

Engineers systematically compare competing designs. For a new product, they might test designs under the same conditions to see which is better. For a design that is used onsite at a location such as a wastewater treatment system, they might compare data about how well the design performs. They evaluate possible design solutions based on the criteria and constraints, or the limitations of the possible engineering design.

The Arcata Marsh in California is an example of a constructed wetland. A constructed wetland is an engineered wastewater system that cleans water the way a natural wetland does, using plants, microorganisms, and soil. Constructed wetlands can be used for many applications, from private homes to whole towns.

You need to evaluate the two designs using the criteria and constraints for the town's system. The criteria state that it needs to serve a certain number of people. It must remove large and small solid particles from the water. It must kill bacteria and other microorganisms that cause disease. Your town plan also requires an animal habitat and outdoor spaces for people to enjoy. One constraint is the cost of the water treatment system. Although you have a lot of land to use, you need to keep the cost low.

Both designs can serve the population and meet almost all the criteria, however, the constructed wetland provides an animal habitat and outdoor spaces. It also costs less than a typical system, which is important. Based on careful consideration of the competing solutions, which design would you choose to clean the town's wastewater?

This wastewater treatment system design cleans water using a series of pipes, pumps, tanks, and filters. Wastewater systems must be evaluated based on the criteria and constraints of the design.

LESSON SUMMARY

Water and the Weather

Sun, Gravity, and the Water Cycle Water is constantly moving through the Earth system. The water cycle is driven by energy from the sun and gravity. Water changes state throughout the cycle.

Evaporation and Transpiration Powered by energy from the sun, water vapor enters the atmosphere mainly through the processes of evaporation of liquid water in bodies of water and the ground, and in transpiration of water from plants.

Humidity Humidity is the amount of water vapor in the air. Relative humidity is the ratio of the amount of water vapor in the air to the amount of water vapor the air can hold at a given temperature. Relative humidity depends on temperature because warmer air can hold more water vapor.

Dew and Condensation Air becomes saturated with water vapor at the temperature called the dew point. Water vapor condenses to form water droplets on surfaces below the dew point.

Clouds Clouds form when moist air rises and cools to the dew point, allowing water droplets or ice crystals to form. Clouds are classified by their height in the sky, their shape, and if they bring rain.

Precipitation Precipitation is any liquid or solid water that falls from clouds and is pulled to the ground by gravity. It includes rain, snow, hail, and sleet.

Engineering Design: Cleaning Wastewater with Plants In designing a wastewater treatment system, engineers evaluate possible designs based on criteria and constraints.

The Mysterious Sources of Earth's Water

In December 1972, an astronaut on the Apollo 17 mission to the moon turned his camera back toward Earth and took a photo. That photo, which shows the whole Earth, was named "The Blue Marble" because the combination of the blue oceans and the swirling white clouds made Earth look like a marble. You know that a large part of Earth's surface is covered with water. Where did all that water come from?

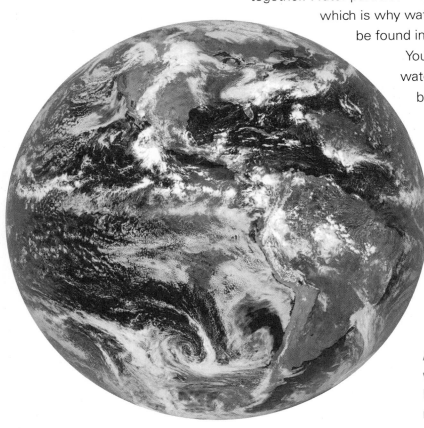

The water on Earth is essential to all life on the planet, but scientists are not sure where it came from. Scientists do, however, have hypotheses on how and when water came to Earth.

Although no humans were around when the solar system formed, scientists theorize that the sun and all the planets, including Earth, formed when gas and dust from a nebula clumped together. Water particles made up part of the gas in the nebula, which is why water vapor, liquid water, and ice can be found in different parts of the solar system. Young Earth may have had some water on it or in it from its formation, but scientists speculate that all that water evaporated because it was so hot. In the early solar system, Earth did not have an atmosphere to insulate it or to trap water particles. The energy from the sun would have driven those water particles off into space. So, scientists concluded that Earth's water had to come from somewhere else.

A large part of Earth's surface is covered with liquid water, which makes the planet look like a giant blue marble. Scientists are not sure where Earth's water came from.

Snowball Fight?

One proposed hypothesis is that comets may have brought water to Earth. A comet is a chunk of ice, rock, and dust that orbits the sun. Because they contain so much ice, they are sometimes described as dirty snowballs. When a comet gets close to the sun, some of the ice turns into water vapor, which streams off the snowball along with dust and other gases to form the comet's tail.

Comets seemed to be a logical source for Earth's water because they contain a lot of water themselves, and the comet hypothesis was favored for years. However, recent evidence does not support the hypothesis. Here's why: every water particle, or molecule, is made of one oxygen atom and two hydrogen atoms. Two kinds of hydrogen atoms are found in nature: one twice as heavy as the other. Water on Earth has a certain ratio of heavy hydrogen to light hydrogen, and the source of Earth's water should have this same ratio because it would be the same water. Recently, scientists found that the ratio of heavy hydrogen to light hydrogen in comets' water is much greater than the ratio of water on Earth. So, they now question whether the comet hypothesis could be wrong.

With evidence questioning the comet hypothesis, one thing that scientists theorize is that, during Earth's past, it was bombarded by objects from space. Impact sites from bombardment have been erased from view by weathering, erosion, and plate tectonic movement. However, scientists have gathered evidence from computer models, moon rocks from Apollo missions to the moon, and impact records from the moon, Mars, and Mercury. So, objects hit Earth, and some of those objects may have delivered water to the planet.

Comets are called dirty snowballs because they are made of ice, dust, and rock. Scientists once hypothesized that comets delivered water to Earth because they contain so much water in the form of ice.

Vesta is the second-largest asteroid in the asteroid belt. It and other asteroids in the asteroid belt have water under their surfaces. Scientists think that meteorites from the asteroid belt may have brought water to Earth.

Asteroid Attack

Another hypothesis for the source of Earth's water is that it came from meteorites that hit the planet a long time ago. Meteorites are particles that can come from asteroids and have reached Earth's surface. Meteorites may not seem like sources of water—they look like dry rocks in the photos that you see of them. But scientists have evidence that meteorites that have hit Earth and asteroids in space both contain water beneath their surfaces.

In 2016, scientists announced that they found a meteorite in Antarctica that had opal in it. Opal is a mineral that can be found on Earth. From studying opal on Earth, scientists know that opal forms with the help of flowing water. So, the presence of opal in the meteorite suggests that the meteorite had water or ice inside it. If that meteorite had water in it, perhaps meteorites that hit Earth ages ago did, too.

Scientists have also found evidence that water may have once flowed on Vesta, a large asteroid in the asteroid belt of the solar system. Photos of Vesta show what look like creek beds carved by running water. Scientists suspect that the ice that exists under Vesta's surface melted and came to the surface when Vesta was hit by a smaller asteroid.

Scientists have studied water found in meteorites that broke off Vesta and in other meteorites from the asteroid belt. They discovered that this water has a similar ratio of heavy-to-light hydrogen as Earth's water has. All this evidence supports the hypothesis that meteorites from asteroids were the source of much of Earth's water.

Here All Along?

One more hypothesis about Earth's water is that at least some of it was here all along. As stated earlier, scientists speculate that water was part of Earth when it formed, and new research suggests that not all of this water evaporated into space.

Scientists studying some of the oldest rocks on Earth found glass crystals in them that contained tiny droplets of water. They analyzed the water and found that its heavy-to-light hydrogen ratio is similar to the ratio predicted to have existed when the solar system was forming. These scientists suspect that this water must have been trapped deep within Earth's surface when the planet first formed. Because it was trapped, it could not evaporate.

However, water trapped when Earth was formed does not have the same heavy-to-light hydrogen ratio as water found on Earth's surface today. So, scientists hypothesize that only some of Earth's water was trapped and that the rest of it was delivered by meteorites. This "double source" of water would help explain why Earth has so much water.

Scientists may never know exactly how or when water arrived on Earth, but thankfully it did. If it hadn't, you and the scientists working on this puzzle wouldn't be alive today! ◆

Where did the water that fills Crater Lake in Oregon come from? Some of it may have come from asteroids, but some of it may have been on Earth since the planet formed.

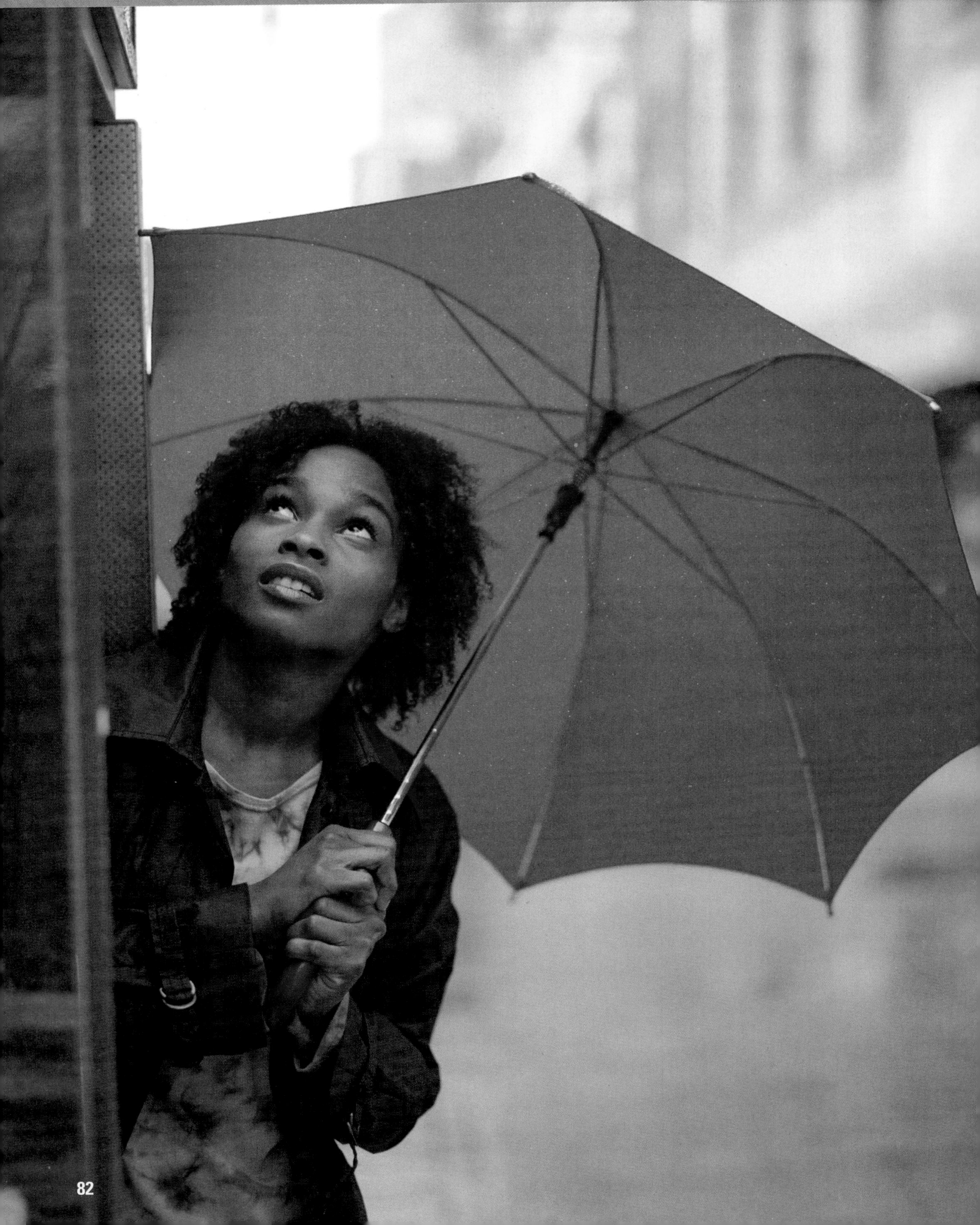

Air Masses and Changing Weather

....

How do giant masses of air that move around the world change weather?

Introduction

You've just left home with your umbrella and are headed for the bus stop. There is a light rain with some wind, but you see the sky to the west is bright. What will the weather be like for the rest of the day? Will the rain get worse? Or will it become clear and calm?

Throughout history, people have studied nature carefully and have identified cause-and-effect relationships in the patterns they observe that help them predict the weather. For instance, thick dark clouds may indicate rain is coming, and wind speed often increases with a greater difference in temperature.

But how do modern scientists use these cause-and-effect relationships to understand the weather? In what ways does investigating moving air masses help explain changes in weather? Scientists also use these relationships to analyze weather data from all over the world to make detailed weather forecasts. The resulting forecast includes the five elements of weather you already know about—wind, temperature, humidity, pressure, and precipitation—and answers many everyday weather questions you might ask. However, they also need to understand the models of air masses, fronts, and pressure systems that form the basis for making these forecasts.

In this lesson, you will learn how elements of weather relate to huge volumes of air called *air masses*. By the end of this lesson, you will understand how scientists use these relationships along with weather stations and radar to predict your local weather.

air mass a huge volume of air that has a uniform temperature and humidity at a given altitude

weather front the boundary where two air masses meet

cold front a weather front in which a cold air mass advances to replace a warm air mass

warm front a weather front in which a warm air mass advances to replace a cold air mass

stationary front a boundary between a cold air mass and a warm air mass that is not moving

occluded front a boundary between one warm air mass and two cold air masses, in which the warm air mass is pushed above the two cold air masses

low pressure system an area within the atmosphere where air is rising and winds blow toward the center

high pressure system an area within the atmosphere where air is sinking and winds blow away from the center

isobar a line on a weather map that connects places that have the same air pressure

---

Next Generation Science Standards

Performance Expectations
MS-ESS2-5. Collect data to provide evidence for how the motions and complex interactions of air masses results in changes in weather conditions.

Science and Engineering Practices
Planning and Carrying Out Investigations
Collect data to produce data to serve as the basis

for evidence to answer scientific questions or test design solutions under a range of conditions.

Crosscutting Concepts
Cause and Effect Cause and effect relationships may be used to predict phenomena in natural or designed systems.

Disciplinary Core Ideas
ESS2.C. The complex patterns of the changes and the movement of water in the atmosphere, determined by winds, landforms, and ocean temperatures and currents, are major determinants of local weather patterns.

ESS2.D. Because these patterns are so complex, weather can only be predicted probabilistically.

1. Air Masses

It is a warm, pleasant morning as you head out the door for soccer practice. By break time, you see gray clouds gathering and trees being whipped by winds. By the time you leave practice, rain is pouring down and it is cold. How can understanding air masses explain a sudden change in the weather?

An **air mass** is a huge volume of air that has a uniform temperature and humidity at a given altitude. Air masses may be warm or cold and moist or dry. They may be thousands of kilometers wide, reaching to the top of the troposphere! As the wind pushes them around the atmosphere, air masses bring their weather characteristics with them as they travel from place to place. Thus, the varying characteristics of air masses bring changing weather.

Air masses form when air stays over an area of land or water for a long time. The properties of the land or water determine their temperature and humidity. Air masses that form over the ocean tend to be moist because they absorb a large amount of water evaporating from the ocean. Air masses that form over land tend to be drier.

Scientists can predict where cold and warm air masses will form by using what they know about the variation of temperature with latitude. Cold air masses form at high latitudes, where the land and water are colder. Warm air masses form closer to the equator, where the land and water are warmer. Notice where each of the warm, cold, dry, and moist air masses form in Figure 6.1. The map shows the cause-and-effect relationship between air masses and the places where they form. According to Figure 6.1, what kind of air mass might be typical for the region where you live? What properties of local land or water cause this?

Figure 6.1

An air mass is a large volume of air that has uniform temperature and humidity. Air masses may be cold or warm and dry or moist, depending on where they form. Meteorologists use mP, cP, mT, and cT to describe how air masses form because these abbreviations are short and fit easily on maps.

Air Masses of North America

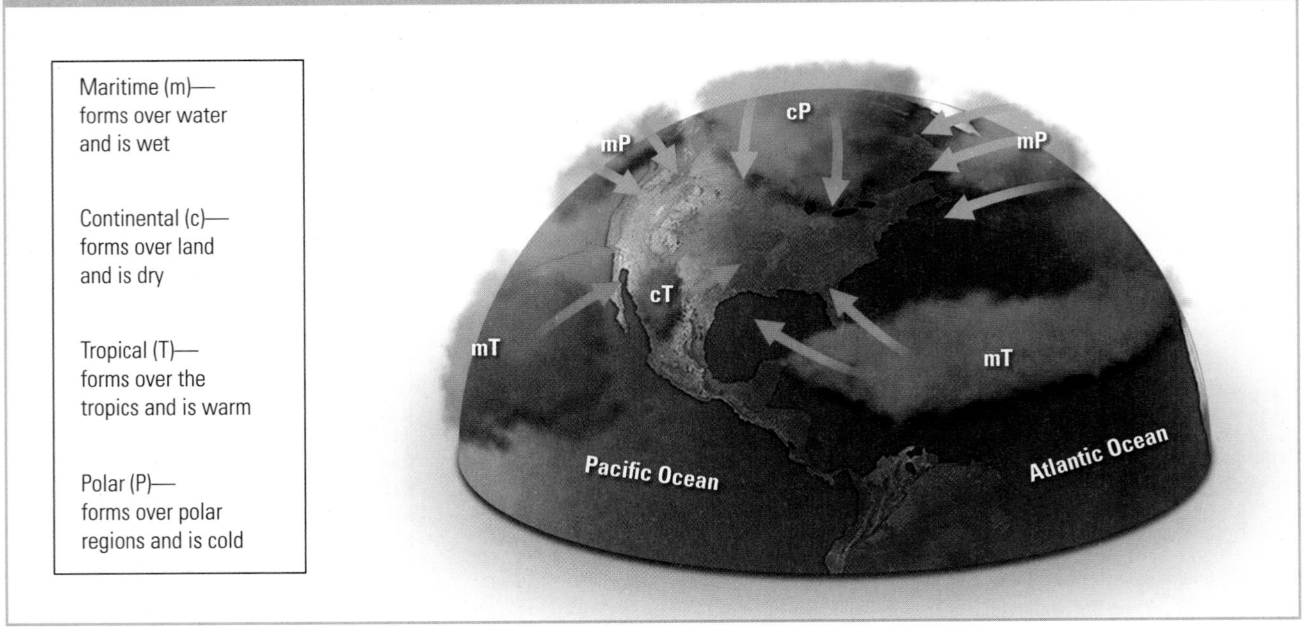

Maritime (m)—
forms over water
and is wet

Continental (c)—
forms over land
and is dry

Tropical (T)—
forms over the
tropics and is warm

Polar (P)—
forms over polar
regions and is cold

Classifying Air Masses Did you notice that each air mass in Figure 6.1 was labeled with two letters—a combination of "m" or "c" and "P" or "T"? These letters are shorthand notation that represents the moisture and temperature characteristics of air masses and helps to classify them. Each letter gives you information about where the air mass formed and also tells you the properties of the air mass. The letter "m" stands for "maritime," which means the air mass formed over bodies of water, such as oceans, and is moist. The letter "c" stands for "continental"—the air mass formed over land and is dry. The "P" stands for "polar," and represents a cold air mass. The letter "T" stands for "tropical," and denotes a warm air mass. These characteristics are used to describe four common types of air masses that affect the United States: mP, mT, cP, and cT.

Moving Air Masses If air masses stayed where they formed, the weather would not be very interesting. Instead, they move from areas of high pressure to areas of low pressure. Moving air masses around the globe bring changing temperature and moisture conditions.

The photos show the type of weather that different air masses are associated with and can bring to locations they travel to. A moist, cool mP air mass forms in the northern Pacific Ocean. This air mass brings cool rainy weather to Seattle and other cities in the Pacific Northwest when it moves onshore. A dry, cold, cP air mass that forms in Canada can bring frigid but fair weather to cities in the Midwest, such as Minneapolis, in the winter. When the moist, warm mT air mass that forms in the tropical parts of the Pacific Ocean travels to coastal regions of southern California, such as the city of San Diego, it brings warm, humid weather.

A location's weather depends on the air mass over it. When they move, air masses change the weather in their path. They are classified based on where they are from using the letters m, c, P, and T.

Seattle
mP

Minneapolis
cP

San Diego
mT

2. Weather Fronts

On the soccer field, you bounce off another player when you accidentally collide. Moving air masses collide, too, but they do not bounce off each other. What happens where two air masses meet?

A boundary forms between air masses where they collide because a dense, cold air mass and a less dense, warm air mass simply do not mix together. The boundary where two air masses meet is called a **weather front**. There are four types of weather fronts—cold, warm, stationary, and occluded, as seen in Figures 6.2A and 6.2B. Fronts travel as the air masses move, and a passing front often brings sudden changes in weather. Scientists continuously gather data that allow them to identify the locations and possible movement of fronts. Using this data, scientists can predict the general weather patterns each front is likely to bring by knowing how fronts interact.

Cold Front A **cold front** is a weather front in which a cold air mass advances to replace a warm air mass. Cold air is denser than warm air. So, the cold air pushes under and lifts the warm air. A cold front brings colder air, and you can feel the temperature dip as it passes. Cold fronts often bring stormy weather because the warm, lifted air cools and may condense to form cumulonimbus clouds in the upper atmosphere. Cold fronts can pass through a location in only a few hours.

Figure 6.2A

A weather front develops along the boundary where two air masses meet. A cold front forms where a dense, cold air mass pushes under a less dense, warm air mass. A warm front forms where a warm air mass slides over a cold air mass that is being pushed ahead by the warmer air.

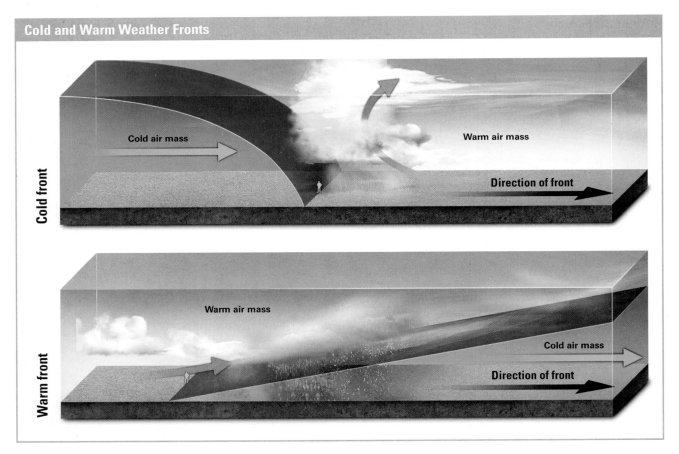

Cold and Warm Weather Fronts

Cold front
Cold air mass
Warm air mass
Direction of front

Warm front
Warm air mass
Cold air mass
Direction of front

Warm Front A **warm front** is a weather front in which a warm air mass advances to replace a cold air mass. When the dense, cold air mass moves ahead of the less dense, warm air mass, the warm air takes its place. Warm fronts can pass slowly through a location and are associated with stormy weather. However, the precipitation is steadier and gentler than at a cold front.

Stationary Front A **stationary front** is a boundary between a cold air mass and a warm air mass that are not moving. Like cold and warm fronts, a stationary front forms where a cold and warm air mass meet. However, neither air mass moves past one another. The weather at a stationary front is similar to that at a warm front. It may last for many days until the front begins to move to become a warm or cold front again.

Occluded Front An **occluded front** is a boundary between one warm air mass and two cold air masses, in which the warm air mass is pushed above the two cold air masses. Occluded fronts form when a cold air mass meets a warm air mass and a second cold air mass moves under the warm air mass, pushing the warm air above both cold air masses. Occluded fronts can bring light, moderate, or heavy precipitation.

Figure 6.2B
A stationary front forms between a cold air mass and a warm air mass that cannot move past each other. An occluded front forms when two cold air masses meet one warm air mass and push it up above them. All fronts are associated with precipitation, but cold fronts tend to bring severe storms.

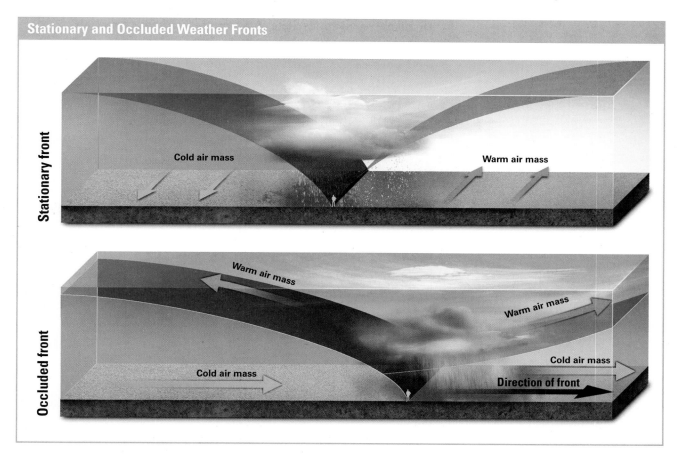

Stationary and Occluded Weather Fronts

Stationary front

Cold air mass   Warm air mass

Occluded front

Warm air mass

Warm air mass

Cold air mass

Cold air mass

Direction of front

Decreasing air pressure, as measured with a barometer such as this one, may mean a low pressure system is approaching. Cloudy, stormy weather may be on its way. Increasing air pressure means fair weather is likely because a high pressure system is approaching.

3. Low Pressure and High Pressure Systems

While stormy weather is associated with low pressure, fair weather is often associated with high pressure. Barometers can measure the changes in pressure that occur when a low or high pressure system is approaching. These changes in pressure data can be used to predict fair or stormy weather. How does air pressure relate to weather fronts and changes in weather?

A **low pressure system** is an area within the atmosphere where air is rising and winds blow toward the center. The diagram of the low pressure system in Figure 6.3 shows arrows modeling the directions that air flows. As you can see, the pressure is lowest at the center of a low pressure system because air is rising due to warmer temperatures. Air flows toward the center of the low pressure system to replace the rising air. As it does, it curves and whirls because Earth is spinning. The whirling mass of air forms the low pressure system, which is also called a *cyclone*.

A **high pressure system** is an area within the atmosphere where air is sinking and winds blow away from the center. Compare the high pressure system with the low pressure system in Figure 6.3. Notice that the air is sinking at the center—the pressure is highest there. Then, the air whirls away from the center, spinning in the opposite direction as a low pressure system. Because air flows in the opposite direction as a cyclone, high pressure systems are called *anticyclones*. In the Northern Hemisphere, an anticyclone curves in the clockwise direction.

Rising or sinking air can mean the difference between a fair or stormy day. A decrease in air pressure may mean a low pressure system is approaching, possibly bringing precipitation and strong winds. Clouds form because the rising air cools and can hold less water. The opposite happens in high pressure systems. The sinking air warms and can hold more water, causing clouds to evaporate. So, rising atmospheric pressure means a high pressure system may bring clear, fair weather.

Figure 6.3

In a low pressure system, air whirls inward to replace air that is rising in the center. In a high pressure system, air whirls outward as it is pushed out by air that is sinking in the center. This rising and sinking of air can mean the difference between a cloudy, rainy day and a fair, sunny day.

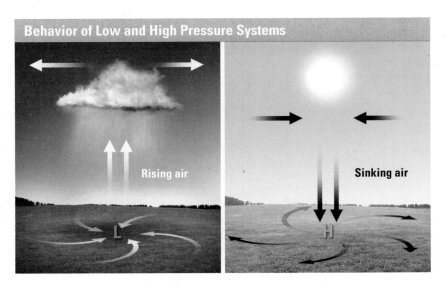

Behavior of Low and High Pressure Systems

Rising air

Sinking air

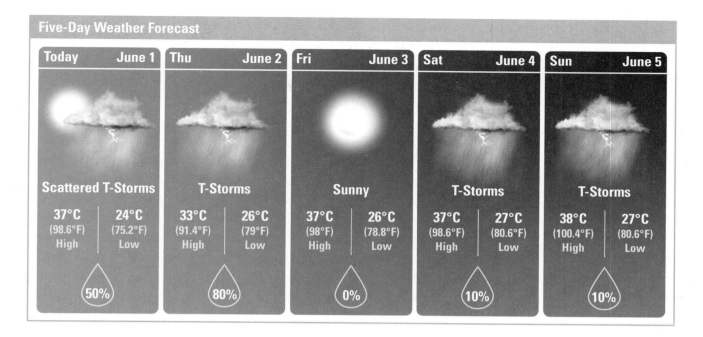

Five-Day Weather Forecast

Today June 1	Thu June 2	Fri June 3	Sat June 4	Sun June 5
Scattered T-Storms	T-Storms	Sunny	T-Storms	T-Storms
37°C (98.6°F) High / 24°C (75.2°F) Low	33°C (91.4°F) High / 26°C (79°F) Low	37°C (98°F) High / 26°C (78.8°F) Low	37°C (98.6°F) High / 27°C (80.6°F) Low	38°C (100.4°F) High / 27°C (80.6°F) Low
50%	80%	0%	10%	10%

4. Weather Reporting

You have learned that air masses, weather fronts, and low or high pressure systems may cause changes in the weather. Suppose that you want to know whether you will need your umbrella on your walk home from soccer practice. Where can you find out what the weather will be?

You can find a local weather report in many places. Weather-related apps and websites provide reliable information about the weather almost anywhere in the world. Local TV stations and newspapers also give forecasts. Checking forecasts for weather can help you decide whether to take your umbrella or wear sunscreen.

Many five-day forecasts predict the daily temperature ranges and the chance of precipitation. Notice the forecast in Figure 6.4, with a column for each day. A quick look will tell you that today and tomorrow may be stormy, while Friday may be sunny. Detailed weather reports also include wind speed, humidity, and whether the air pressure is rising or falling.

Since weather patterns are very complex, scientists can only predict the probability, or likelihood, of a certain type of weather. For example, although they may predict thunderstorms on Thursday, you may not have a thunderstorm that day. The bottom row of Figure 6.4 shows the probability of precipitation. A higher percentage suggests precipitation is more likely to occur. Today, the probability of a thunderstorm is 50 percent, so the chance of a storm occurring where you are is equally as likely as the chance that there will not be a storm. On Thursday, the probability is 80 percent, so you are more likely to have a storm than not. Over the weekend the chance is only 10 percent. That suggests a storm is possible but not likely.

Figure 6.4

A simple five-day weather forecast summarizes the high and low temperatures for each day and the chance, or probability, of precipitation. Scientists give the probability of precipitation as percentages because weather is so complex that they usually cannot predict the weather with absolute certainty.

5. Weather Maps

On weather sites, scientists may use a map of your area or the United States to explain the forecast. While these weather maps may look complicated, you already know almost everything that they include. What do they show?

Weather maps use symbols to show the location of fronts over a large area at a certain point in time. Fronts are represented by colored lines with triangles or semicircles. Warm fronts are shown by a red line with semicircles, while a cold front is shown by a blue line with triangles. The semicircles or triangles point in the direction that the front is moving. Can you identify the weather associated with each type of front on the map in Figure 6.5? On the map, north of Montana, alternating red semicircles and blue triangles point in opposite directions, representing a stationary front. A purple line with semicircles and triangles pointing in the same direction represents an occluded front north of Michigan.

Weather maps also show low and high pressure systems. A low pressure system is represented by a large red "L," while a high pressure system is shown by a large blue "H." The lines around the Ls and Hs are called *isobars*. An **isobar** is a line on a weather map that connects places that have the same air pressure. The numbers near these lines indicate the pressure. Notice that the isobars show pressure decreases going away from an H and toward an L. Closer isobars mean the pressure is changing more quickly and winds will be faster.

Figure 6.5

Weather maps show the weather patterns within a certain point in time over a large area, such as the entire United States. They include symbols that represent each type of front that is occurring, low and high pressure systems, and isobars that show air pressure and how it changes.

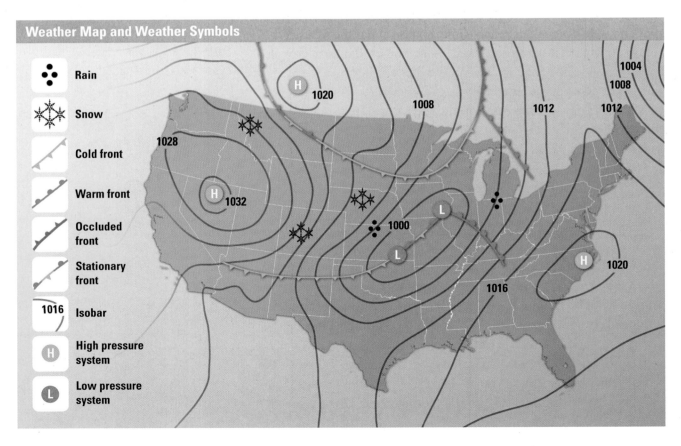

Relating Air Masses, Fronts, and Pressure Systems

This weather map uses symbols to show the weather conditions on a winter day in the United States at 2 P.M., Central Standard Time. The models of the fronts show what is happening where the air masses meet. The photos show the actual weather in specific locations. How can you explain the weather at each location using the cause-and-effect relationships you have learned?

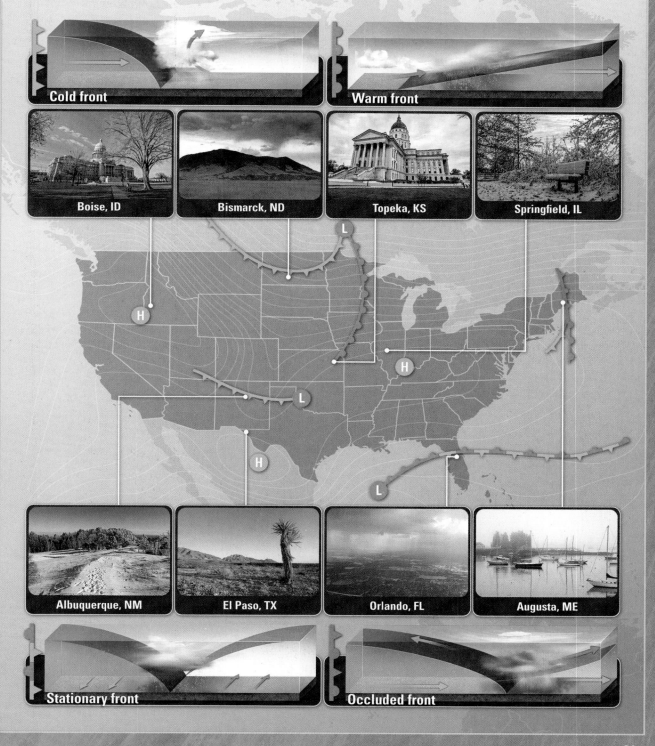

Cold front

Warm front

Boise, ID

Bismarck, ND

Topeka, KS

Springfield, IL

Albuquerque, NM

El Paso, TX

Orlando, FL

Augusta, ME

Stationary front

Occluded front

91

6. Tools of Weather Forecasting

The weather forecast says that a cold front is moving through your area on Saturday. There is an 80 percent chance of thunderstorms, so the soccer game might be canceled. How do scientists determine that a cold front is moving toward your area?

What kind of data do scientists need to analyze and forecast weather? Scientists gather large amounts of data about the state of the atmosphere to make weather maps and accurately predict local weather. Weather stations, weather balloons, radar, and satellites measure atmospheric pressure, wind, temperature, humidity, and precipitation. Think back to the weather map in Figure 6.5. Pressure data from all over the United States were taken to make this map.

Scientists have placed thousands of weather stations all around the world to gather enough information to provide the evidence necessary to predict the weather. Weather stations include the tools scientists use to collect weather-related data on the ground: thermometers to measure temperature, barometers to measure pressure, anemometers to measure wind speed, rain gauges to collect and measure precipitation, and hygrometers to measure humidity.

Scientists also gather data about the conditions high up in the atmosphere using weather balloons and satellites. Weather balloons carry instruments that collect information from weather stations and satellites at altitudes of more than 30 km. As they rise, they transmit data about temperature, air pressure, wind speed and direction, and relative humidity at different altitudes. Satellites that orbit high above Earth accumulate data about temperature, humidity, and cloud cover. This data is then translated into images for analysis. Scientists look for patterns in satellite images that provide evidence for how storms develop and change over the entire planet.

This is the Aqua satellite, which was launched by NASA to help answer questions about the water cycle. It collects and transmits data about clouds, precipitation, air temperatures, and other variables. Scientists use satellites like this along with weather stations and weather balloons to gather and analyze data in efforts to predict local weather.

One of the most important tools scientists use to detect precipitation is radar. Radar antennas, such as the one inside the sphere on the tower in the photo, send out radio waves. These waves bounce off clouds, rain, snow, hail, or other types of precipitation. The antenna then detects these waves as they return. The radar can detect the intensity of the precipitation and the direction of the storm. The resulting data is used to create maps of clouds and precipitation. The maps can provide evidence that thunderstorms or snow clouds are forming.

Scientists accumulate data from radar, satellites, and weather stations and balloons to give current weather conditions. These data are then processed through computer models to analyze weather patterns and make a variety of forecasts. The models use mathematical formulas to find the probability of weather conditions and can predict how complex weather patterns can change. For example, they may predict that there is an 80 percent chance of rain on Saturday. That suggests there is a 20 percent chance that there will not be rain. But, an 80 percent chance of rain means you should be prepared for rain. Pack an umbrella.

Scientists use Doppler radar systems like this one to gather data about precipitation. They use computer models to analyze the data from radar, weather stations, instruments on weather balloons, and satellites, allowing them to predict complex weather patterns.

LESSON SUMMARY

Air Masses and Changing Weather

Air Masses The large volume of air in an air mass has uniform temperature and humidity at a certain altitude. The properties of an air mass are determined by where the air mass forms. Air masses affect weather as they move around the globe.

Weather Fronts Weather fronts form where warm and cold air masses meet. Cold fronts, warm fronts, stationary fronts, and occluded fronts are each associated with typical types of weather.

Low Pressure and High Pressure Systems Low pressure systems form where air is rising. They are associated with stormy weather. High pressure systems form where air is sinking. They are associated with fair or clear weather.

Weather Reporting Weather forecasts are predicted using probability. A typical forecast includes possible high and low temperatures as well as the likelihood of precipitation and wind.

Weather Maps Weather maps use symbols to represent fronts and high and low pressure systems over a large area at a specific time.

Tools of Weather Forecasting Scientists use weather stations, radar systems, weather balloons, and satellites to gather weather data. They use computer models to analyze the data so that they can predict weather conditions.

Severe Weather

What is severe weather, and how do scientists predict where will it occur?

Introduction

As it touches the ground and sucks up dirt and debris, the funnel cloud darkens. The tornado's whirling winds will wreak havoc and cause damage for miles along its path. How can you tell if dangerous weather such as a tornado is on its way? What can you do to stay safe?

Severe weather can damage buildings, trees, and crops, cause power outages, shut down highways and bridges, and injure or even kill people. There are many kinds of severe weather, including blizzards, heat waves, severe thunderstorms, tornadoes, hurricanes, droughts, and ice storms. Severe weather conditions may cause additional dangers such as wildfires, landslides, or flash floods. The type of severe weather you need to prepare for depends on local weather patterns. Maps of past severe weather can reveal patterns that show where similar events are likely to occur again.

In this lesson, you will learn about five kinds of severe weather. You will discover the damage they cause, where they are likely to occur, why they occur, and how to withstand their effects. You will also find out how weather forecasters analyze satellite and radar images so they can warn people of severe weather.

Vocabulary

severe weather weather such as blizzards, heat waves, severe thunderstorms, tornadoes, and hurricanes that can damage buildings or cause loss of life

blizzard a winter storm that lasts for at least three hours with winds greater than 56 km/h and large amounts of blowing snow

heat wave a period of unusually hot, and often more humid, weather than is typical for a region

heat index the temperature that the air feels like to people when humidity is combined with the actual air temperature

severe thunderstorm a thunderstorm that has wind speeds of 93 km/h, hail that is at least 2.5 cm wide, or a tornado

tornado a rotating column of air with extremely high wind speeds of 117 km/h or higher that touches the ground

hurricane a huge, rotating, low pressure storm system that forms over warm water near the equator and has sustained wind speeds of 119 km/h or higher

---

Next Generation Science Standards

Performance Expectations

MS-ESS3-2. Analyze and interpret data on natural hazards to forecast future catastrophic events and inform the development of technologies to mitigate their effects.

MS-ETS1-4. Develop a model to generate data for iterative testing and modification of a proposed object, tool, or process such that an optimal design can be achieved.

Science and Engineering Practices

Analyzing and Interpreting Data Analyze and interpret data to determine similarities and differences in findings.

Developing and Using Models Develop a model to generate data to test ideas about designed systems, including those representing inputs and outputs.

Crosscutting Concepts

Patterns Graphs, charts, and images can be used to identify patterns in data.

Influence of Science, Engineering, and Technology on Society and the Natural World

Disciplinary Core Ideas

ESS3.B. Mapping the history of natural hazards in a region, combined with an understanding of related geologic forces can help forecast the locations and likelihoods of future events.

ETS1.B. • A solution needs to be tested, and then modified on the basis of the test results, in order to improve it. • Models of all kinds are important for testing solutions.

ETS1.C. The iterative process of testing the most promising solutions and modifying what is proposed on the basis of the test results leads to greater refinement and ultimately to an optimal solution.

1. Blizzards

Winds howl and snow swirls all around. Luckily, school was canceled because of a severe weather warning—a blizzard. How is severe weather different from other types of weather?

Severe weather is weather that can damage buildings or cause loss of life. It includes blizzards, heat waves, severe thunderstorms, tornadoes, and hurricanes. The National Weather Service (NWS) is the official U.S. agency that monitors the weather. The NWS is authorized to issue storm watches and warnings to inform people of severe weather events.

A **blizzard** is a winter storm that lasts for at least three hours with winds greater than 56 km/h (34.7 mph) and large amounts of blowing snow. As seen in the photo, visibility is nearly zero because so much snow is blowing. Below-freezing temperatures create icy conditions on roads and sidewalks that make driving and walking hazardous. The very low wind chill temperature increases the chance for frostbite, or damage to the skin from freezing, and hypothermia. Hypothermia occurs when body temperature falls below 35°C (95°F) and internal organs begin to fail. During blizzards, piles of snow can block roads, cause power outages, and trap some people in their homes for days.

Understanding how blizzards form and where they are likely to happen allows the NWS to warn people of an approaching storm. Blizzards develop when a low pressure system has formed where moist, warm air rises over cold air, producing lots of snow and high winds. The NWS analyzes data from satellite images, weather stations, and weather balloons for potential blizzard activity. The NWS also keeps historical data of blizzards by city and region so it can predict where future ones are likely to occur. The data show that blizzards in the United States are common in the Midwest, the Northeast, and mountainous areas. What clues in the satellite image show which section of the country may be experiencing a blizzard?

Blizzards are particularly dangerous winter storms with high winds and poor visibility that can cause freezing conditions and loss of life.

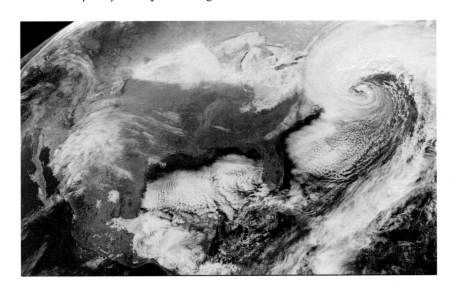

This satellite image of a major winter storm hitting the East Coast of the United States was taken by NOAA's GOES-16 satellite in 2018. Using images such as this, along with other data gathered from monitoring the storm system, helped the NWS in issuing a blizzard warning for the Mid-Atlantic region of the country.

2. Heat Waves

You have probably never experienced a blizzard if you live in southern California or Florida. But you may have been very hot in the summer. Beyond uncomfortable, when is hot weather hazardous?

A **heat wave** is a period of unusually hot, and often more humid, weather than is typical for a region and can be very dangerous. A heat wave lasts at least two days or longer. The hot temperatures can harm people, particularly elderly people and babies, and people without air conditioning. Heat waves can be more dangerous in cities than the surrounding areas. This is because buildings and concrete make cities hotter. Heat waves also increase the risk of wildfires.

During a heat wave, people are in danger when they cannot maintain normal body temperature. They may suffer heatstroke when the body temperature rises above 41°C (106°F). Heatstroke needs to be treated right away. If it is not, the person may suffer permanent brain damage and even die. Hundreds of people die each year in the United States due to hot temperatures.

It is important to stay cool during a heat wave, which is a period of unusually hot and often humid weather. The heat index is the temperature that tells you how hot it actually feels during a heat wave because of high humidity.

Humidity makes things worse during a heat wave because sweat does not evaporate well in humid air. So, the body cannot cool itself efficiently and the air temperature feels hotter. The **heat index** is the temperature that the air feels like when humidity is combined with the actual air temperature. For example, when relative humidity is 75 percent and the air temperature is 32°C (90°F), the heat index is 43°C (109°F). That is dangerously hot.

Heat waves occur in many parts of the United States in the summer. To predict heat waves, forecasters look for increasing temperatures and humidity within high pressure systems stalled over a region. Air that is sinking in the middle of a high pressure system keeps the hot air near the ground from rising. The trapped air gets hotter because it is under pressure and because the ground heats up during fair, sunny weather and transfers thermal energy to the air.

People can lessen the effects of a predicted heat wave. Some people may buy air conditioners or fans to stay cool. Cities may open cooling centers in public buildings, such as libraries, where people can stay cool. To avoid heatstroke during a heat wave, you should avoid strenuous activities, stay out of the sun, and drink plenty of water.

Lightning, thunder, and heavy rain are a part of every thunderstorm. A severe thunderstorm also has high winds, large hail, or a tornado. So, it can be very destructive. You should seek shelter during a thunderstorm and stay away from windows and corded electronic devices in case of a lightning strike.

3. Severe Thunderstorms

Dark clouds, bright flashes of lightning, booming claps of thunder, and pouring rain mean one thing—a thunderstorm. While some think a thunderstorm is more frightening than a heat wave, most thunderstorms are not classified as severe weather. So, how are severe thunderstorms different?

A normal thunderstorm includes lightning, thunder, and heavy rain. A **severe thunderstorm** is a thunderstorm that has wind speeds of greater than 93 km/h (57.7 mph), hail that is at least 2.5 cm (0.98 in.) wide, or the development of a tornado. A severe thunderstorm may last for several hours and has the potential to be much more destructive than ordinary thunderstorms. The very strong winds may blow down trees and power lines. Hail can damage cars and plants, and harm animals that do not have shelter from the storm. Heavy rains may also cause flash flooding. Trees and buildings may be struck and burned by lightning or damaged by wind and floodwater. After a severe thunderstorm, people may be without power and roads may be blocked by downed trees or floodwater.

You can take steps to protect yourself before a severe thunderstorm. During any thunderstorm, go inside or seek shelter, and stay away from windows. Avoid trees, water, and electrical devices with cords to reduce your risk of getting struck by lightning. Never try to cross roads that are flooded by water, even if you are in a car, because a car can be carried away in waters less than a foot deep.

Understanding how thunderstorms form helps scientists predict severe thunderstorms. To do this, scientists must use a variety of data received from satellite and radar imagery. They look for tall clouds and a large amount of precipitation in satellite images. They also look for specific wind patterns in radar images.

Most thunderstorms develop where warm, moist air near the ground meets cold, dry air above it. The warm air may be pushed up at a cold front, causing the water in the air to condense to form a large cumulus cloud as seen in Figure 7.3. As the air continues to rise as an updraft, the cloud grows into a tall cumulonimbus cloud. Precipitation starts to fall and a downdraft, or cool air that is moving downward, develops. In normal thunderstorms, the cool downdraft eventually dominates over the warm updraft, ending the updraft and the storm. In a severe storm, the warm updrafts and cool downdrafts are farther apart, allowing the storm to grow bigger. Strong updrafts continue to feed the storm and push ice particles upwards, forming them into hail. A funnel cloud may also develop if a thundercloud starts to spin, rotated by strong winds.

The frequency of severe thunderstorms depends on where you live. There are about 10,000 severe thunderstorms in the United States each year. Most of these occur in the middle of the country between Texas and Minnesota. Regions with severe thunderstorms are also likely to have tornadoes, when developing funnel clouds touch ground.

Figure 7.3
Severe thunderstorms can form at cold fronts where warm, moist air is pushed upwards. All thunderstorms form as the water vapor in the rising air condenses to form a cloud that grows into a cumulonimbus cloud. In severe thunderstorms, the updrafts and downdrafts are separated, allowing the storm to grow bigger and create hail.

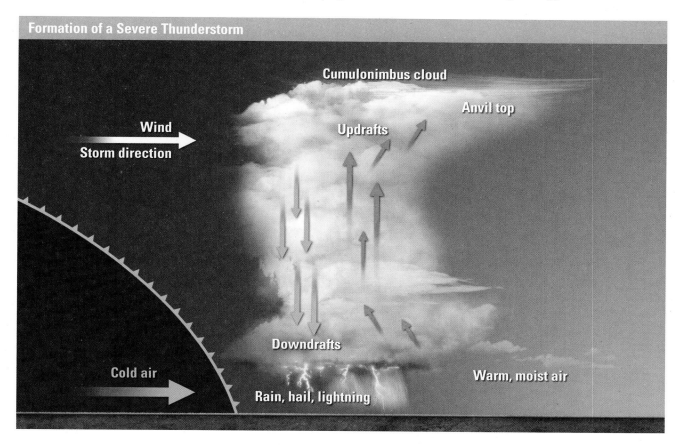

Formation of a Severe Thunderstorm

Cumulonimbus cloud

Anvil top

Wind
Storm direction

Updrafts

Downdrafts

Cold air

Rain, hail, lightning

Warm, moist air

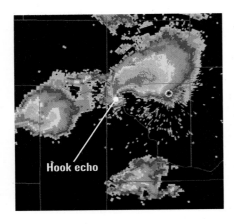

This radar image shows a "hook echo" forming within a severe storm. A hook, such as this one, indicates favorable conditions for a tornado.

4. Tornadoes

A tornado like the one in the photo at the beginning of this lesson typically lasts just a few minutes, but it can leave a trail of destruction in its path. What is a tornado, and how can people stay safe during one?

A **tornado** is a rotating column of air with extremely high wind speeds of 117 km/h (73 mph) or higher that touches the ground. The damage done by a tornado is proportional to wind speed, so the higher the winds, the more destructive they are over a relatively small area. Tornadoes can knock down power lines, uproot trees, rip off rooftops, destroy buildings and scatter debris. Flying debris can be highly dangerous. After a tornado, people may be left homeless or without power, natural gas lines can be damaged causing leaks that increase the risk of fire, and survivors may face months of rebuilding.

More than 1,000 tornadoes occur in the United States every year. Florida, and the states in Tornado Alley, including Texas, Kansas, and Oklahoma, experience the most tornadoes. Figure 7.4 shows the average number of tornadoes that occurred each June from 1989–2013. Scientists are working to understand exactly how tornadoes develop by using satellite and radar images. They know that tornadoes often form during severe thunderstorms. Specific patterns such as the characteristic "hook echo" in radar images may indicate a tornado is forming. The shape of the hook is formed from strong drafts of wind blowing downward as precipitation is wrapped around strong drafts of wind blowing upward.

In places where tornadoes are common, local governments often use sirens to warn people about tornadoes. Some buildings also have underground storm shelters where people can stay during a tornado. If you cannot get to a storm shelter, seek refuge in a basement or a room away from windows and outside walls, such as a hallway.

Figure 7.4
This map shows the average number of tornadoes that occurred across the United States during the month of June for the time period from 1989–2013.

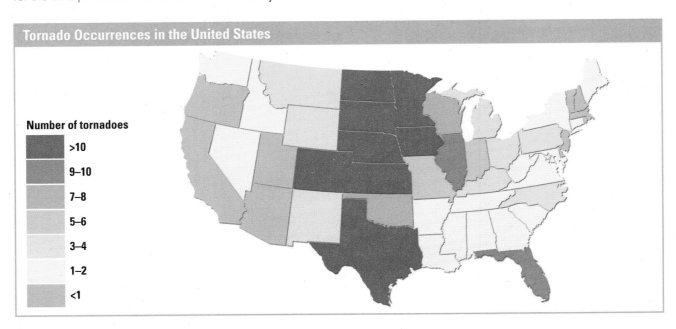

Tornado Occurrences in the United States

Number of tornadoes

- >10
- 9–10
- 7–8
- 5–6
- 3–4
- 1–2
- <1

Rising, warm, moist air condenses as clouds

Wind speed: 120.7 km/h

Eye

Eyewall

Warm, moist air rises rapidly in updrafts near the center

Rainbands

5. Hurricanes

People in Kansas or Oklahoma need to be prepared for tornadoes. But, they are unlikely to experience a hurricane like people who live along the Gulf Coast or East Coast. What is a hurricane, and why do they only affect certain parts of the country?

A **hurricane** is a huge, rotating, low pressure storm system that forms over warm water near the equator and has sustained wind speeds of 119 km/h (73.9 mph) or higher. Like other low pressure systems, hurricanes that form in the Northern Hemisphere rotate counterclockwise. Satellite images, such as the one in Figure 7.5A on the left, show the rotating pattern of the clouds. The clouds span an area over the Bahamas and Cuba off the southeast coast of Florida.

Hurricanes form as warm air travels over warm oceans. Water evaporates, making the air very moist. As the air rises, it cools and water vapor condenses to form clouds. Energy is released by condensation into the air and fuels the growing storm. The less dense warm air continues to rise, creating a low pressure system. At the bottom of this system, warmer, moist air flows in to replace the rising air. Strong winds form. The clouds may begin to rotate noticeably, forming a tropical storm, which may continue to grow into a hurricane if atmospheric conditions are right.

Figure 7.5A also shows a model of the resulting structure on the right. The eye is the center of the hurricane, where air pressure is lowest near sea level compared to the rest of the storm. Inside the eye, winds are relatively calm and the sky is clear, as seen in the photo. The eyewall is a wall of tall cumulonimbus clouds that surrounds the eye. Strong thunderstorms and the highest winds in the hurricane occur here. The spiraling bands of clouds and rain around the eyewall are called *rainbands*. Rain can occur between these bands but is very heavy inside of them and accompanied by intense winds.

Figure 7.5A

The satellite image on the left shows a hurricane, which is a huge, rotating storm system with extremely high winds. The model of the hurricane on the right shows its structure.

This photo taken from a NOAA P-3 hurricane hunter aircraft shows the eye and the dense eyewall of Hurricane Katrina.

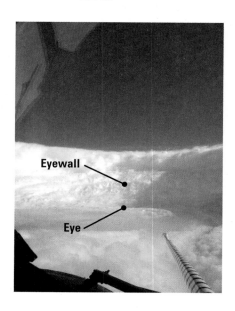

Eyewall

Eye

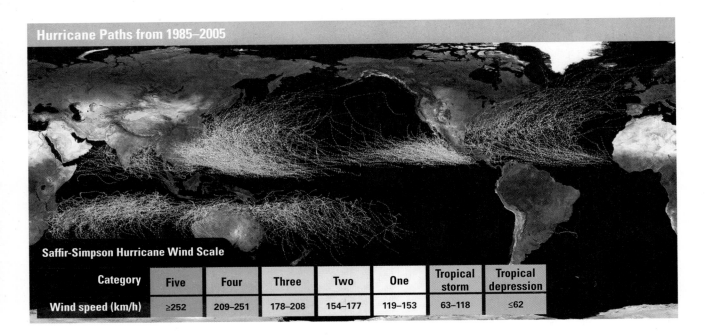

Hurricane Paths from 1985–2005

Saffir-Simpson Hurricane Wind Scale

Category	Five	Four	Three	Two	One	Tropical storm	Tropical depression
Wind speed (km/h)	≥252	209–251	178–208	154–177	119–153	63–118	≤62

Figure 7.5B

This map shows the paths of various hurricanes over a 20-year period. Each path is shown in a different color, depending on the strength of the storm as categorized by the Saffir-Simpson Hurricane Wind Scale. The 1 to 5 rating categorizes hurricanes based on sustained wind speed and the amount of resulting property damage.

Figure 7.5B shows the history of hurricane paths from 1985–2005. It was created using data collected by the NWS and the U.S. military. The lines show that the hurricanes formed near the equator and their paths follow a general pattern, often moving in a west-northwest direction. Hurricanes are most likely to form during certain times of the year. In the North Atlantic Ocean, hurricane season is from the beginning of June to the end of November, when the water there is warmest. On average, six hurricanes form in the Atlantic each year, but they do not all reach land. Why do hurricanes that form in the Eastern Pacific Ocean rarely reach the West Coast of the United States? This same west-northwest movement pushes them away from the West Coast and weakens the storm. The ocean there is cold, so it does not have enough thermal energy to sustain hurricanes.

Hurricanes that reach land bring dangerously high winds and heavy rains that can cause flooding to a wide area near landfall. They also cause a storm surge, which is a rise in ocean water that may be up to 6 meters high. Storm surges can cause massive flooding. As the storm moves over land, it quickly becomes weaker because warm ocean water no longer provides water and energy. But, the storm can still bring heavy rains and flooding to inland areas.

Scientists use satellite and radar images to track storms that may develop into hurricanes. They also send airplanes into the storm to collect data about the conditions inside the storm. Computer models help scientists predict whether a storm will turn into a hurricane and what path it is likely to follow. Historical maps, such as Figure 7.5B, that show the formation and movement of past hurricanes, are also used to help forecast future storms. If the models predict that a hurricane may reach land, the NWS has time to issue a warning.

Severe Weather Safety

Historical data and maps of severe weather reveal patterns in where and how often severe weather occurs in different regions. You should know how to get information about severe weather risks and be sure to act in response to a watch or warning. Developing and following an emergency plan for the kinds of severe weather that occur in your area will help you and your family stay safe.

I live in Oklahoma where about 60 tornadoes occur every year. Some are mild while others are violent. We have an underground storm shelter where I go when I hear the tornado warning siren.

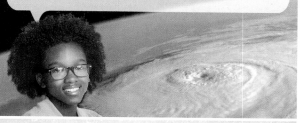

In Louisiana, we can get strong winds, heavy rains, and storm surges. Once every 3 to 11 years or so, we get a hurricane. To prepare, we gather supplies and board up windows. If it floods, we may evacuate.

In Florida, we can get heat waves. Between 1997 and 2017, we have had five heat waves. When one occurs, I avoid exercising outside, drink lots of water, and stay inside where there is air conditioning.

In Nebraska, we can get lots of snow and ice storms with a 50 percent chance of a blizzard in any given year. During blizzards, we stock up on supplies and stay inside if possible. We limit our time outside and dress warmly.

You can follow these steps:

1 Know your risks

Identify what types of severe weather occur where you live and when they occur.

2 Do your research

Learn how to prepare for storms from sources like the National Weather Service.

3 Plan and prepare

Make an emergency plan and kit with your family. Know where shelters are located.

4 Listen to watches and warnings

Watches mean severe weather may occur. *Warnings* mean that severe weather is happening.

5 Follow the emergency plan

Listen to official guidelines. Stay inside until the severe weather is over, but evacuate if necessary.

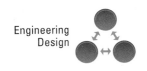

Engineering
Design

6. Improving Severe Weather Forecasting

For regions that have a history of tornadoes, a warning system is especially important. As of 2017, warnings are sometimes issued less than 13 minutes before the tornado strikes. Those few minutes are not much time for some people to get to a safe place. However, forecasters presently have no way to predict tornadoes further in advance. They can only issue a tornado warning after they observe signs in radar data that a tornado is forming. What are scientists doing to develop a faster and more accurate way to forecast severe weather?

The NOAA National Severe Storms Laboratory continues to develop and improve a state-of-the-art computer modeling system to accurately predict severe weather, including tornadoes, thunderstorms, and flash floods. The main criterion is that the system is able to issue warnings 30 to 60 minutes in advance to save more lives. The system combines many computer-based weather models, so it can produce more detailed outputs. For example, it can predict the likely path of a tornado and will allow forecasters to predict tornadoes before they can be observed on the radar. To do this, computers calculate complex equations using a large amount of weather data. Running the models requires a huge amount of computer power.

Scientists use storm data to test storm-forecasting models to predict severe weather events such as tornadoes and flash floods up to an hour before they strike.

Before these systems become operational, they must be tested, improved, and tested again. To develop the models in the system, both records of historical severe weather events, and a database of specific severe weather events were used. This includes events such as severe thunderstorms that form or do not form a tornado. The data are compiled from historical maps, radar, satellites, and weather balloons and stations. These data are entered into computer models as input. The predictions of the models, or output, are compared to the actual observations of an occurring storm. Models are constantly refined and retested to accurately predict the weather.

The system is then tested using real-time weather data at the Hazardous Weather Testbed (HWT). The HWT specializes in testing forecasting and warning methods. The system is tested by scientists working on the models and by the forecasters who will use the system. Here, the system is further optimized to accurately predict where a tornado will strike. It is also improved so that forecasters can easily use it to issue tornado warnings.

Would an extra 45 minutes of advanced warning help people to better prepare in the event of a tornado? Developing and testing the computer modeling system will improve scientists' ability to forecast tornadoes accurately and provide warning in advance.

LESSON SUMMARY

Severe Weather

Blizzards Severe winter storms such as blizzards can create icy conditions and power outages, block roads with snow, and result in loss of life. Historical data of blizzards help the National Weather Service predict where future ones are likely to occur.

Heat Waves A period of weather that is unusually hot and humid for a region is known as a heat wave. To predict heat waves, forecasters look for increasing temperatures and humidity.

Severe Thunderstorms In addition to lightning, thunder, and heavy rain, severe thunderstorms have strong winds and large hail. To help predict severe thunderstorms, scientists look for tall clouds and large amounts of precipitation in satellite images, and wind patterns in radar images.

Tornadoes Tornadoes are rotating columns of air that touch the ground. Scientists identify specific patterns in satellite and radar images that may indicate a tornado is forming and where it will touch ground. They use these data to provide advanced warnings.

Hurricanes Hurricanes are large, rotating, low pressure systems with wind speeds of at least 119 km/h. Historical maps showing the formation of hurricanes and hurricane paths can help forecast future storms.

Improving Severe Weather Forecasting Computer modeling combines current and historical models to predict severe weather. Storm warning models must be tested, improved, and retested.

On the Front Lines of Disaster

A crew of smokejumpers waits by the open door of a low-flying plane for the signal to jump out. They are specially trained firefighters who battle forest fires in remote locations. After they jump, their food, water, and firefighting gear will be dropped down to them. Once they are on the ground, they may stay there working for days. What do smokejumpers and other first responders do during natural disasters?

The work of smokejumpers is different from the work of firefighters in cities. They don't use fire trucks and hoses because the fires they fight are located deep in the woods, far from roads and hydrants. Most of these wildfires are caused by humans.

The main job of smokejumpers is to build firebreaks around fires. Created to stop a fire from spreading, a firebreak is an area cleared of all materials that can burn. Smokejumpers build firebreaks by cutting trees, clearing underbrush, and digging trenches, and they can use natural barriers such as streams as part of their firebreaks.

Because smokejumpers are dropped into remote locations for days at a time and often move from place to place, they carry all their equipment in backpacks. The equipment includes chainsaws, shovels, axes, and a fireproof tent that can protect them if they are caught in a fast-moving fire.

Smokejumpers may help or get help from other firefighters. Smokejumpers can help fire crews who are fighting wildfires in places that cannot be reached by truck. Sometimes other firefighters help smokejumpers by dropping water and fire-retardant substances from planes and helicopters.

Smokejumpers fight fires in remote locations. Some firefighters drop water from helicopters to help smokejumpers and others working on the ground.

Help Floods In

Fires aren't the only natural disasters that require brave first responders in uncommon modes of transportation. When a flood happens, first responders can't drive firetrucks, ambulances, or police cars to rescue people. If water gets into the engines of such vehicles, they can stop running and leave everyone inside stranded.

During a flood, rising waters can trap people because they should not walk through floodwaters to get to safety. The water may not be clear, so people cannot tell how deep it is and may trip over objects hidden by the water. So, people must wait to be rescued.

The most common way first responders travel to flood victims is in boats. Small, flat-bottomed boats are piloted along flooded rivers, roads, and other areas. These boats are good for rescues because they are easy to steer and can fit through narrow passages. Because of their flat bottom, they can be used in shallow water, such as flooded streets. However, these boats cannot hold many people, and they can only be used in water deep enough for them to float.

First responders in cities that flood regularly, such as Houston, Texas, also use high-water rescue trucks to save flood victims. These trucks can drive in deep water without stalling, and they can carry up to 17 people including 2 crewmembers. These trucks are so tall that people need to climb a ladder to get aboard them!

First responders often need to save stranded people during floods. These people are riding in a high-water rescue truck after being rescued during a flood in south Texas after Hurricane Harvey hit.

A landslide is a downhill movement of rock and soil. In March 2014, a landslide of mud and debris covered a small community outside of Oso, Washington, in less than a minute. Large amounts of rain had saturated the ground and made the mountainside unstable.

After a landslide, first responders often have a difficult time locating trapped people. This rescue worker encounters numerous hazards from debris while searching for survivors.

Landslide!

In addition to floods, heavy rains can cause another kind of natural disaster: a landslide. A landslide is a downhill movement of rock and soil in which the moving matter slides down as one mass. A landslide can happen when rainwater weakens the ground on a slope, allowing gravity to pull part of it down.

As during floods, first responders at a landslide must rescue people. However, rescuing after a landslide is especially challenging because victims can be stuck or even buried in mud and debris. The debris can also cover roads and bury or move buildings, which makes it difficult to find where people are trapped.

On March 22, 2014, a huge landslide covered dozens of homes and structures, killing 43 people in a community located 6.4 km (4 mi) east of Oso, Washington. In less than a minute, approximately 8 million cubic meters (10,463,604.9 cu yds) of rock and soil covered an area of about 2.5 km (0.96 sq mi). The road into the area was covered with mud and debris from the mountainside. Although first responders arrived on the scene within minutes, the unstable ground made it difficult to search for survivors. They flew helicopters over the area to search for people by sight and by using cameras. First responders who searched on foot used infrared detectors, which can sense body heat emitted from people and other living things, and dogs that could sniff out the locations of survivors and victims. As they searched, the people and the dogs had to be careful not to get stuck in the mud themselves.

Avalanche Rescue

Another kind of natural disaster that can bury people is an avalanche. Like a landslide, an avalanche is a downhill movement of material, but the material in an avalanche is mostly snow. An avalanche can reach speeds of 130 km/h (80.7 mph)—that's faster than cars drive on freeways! The rushing snow can knock down trees and quickly bury any person in its path under its tremendous weight. Most of the people who get buried by avalanches are skiers and other people participating in winter sports.

First responders must work quickly when rescuing people buried by avalanches because people can suffocate if they are trapped under snow for too long. The first responders who perform most avalanche rescues are members of the ski patrol.

The ski patrol uses different methods to locate buried people. One method is to use probe poles, which are long, skinny poles that are pushed into the snow at regular intervals. When a pole hits something under the snow, the ski patrol starts digging, hoping that the "something" is the "someone" they are searching for. A quicker method is to use avalanche dogs, which are dogs that use their sense of smell to find people. One avalanche dog can search an area in a fraction of the time needed by 15 to 20 people searching with probe poles.

During any natural disaster, first responders must act quickly to save lives and property. Whether they jump out of planes, work side-by-side with dogs, or ride on a truck, they are all brave heroes. ◆

An avalanche can quickly bury people in snow. First responders often use dogs to locate someone buried under snow.

UNIT 3

Climate

OVERVIEW

The mud in this valley hardens and cracks as changing global weather patterns create shifts in temperature and precipitation. How do these changes impact climate? In this unit, you will learn what controls climate and examine evidence of historic and future climates. Using models, you will explore the difference between weather and climate and learn how global wind patterns and the ocean influence climate. Then, you will identify evidence of rapid climate change and develop a strategy to address a problem associated with it.

Phenomenon-Based Storyline

A rise in average global temperature may result in major impacts to Earth. What specific problems can you identify that are associated with climate change?

UNIT CONTENTS

Investigations Compare weather and climate, and develop and use a model to describe the uneven heating of Earth's surface.

UNIT 3

Performance Expectations

MS-ESS2-6. Develop and use a model to describe how unequal heating and rotation of the Earth cause patterns of atmospheric and oceanic circulation that determine regional climates.

MS-ESS3-3. Apply scientific principles to design a method for monitoring and minimizing a human impact on the environment.

MS-ESS3-5. Ask questions to clarify evidence of the factors that have caused the rise in global temperatures over the past century.

MS-ETS1-1. Define the criteria and constraints of a design problem with sufficient precision to ensure a successful solution, taking into account relevant scientific principles and potential impacts on people and the natural environment that may limit possible solutions.

Science and Engineering Practices

Asking Questions and Defining Problems
Define a design problem that can be solved through the development of an object, tool, process or system and includes multiple criteria and constraints, including scientific knowledge that may limit possible solutions. • Ask questions to identify and clarify evidence of an argument.

Developing and Using Models
Develop and use a model to describe phenomena.

Constructing Explanations and Designing Solutions
Apply scientific ideas or principles to design, construct, and test a design of an object, tool, process or system.

Crosscutting Concepts

Cause and Effect
• Relationships can be classified as causal or correlational, and correlation does not necessarily imply causation. • Cause and effect relationships may be used to predict phenomena in natural or designed systems.

Scale, Proportion, and Quantity
Time, space, and energy phenomena can be observed at various scales using models to study systems that are too large or too small.

Systems and System Models
Models can be used to represent systems and their interactions—such as inputs, processes, and outputs—and energy, matter, and information flows within systems.

Energy and Matter
The transfer of energy can be tracked as energy flows through a designed or natural system.

Stability and Change
Stability might be disturbed either by sudden events or gradual changes that accumulate over time.

Connections to Engineering, Technology, and Applications of Science: Influence of Science, Engineering, and Technology on Society and the Natural World
• All human activity draws on natural resources and has both short and long-term consequences, positive as well as negative, for the health of people and the natural environment. • The uses of technologies and limitations on their use are driven by individual or societal needs, desires, and values; by the findings of scientific research; and by differences in such factors as climate, natural resources, and economic conditions.

Disciplinary Core Ideas

ESS2.C: The Roles of Water in Earth's Surface Processes
Variations in density due to variations in temperature and salinity drive a global pattern of interconnected ocean currents.

ESS2.D: Weather and Climate
• Weather and climate are influenced by interactions involving sunlight, the ocean, the atmosphere, ice, landforms, and living things. These interactions vary with latitude, altitude, and local and regional geography, all of which can affect oceanic and atmospheric flow patterns. • The ocean exerts a major influence on weather and climate by absorbing energy from the sun, releasing it over time, and globally redistributing it through ocean currents.

ESS3.C: Human Impacts on Earth Systems
• Human activities have significantly altered the biosphere, sometimes damaging or destroying natural habitats and causing the extinction of other species. But changes to Earth's environments can have different impacts (negative and positive) for different living things. • Typically, as human populations and per capita consumption of natural resources increase, so do the negative impacts on Earth unless the activities and technologies involved are engineered otherwise.

ESS3.D: Global Climate Change
Human activities, such as the release of greenhouse gases from burning fossil fuels, are major factors in the current rise in Earth's mean surface temperature (global warming). Reducing the level of climate change and reducing human vulnerability to whatever climate changes do occur depend on the understanding of climate science, engineering capabilities, and other kinds of knowledge, such as understanding of human behavior and on applying that knowledge wisely in decisions and activities.

ETS1.A: Defining and Delimiting Engineering Problems
The more precisely a design task's criteria and constraints can be defined, the more likely it is that the designed solution will be successful. Specification of constraints includes consideration of scientific principles and other relevant knowledge that are likely to limit possible solutions.

Connect Your Learning

Most people consider the local weather for today, tomorrow, and maybe the week. If you think about weather patterns over years, you are examining *climate*. Natural processes and events affect Earth's global climate, but human activity impacts climate as well. Certain recent phenomena, such as more frequent hurricanes, show this impact. How is understanding climate on a global, as well as local, level important to your life?

Climate

Sailing ships rely on wind and global ocean currents, which, along with other factors, affect climate. Whether you live inland or along a coast, how do wind and ocean currents affect your local climate?

The Arctic is seeing big impacts from changes to its climate. As a result, polar bears are threatened by a changing ecosystem as sea ice shrinks. How is rapid climate change affecting where you live?

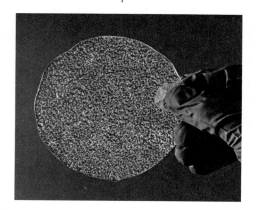

This thin wafer of ice is a slice from a core sample taken from a glacier or ice sheet. How do scientists use ice samples as evidence of Earth's climatic history?

Climate Patterns

What factors control climate?

Introduction

Someday you might be packing for a summer vacation on an island in Hawaii. You might be heading there to surf, watch whales, or relax on a beach like the one shown in the photo. The vegetation is green and lush. If you were there, you'd feel the warm, humid air on your skin. But, what if you were to visit that beach in October, January, or March? What weather could you expect? How could you find out?

You will have a good idea of what to expect based on the climate of your destination and the season. Climate gives you an idea of what weather to plan for because it describes the long-term weather conditions in a place. So, although you might wear shorts in Hawaii in the summer, you may find out that you will need a jacket there in the winter, but not a parka. Models of climate have been developed to explain why climate patterns vary in regions around the world.

In this lesson, you will learn how the elements of weather are related to climate. You will also explore how latitude, elevation, and nearness to large bodies of water contribute to the climate patterns on Earth and how those many different climates affect human culture, plants, and wildlife. Last, you will learn how scientists use data from past and present weather conditions to model current climate patterns and predict future ones.

Vocabulary

climate the long-term weather pattern for a given area

climate zone a region on Earth that has a particular average temperature because of its latitude

polar refers to the climate zones closest to the North Pole and South Pole, where the average temperatures are cold all year

temperate refers to the climate zone between the tropical and polar zones, with warm summers and cool winters

tropical refers to the climate zone centered at the equator, where the average temperatures are warm all year

Next Generation Science Standards

Performance Expectations
MS-ESS2-6. Develop and use a model to describe how unequal heating and rotation of the Earth cause patterns of atmospheric and oceanic circulation that determine regional climates.

Science and Engineering Practices
Developing and Using Models Develop and use a model to describe phenomena.

Crosscutting Concepts
Systems and System Models Models can be used to represent systems and their interactions—such as inputs, processes, and outputs—and energy, matter, and information flows within systems.

Disciplinary Core Ideas
ESS2.D. • Weather and climate are influenced by interactions involving sunlight, the ocean, the atmosphere, ice, landforms, and living things. These interactions vary with latitude, altitude, and local and regional geography, all of which can affect oceanic and atmospheric flow patterns. • The ocean exerts a major influence on weather and climate by absorbing energy from the sun, releasing it over time, and globally redistributing it through ocean currents.

Extremely Hot: Lut Desert, Iran

Extremely Cold: Svalbard, Norway

Extremely Dry: Atacama Desert, South America

Extremely Wet: Cherrapunji, India

1. Understanding Climate

You might expect summers to be warm and humid or hot and dry, and winters to be cold and snowy or mild and rainy. Why can you expect certain types of weather to occur at the same time every year where you live?

You can expect certain weather at a given place and time because weather follows a general pattern, repeating year after year. In other words, each location on Earth has a characteristic **climate,** or the long-term weather pattern for a given area.

The photos show regions with very hot, cold, dry, and wet climate patterns. The Lut Desert in Iran has one of the hottest climates on Earth, while Svalbard, Norway, is one of the coldest habitable places. The Atacama Desert in South America is extremely dry, receiving less than 2.5 cm (about 1 in.) of rain each year. Cherrapunji, India, is in one of the wettest regions on Earth, receiving an average of 1,143 cm (450 in.) of rain per year. Climate is described mainly by average temperature and precipitation, although patterns often include the effects of changing wind, humidity, and pressure.

The weather that you experience from day to day may differ from the expected climate. For example, Svalbard is a group of islands in the Arctic where the average temperature is a frigid −16°C (3°F) in February. This temperature describes the climate pattern because it is the average temperature for all the days in February over many years. However, one day in February might have a high temperature of 4°C (39°F). The next day might have a high of −12°C (10°F).

Climate affects what life forms occur in a given place. Elephants thrive in the lush forest near Cherrapunji, and reindeer depend on grasses adapted to the climate in Svalbard. Very little life exists in the parched Atacama Desert, yet in the Lut Desert, insects, reptiles, and desert foxes can survive.

These locations have extreme climate patterns. Climate is not the same as the weather, which describes atmospheric conditions from day to day. Instead, climate is the average weather over many years.

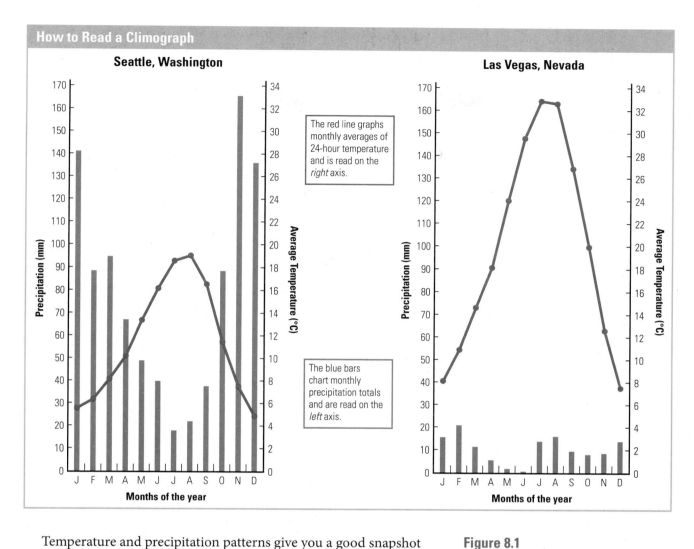

Seattle, Washington

The red line graphs monthly averages of 24-hour temperature and is read on the *right* axis.

The blue bars chart monthly precipitation totals and are read on the *left* axis.

Precipitation (mm)

Average Temperature (°C)

Months of the year

Las Vegas, Nevada

Precipitation (mm)

Average Temperature (°C)

Months of the year

Temperature and precipitation patterns give you a good snapshot of the aspects of climate that have a big impact on living things. A *climograph* shows the average temperature and amount of precipitation of a location for each month of the year. It is made by compiling many years of weather data. Look at the climographs for Seattle in Washington and Las Vegas in Nevada in Figure 8.1. The blue bars show the average precipitation each month. The red lines represent the monthly average temperature of a 24-hour period. How would you compare the climates of these two cities based on the patterns in the data? The blue bars show that Seattle gets more rain in the winter than in the summer. It also gets more rain all year than Las Vegas. The red lines show Seattle is much cooler than Las Vegas in the summer. The winter temperatures are mild in both cities. Seattle is lush and green because it has a moderate, rainy climate. The dry climate of Las Vegas indicates that it is a desert.

Climate scientists use current and historical weather data to describe the variety of climate patterns around the world. They also analyze the causes of changing climate patterns and provide data that societies need to make decisions that affect people, businesses, and the environment.

Figure 8.1

These climographs show the temperature and precipitation patterns for two different cities. In them, temperatures are shown by the red lines and precipitation is shown by the blue bars. Climographs can show the averages for monthly temperature and rainfall.

2. Latitude Controls Climate

You could pack swim trunks if you traveled to Hawaii, but you would need to pack a parka if you traveled to Antarctica. Can you predict the climate of a place by knowing its latitude?

A **climate zone** is a region on Earth that has a particular average temperatures because of latitude. Earth can be modeled as having three main climate zones in each hemisphere, as Figure 8.2A shows. The zones in the figure are approximations, but notice that one zone is near the equator, one is near each pole, and one is in between each pole and the equator. How do you think latitude affects the temperature patterns of these climate zones?

The temperature in climate zones generally increases going from the poles to the equator. The climate zone closest to the North Pole and the South Pole, where the average temperatures are cold all year, is called **polar**. The polar zones are found between 60° to 90°N and 60° to 90°S. Antarctica is in this zone, and the average temperature in summer there is less than 0°C. The climate zone between the tropical and polar zones, with warm summers and cool winters, is called **temperate**. The two temperate climate zones are found between 25° to 65°N and 25° to 65°S. The climate zone between about 25°N and 25°S near the equator, where the average temperatures are warmest all year, is called **tropical**. Hawaii is in this zone. The average temperature in the tropical zone typically does not fall below 18°C (64.4°F) and precipitation patterns vary.

Figure 8.2A

This model shows how Earth can be divided into three climate zones in each hemisphere—polar, temperate, and tropical—based on latitude. Temperatures within a climate zone are similar because of the angle in which the sun hits Earth's surface at these latitudes does not vary too much.

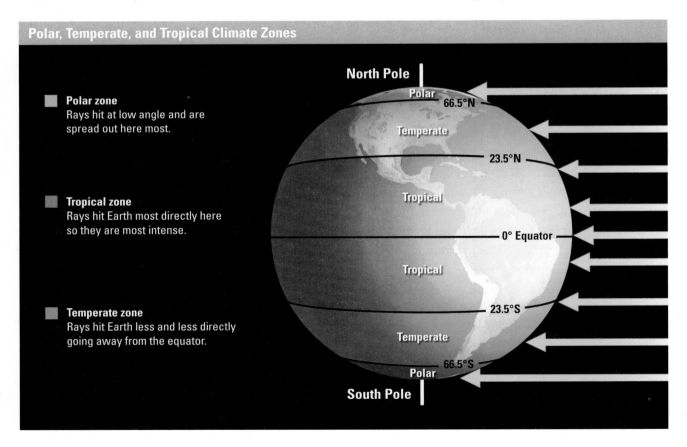

Polar, Temperate, and Tropical Climate Zones

Polar zone
Rays hit at low angle and are spread out here most.

Tropical zone
Rays hit Earth most directly here so they are most intense.

Temperate zone
Rays hit Earth less and less directly going away from the equator.

North Pole
Polar
66.5°N
Temperate
23.5°N
Tropical
0° Equator
Tropical
23.5°S
Temperate
66.5°S
Polar
South Pole

Summary of Climate Zones

Zone	Sun's Rays	Temperature	Day/Night Length	Example Location
Polar	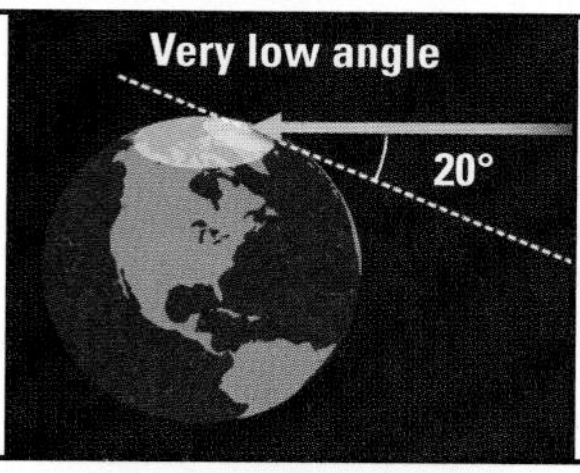 Very low angle — 20°	• Coldest of all zones • Temperature usually below freezing	• Days up to 24 hours long in summer • Nights up to 24 hours long in winter	 Barrow, Alaska
Temperate	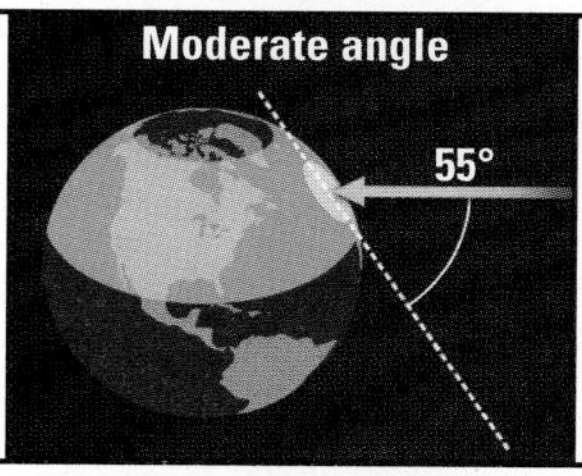 Moderate angle — 55°	• Contains most of Earth's land • Usually moderate temperatures year round	• Longer days in summer • Shorter days in winter	 New York, New York
Tropical	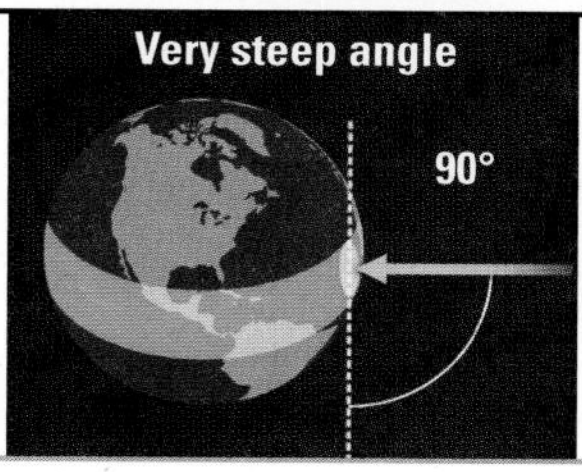 Very steep angle — 90°	Warmest average temperatures of all Earth's zones	Day and night are almost always equal in length	 Barbados

Why does latitude affect temperature? As you learned in Lesson 2, latitude determines how much of the sun's energy any place on Earth receives. Recall that the sun's rays strike Earth at different angles because of Earth's curvature, as shown in Figure 8.2B. Polar locations receive the least energy due to the low angle of the sun's rays, so they are cold climates. Tropical locations receive more energy from the sun because the angle of the sun's rays is near 90°. The rays are nearly perpendicular to Earth's surface, so tropical climates are hot.

Temperature is also affected by the length of day at a given location. Remember, the angle of the rays striking Earth changes with the seasons. Because of Earth's axis tilt, the length of day changes by the season. In winter in the Northern Hemisphere, the north pole tilts away from the sun. Rays of sunlight hit the Northern Hemisphere less directly, which makes days shorter. In the tropical zone, the hours of day and night are about the same year round. Figure 8.2B summarizes the day lengths.

Unequal heating of Earth due to its round shape and the angle of the sun's rays affects climate patterns in general. Energy flows from the warmer equator to the cooler poles through the atmosphere and the ocean, which moderates climates on Earth. The effect of latitude on energy flow and weather patterns does not change from year to year because Earth's curvature and tilt do not change very much over time. For these reasons, latitude affects climate patterns on a global level.

Figure 8.2B

Latitude affects climate because the angle at which the sun's rays strike Earth is different from zone to zone. In polar and temperate zones, the day length also varies throughout the year because the angle of the sun's rays changes with the seasons.

3. Elevation Controls Climate

It is a warm spring day and you decide to check out some sights. There is a tram that can take you to the top of Mount San Jacinto near Palm Springs, California. Even though you can wear a t-shirt and shorts at the bottom of the mountain, you will want a jacket for the cold wind and perhaps snow, too, when you get off the tram at the mountaintop. How can the top of Mount San Jacinto be covered in snow when its base is warm and desert-like?

Latitude is not the only factor that influences the climate at a location. Changes in elevation can create very different climates for places that are close together. You can see these changes riding the tram up Mount San Jacinto. Recall that the temperature of the troposphere decreases as the height above sea level increases. As you go up a mountain, you are also going higher up in the atmosphere. Mount San Jacinto towers more than 3,000 m (9,843 ft) above the desert. Even though the temperature at the bottom of the mountain may be very warm, as you travel up the mountain, the temperature gets cooler and cooler. Although the conditions at the bottom of a mountain may be hot and dry, as you travel up the mountain, the top may be freezing, even in the middle of summer.

The change in temperature is proportional to elevation and occurs at a specific rate. Figure 8.3A shows this. The rate of cooling is in general 6.5°C per 1,000 m (11.7°F per 3,280 ft). The temperature decreases at a steady rate regardless of how high up in elevation you go. Depending on the height of the mountain and the temperature at sea level, the temperature at high elevations may be below freezing. So, on a winter day, although Palm Springs might reach 21°C (70°F), the top of Mount San Jacinto will only be 10.5°C (50.9°F), even though they are both at the same latitude.

The latitude is the same for the desert at the bottom of Mount San Jacinto in California and the mountain's snow-capped peaks.

Figure 8.3A
Temperature decreases at a specific rate as elevation increases. So, the climate on mountaintops is cooler than the land climate at lower elevations at the same latitude.

Temperature Change with Elevation

Elevation		Temperature
4,000 m	Rate of cooling: 6.5°C for every 1,000 m	4.0°C
3,000 m		10.5°C
2,000 m		17°C
1,000 m		23.5°C
Sea level 0 m		30°C

The Rain Shadow Effect

Precipitation

Windward side

Rising moist air cools and condenses

Leeward side

Dry air descends and warms

Wind

Rain shadow desert

Changes in elevation also affect precipitation patterns. Mountains may cause what is known as the *rain shadow effect*, which happens when one side of a mountain is much wetter than the other side. The model in Figure 8.3B shows how these changes in elevation cause the rain shadow effect. The side where the wind blows toward the mountain is called the *windward* side. The opposite side is called the *leeward* side. When winds blow a warm, moist air mass toward the mountain, the air flows up the windward side. As you learned when you studied precipitation, the air cools as it rises and water vapor condenses. Clouds form and rain or snow falls at higher elevations. Because the air loses moisture on the windward side, drier air flows down the leeward side. The air warms up as it flows downward. Since warm air can hold more moisture, there is little precipitation. Thus, a dry area called a *rain shadow* forms on the leeward side of the mountain. Palm Springs is in the rain shadow of Mount San Jacinto and other nearby mountains.

Elevation also affects other aspects of climate, including pressure and wind. You may have noticed your ears popping when you ride up or down a mountain. Air pressure changes as elevation changes. You can feel this in your ears. "Popping" your ears equalizes the air pressure on either side of your eardrum. Mountains may also be very windy due to pressure differences at various elevations.

Figure 8.3B
This model shows why the windward side of the mountain receives more precipitation than the leeward side. The dry area on the leeward side is called a rain shadow.

4. Nearness to Water Controls Climate

You enjoy the cool breeze as you lounge on the beach. When you leave and travel inland, you notice that the air feels hotter and drier. Your latitude and elevation are the same as at the beach. Why is the beach cooler and more humid than locations far away from the water?

Compare the photo of Honolulu, Hawaii, with those of South Dakota. How would you describe the two climates? Honolulu is on the island of Oahu in the Pacific Ocean and in the tropical zone. South Dakota is in the middle of the United States in the temperate zone. In addition to the temperature differences caused by the differences in latitude, Honolulu's climate is affected by its nearness to water. Large bodies of water control the climates of nearby land because water affects the temperature and moisture of the air over it.

Water Moderates Daily Temperature Locations near large bodies of water have more moderate climate patterns with a narrower daily temperature range than inland locations. Why? Remember that water warm ups and cools down more slowly than land. Water must absorb more energy than land must absorb to raise its temperature. So, it warms up more slowly during the day. Water cools slowly at night as it releases the energy it absorbed during the day. Water affects the temperature of the air above it. The air above the water stays cooler during the day and warmer at night. Thus, the daily temperature range is smaller.

Honolulu, Hawaii, has a mild climate because it is near the Pacific Ocean. Locations near large bodies of water have a narrow temperature range. Water moderates the temperature of nearby areas because it absorbs a large amount of energy before it changes temperature.

Water Reduces Seasonal Variations

Climate is influenced by more than just temperature and amount of precipitation. It is also affected by seasonal variations in temperature. Large bodies of water moderate climate patterns by reducing seasonal temperature variations. In the summer, the water stays cooler than the nearby land, so the air above it is cooler. If prevailing winds blow the cool air toward land, they help keep temperatures from being too hot in the summer. In winter, the water stays warmer than the land, so the air above the water is warmer. Winds that blow over water bring the warmer air to land, helping to warm the air temperatures over it. As a result, coastal regions tend to have milder temperatures in both the summer and the winter than areas far away from the water. So, in Honolulu, the average summer and winter temperatures are quite similar because it is close to the ocean. In comparison, South Dakota is located in the Midwest, far from water. The photos show its climate has large seasonal variation in temperature as a result of this. Its temperatures are very warm in the summer and very cold in the winter.

Hot summer climate

Cold winter climate

The Badlands, shown in both photos, along with the rest of South Dakota experiences a wider range of seasonal temperatures than locations near large bodies of water.

Water Affects Humidity and Precipitation Nearness to large bodies of water affects humidity and precipitation patterns. Evaporation adds moisture to air that passes over large bodies of water, and the air becomes more humid. So, coastal areas have higher humidity than nearby inland areas. Because of the additional moisture in the air, coastal areas may also have more precipitation than inland areas. This can be seen in how green the vegetation is in the photo of Hawaii versus the vegetation in the summer photo of South Dakota.

Water Affects Wind Patterns Regions along the coast tend to have certain daily and seasonal wind patterns. For example, daily shifts include sea and land breezes. However, a seasonal change in the strongest winds in a region can result in a *monsoon*. Monsoons are characterized by rainy seasons that alternate with dry seasons, each with its own pattern of prevailing winds that reverse direction because of temperature differences between land and sea.

Climate Controls: Latitude, Elevation, Nearness to Water

Latitude, elevation, and nearness to water are climate controls—they are three major factors that strongly influence climate patterns. These controls work together to produce varied climates all around the globe. What types of climate do you expect to find in Australia, the world's largest island and smallest continent?

Florence Falls lies in the Northern Territory, close to water. Being in the tropical zone tends to produce high temperatures. But nearness to water moderates these extremes. Florence Falls has a moderately high-temperature climate.

Cobar is located on the leeward side of the Great Dividing Range. It is a rain shadow desert, so it is very dry. Besides the rain shadow effect, Cobar is hot because its latitude lies in the tropical zone.

Indian Ocean

Pacific Ocean

Australia

Ayers Rock is far away from water. Located in Uluru in the middle of the Australian continent, Ayers Rock experiences extreme high and low temperatures and low humidity.

Indian Ocean

Kempsey is a town on the windward side of the Great Dividing Range. It is rainy, lush, and green there due to the rain shadow effect.

Perth enjoys a moderate climate due to its proximity to the Indian Ocean. Its temperatures are mild and seasonal because this city lies in the temperate zone.

Tasmania is an island that lies in the temperate zone. Its middle latitude and nearness to water are the major reasons that Tasmania contains large amounts of temperate rainforest—dense forest with moderate temperatures and low seasonal variability.

The Snowy Mountains exist at high elevations along the Great Dividing Range. Due to their high elevation, the Snowy Mountains are cold and snowy much of the year.

5. Modeling Earth's Climate

Based on the data in a climograph for your region, you would expect the weather next winter to be similar to the average winter for your area. However, climate scientists can predict that next winter is not likely to be average. How do they predict future climate?

Climate scientists use climate models to predict how climate may change. Climate models use mathematical equations to describe the complex climate system. Scientists can adjust variables in the equations to predict how climate may change over time. For example, climate models might simulate how energy is transferred within the atmosphere. Scientists can adjust the composition of the atmosphere in the model to view different outcomes. These system models simulate processes that contribute to climate and interactions between parts of the Earth system. They show how energy flows between the parts of the Earth system and may include other important inputs, such as energy from the sun.

Using climate models, climate scientists may predict the probability of possible climate conditions beyond a region's average. Climate scientists can also simulate patterns in global temperatures and precipitation and compare them to what is observed. These outputs help in forecasting future climate under changing conditions caused by factors such as the greenhouse effect.

Climate scientists use computer models to predict future climate. The models are system models that are based on equations to describe the parts of the Earth system and how they interact.

LESSON SUMMARY
Climate Patterns

Understanding Climate The weather in a certain location averaged over a period of many years is called *climate*. Climate includes average temperature, precipitation, wind, humidity, and pressure.

Latitude Controls Climate The tropical, temperate, and polar climate zones have different average temperatures because of their latitude. Regions farther from the equator receive less solar energy.

Elevation Controls Climate Air temperature is proportional to elevation. It decreases at a specific rate as elevation increases. The rain shadow effect is caused when precipitation falls on the windward side of a mountain, leaving dry air on the leeward side.

Nearness to Water Controls Climate Large bodies of water moderate climate by creating smaller daily and seasonal temperature ranges. Nearness to water also increases humidity, affects precipitation, and leads to land breezes and sea breezes.

Modeling Earth's Climate Climate models are system models that describe the processes that produce climate patterns.

Extreme Climates

How do you like your weather? Do you prefer sizzling summers, freezing winters, or mild springs and autumns? Or maybe you'd like to be in one of Earth's extreme, record-breaking climates? Where are these extraordinary places? And what happens there?

The highest air temperature ever recorded was 57°C (134°F) in Death Valley, California, on July 10, 1913. The temperatures in Death Valley do not regularly get higher than 50°C (122°F), but during the summer, the average high temperature stays above 38°C (100°F).

Death Valley's high air temperature has been considered the record for more than 100 years, but scientists continue to search for and note record high temperatures. Although scientists have placed weather stations around the world to measure official air temperatures, few weather stations are placed in the hottest deserts because they are hard to reach. Consequently, this makes weather records difficult to track.

So, where have scientists noted as the hottest place on Earth? Using satellite temperature data, scientists have discovered that, in 2005, the Lut Desert in Iran had a temperature of 71°C (159°F)! That temperature was surface temperature, not air temperature, but it was hotter than any surface temperature measured in Death Valley. Because surface temperature and air temperature are not comparable, two different places could be called the hottest place on Earth.

Salt flats, like these formed from rapidly evaporating water leaving behind minerals, can be found in the arid desert soil of Death Valley. The valley regularly has temperatures over 38°C (100°F) throughout the summer.

Out in the Cold

Although the location of the hottest place on Earth is debatable, the location of the coldest place on Earth is not. Antarctica is the coldest place, with record-setting temperatures measured by an air-temperature thermometer and by satellite. On July 21, 1983, a thermometer at the Vostok Research Station measured the air temperature at a bone-chilling −89°C (−129°F). Then on August 10, 2010, a satellite measured the temperature on a ridge not too far from Vostok at an even colder −93°C (−136°F)!

Vostok is just one of many scientific research stations in Antarctica that have people living in them year round. But it is a research station and people don't tend to settle there or in any of the other stations. Thus, no one lives in Antarctica permanently. So, while Antarctica easily takes the title for the coldest place on Earth, it is not the coldest inhabited place. The coldest inhabited place is practically on the other side of the world from Antarctica.

The towns of Verkhoyansk and Oymyakon in northern Russia recorded air temperatures of −68°C (−90°F) in 1892 and 1933, respectively. These towns are so cold that people use outhouses instead of toilets because indoor plumbing often freezes. They also leave cars running all day because, if they turn them off, the engines may become too cold to start again. There is, however, a benefit to the cold weather: people don't need refrigerators. The ground is permanently frozen, so some people simply put food in their basements to keep it cold.

The coldest inhabited places on Earth are the towns of Verkhoyansk and Oymyakon in Russia. This man is gathering firewood in January in the village of Oymyakon, where winter temperatures average around −50°C (−58°F).

The Atacama Desert in Chile is the second driest place on Earth, following Antarctica. Astronomers from all over the world use telescopes located in the Atacama because the dry conditions lead to normally clear skies and clear images of stars.

Every few years, the Atacama Desert experiences wetter-than-normal conditions. During those times, blooming flowers cover the desert.

Dry as a Bone

Antarctica holds another extreme climate record as the driest place on Earth. According to one source, the region in Antarctica called the Dry Valleys has not had a drop of precipitation in nearly 2 million years. The valleys are so dry that, despite being on a frozen continent, they have no ice or snow in them. The Dry Valleys are close to a U.S. research station, and scientists have visited and investigated the area. They have found that despite the cold temperatures and lack of moisture, some lichen, moss, and bacteria live in the valleys.

The next-driest place on Earth sometimes shows a little more life than the Dry Valleys. Locations across the Atacama Desert in northern Chile average around 5 mm (0.19 in.) of precipitation per year. Most of the time, the Atacama Desert looks the way you would expect a desert to look: dry and sandy with no plants. But every five to seven years, wetter-than-normal conditions occur, which awaken dormant seeds in the ground. Flowers bloom, covering the desert floor in bright colors.

But "wetter-than-normal" in the Atacama is still very dry compared to most places. For example, a rare downpour in 2015 dropped about 24 mm (less than 1 in.) of rain on the desert. Because the Atacama Desert is so dry, it is an ideal place for astronomical telescopes. The night sky over the desert is usually free of clouds, and the lack of water vapor in the air allows light from distant stars to travel to the telescopes without being scattered or absorbed.

Soaking Wet

The difference between the driest place on Earth and the wettest place on Earth couldn't be more extreme. While it never rains in the Dry Valleys, it rains almost every day in Meghalaya, India. In particular, the average rainfall in Mawsynram, Meghalaya, is 11,873 mm per year—that's almost 39 *feet* of rain each year!

The people who live in Meghalaya have found unique ways to deal with the wet climate. They use things called *knups*, which are essentially whole-body umbrellas that are worn on their heads and backs. Because a knup is attached to a person's body, it doesn't need to be held up with a hand, and the person is free to use both hands while farming or doing anything else in the rain.

Another unusual solution that the people of Meghalaya have devised is the building of "living bridges." The constant rain in the area causes wooden structures, including bridges, to rot and fall apart. So, instead of building bridges out of dead wood, the people use living tree roots. The roots of rubber trees are tied and woven together to form a bridge. As time passes, the roots get thicker and stronger until they form a bridge strong enough to support people.

So, do Earth's extreme weather conditions appeal to you? Whatever climate you prefer, you're probably a lot more comfortable where you live than you would be in the hottest, coldest, driest, or wettest places on Earth. ◆

The wettest climate is found in Meghalaya, India. In this area, bridges are made of living tree roots because bridges made from dead wood could likely rot and fall apart.

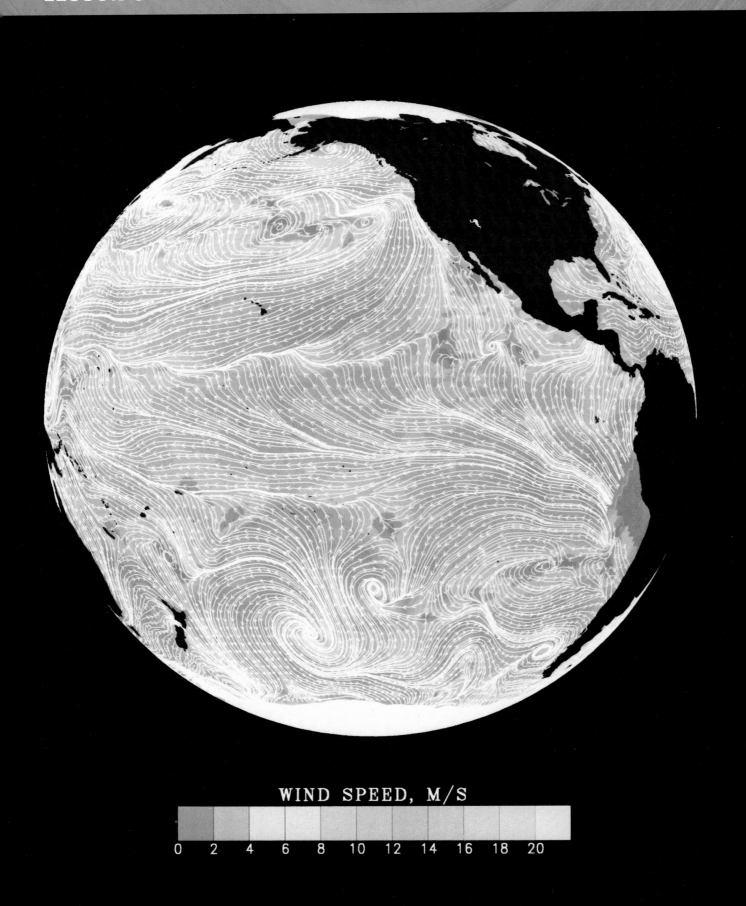

WIND SPEED, M/S

0 2 4 6 8 10 12 14 16 18 20

Global Circulation of the Atmosphere

How do global winds affect climates around the world?

Introduction

This image of Earth may look like a swirling watercolor painting, but it is actually a computer image made from satellite data. The satellite obtained the data with a sensor that detects microwaves to measure wind speeds and their directions over the ocean. The blue color represents slow winds, while the pink and orange colors show faster winds. What patterns do you see in wind speed and direction on Earth?

Images such as this one are valuable for observing and forecasting winds. As you can see, large-scale winds, called *global winds*, move in a twisting pattern around Earth. Why does wind circulate around the planet in these patterns? How is understanding global winds useful to scientists studying Earth's climate? How do humans benefit from using these winds?

In this lesson, you will learn about the scientific model that explains how global winds circulate air and distribute energy. You will explore how engineers are harnessing the global winds to generate electricity. Finally, you will learn about the rivers of air in the upper atmosphere that create an "express lane" for jet planes.

Vocabulary

surface winds winds that blow near Earth's surface

Coriolis effect the apparent curve in the path of an object caused by Earth's rotation

global winds prevailing wind patterns that blow in fairly constant, predictable patterns around Earth

jet stream strong winds in the upper troposphere that exist in relatively narrow bands

---

Next Generation Science Standards

Performance Expectations

MS-ESS2-6. Develop and use a model to describe how unequal heating and rotation of the Earth cause patterns of atmospheric and oceanic circulation that determine regional climates.

MS-ETS1-1. Define the criteria and constraints of a design problem with sufficient precision to ensure a successful solution, taking into account relevant scientific principles and potential impacts on people and the natural environment that may limit possible solutions.

Science and Engineering Practices

Developing and Using Models Develop and use a model to describe phenomena.

Asking Questions and Defining Problems Define a design problem that can be solved through the development of an object, tool, process or system and includes multiple criteria and constraints, including scientific knowledge that may limit possible solutions.

Crosscutting Concepts

Systems and System Models Models can be used to represent systems and their interactions—such as inputs, processes, and outputs—and energy, matter, and information flows within systems.

Influence of Science, Engineering, and Technology on Society and the Natural World

Disciplinary Core Ideas

ESS2.D. Weather and climate are influenced by interactions involving sunlight, the ocean, the atmosphere, ice, landforms, and living things. These interactions vary with latitude, altitude, and local and regional geography, all of which can affect oceanic and atmospheric flow patterns.

ETS1.A. The more precisely a design task's criteria and constraints can be defined, the more likely it is that the designed solution will be successful. Specification of constraints includes consideration of scientific principles and other relevant knowledge that are likely to limit possible solutions.

1. Developing a Model of Global Air Circulation

For centuries, sailors have known that winds at different latitudes blow steadily in certain directions. Yet, little was known about why these winds exist. In 1735, George Hadley, a lawyer who studied climate as a hobby, developed a model to explain them. What was his model?

Hadley's model explains that air circulates around the planet through a system of convection cells. Figure 9.1A shows the Hadley convection cell model. In his model, the atmosphere in the Northern and Southern Hemispheres each have one large convection cell. Air that is warmed at the equator rises. As it rises, the warm air cools. When it reaches the cool upper troposphere, it is at the same temperature as surrounding air. Therefore, it cannot rise any further. Instead, the air spreads out, moving toward the poles. When it reaches the poles, it sinks and circulates back toward the equator.

Hadley's global-scale circulation pattern, based on convection, exists because of the uneven heating of Earth by the sun. Recall that the sun's rays strike the equator more directly than the poles. Therefore, regions near the equator are hotter than those near the poles. But energy always moves from warmer to colder areas, so energy flows away from the equator and toward the poles. Convection cells are how this transfer of energy takes place. Without convection cells, Earth's equator would be much hotter and the poles would be much colder than they are, making it hard for life to exist on Earth.

Air in a convection cell moves vertically. Figure 9.1A models this movement and shows the direction surface winds move. **Surface winds** are winds that blow near Earth's surface. Some surface winds, such as the winds that Hadley set out to explain in his model, are at the bottoms of convection cells.

Figure 9.1A

The Hadley model of convection was developed in the 1700s. It shows the movement of energy as it flows from the equator to the poles and back again through large convection cells in the troposphere. Surface winds flow back toward the equator near the surface.

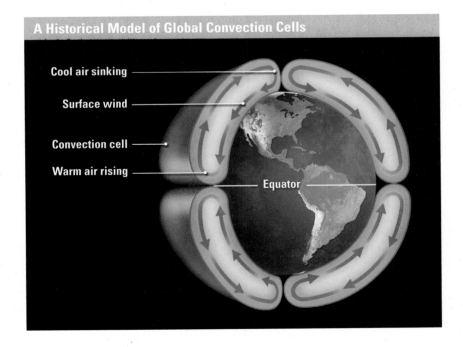

A Historical Model of Global Convection Cells

Cool air sinking

Surface wind

Convection cell

Warm air rising

Equator

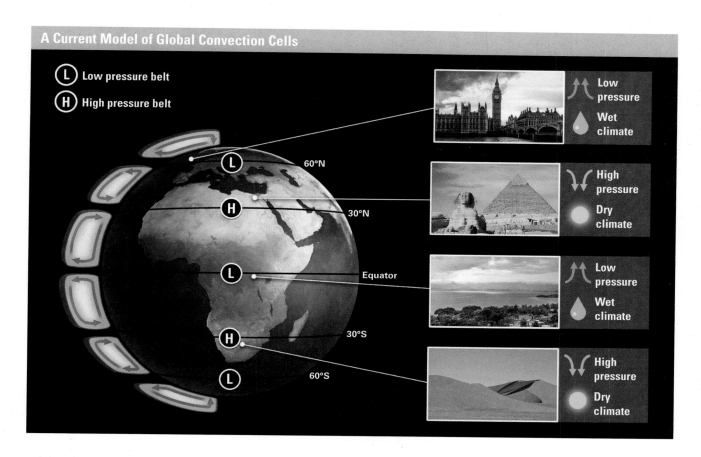

A Current Model of Global Convection Cells

Ⓛ Low pressure belt

Ⓗ High pressure belt

60°N

30°N

Equator

30°S

60°S

Low pressure
Wet climate

High pressure
Dry climate

Low pressure
Wet climate

High pressure
Dry climate

Hadley's simple model could not explain the observed wind and pressure patterns in the mid-latitudes. Surface winds between 30°N and 60°N and between 30°S and 60°S blow toward the poles instead of toward the equator. In 1856, William Ferrel modified Hadley's model to include an additional cell at the mid-latitudes. His model explained the winds that blow poleward. The current model, shown in Figure 9.1B, has three convection cells in each hemisphere. It takes into account Earth's rotation and the seasonal temperature changes caused by Earth's tilt. Notice that at the latitudes where the convection cells meet, regions of high or low pressure form. These regions of high and low pressure are called *pressure belts*. High pressure belts are found at about 30°N and 30°S. Low pressure belts are found at the equator and at about 60°N and 60°S. In each cell in the current model, the surface winds blow from high pressure toward low pressure.

The rising and falling air in the three convection cells in each hemisphere help to explain patterns of wet and dry climates around the globe. Climates near the equator and 60°N and 60°S tend to be wetter because they are in low pressure belts where air rises. The air cools as it rises and clouds form, which can produce stormy weather and rain or snow. The opposite happens near the poles and 30°N and 30°S, where sinking air creates areas of high pressure. The sinking air warms and can hold more moisture, so clouds do not form. The sunny, dry climate explains why many deserts are found there.

Figure 9.1B

This current model shows three convection cells in each hemisphere. Each cell encircles the globe and results in circulation of air in the atmosphere. Pressure belts form where the convection cells meet. Climates are wetter near the low pressure belts and near the equator, and drier near the high pressure belts.

The Coriolis Effect

In the Northern Hemisphere the rotation of Earth makes air particles seem to move in a clockwise direction.

Actual path of air particles

Particles of air

Direction of Earth's rotation

Figure 9.2

The Coriolis effect is the apparent curving of the path of an object due to Earth's rotation. It causes large-scale surface winds to curve clockwise in the Northern Hemisphere and counterclockwise in the Southern Hemisphere.

2. Curving Air—the Coriolis Effect

If the winds traveled straight north or south, captains of sailing ships could not take advantage of surface winds to travel east or west across the oceans. However, they can use surface winds because the paths of the winds curve. What causes the paths of surface winds to curve?

Winds curve because of the **Coriolis effect,** which is the apparent curve in the path of an object caused by Earth's rotation. Although the path of wind is not actually moving off course, it appears to curve because Earth rotates underneath the air as it is moving north or south. Look at what happens to the paths of the air particles in Figure 9.2. In the Northern Hemisphere, the path curves clockwise. In the Southern Hemisphere, the path curves counterclockwise. The paths appear to curve in these directions because Earth is rotating west to east.

However, the Coriolis Effect causes a different pattern of movement for hurricanes. The movement of air from areas of high pressure to low pressure causes hurricanes in the Northern Hemisphere to rotate counterclockwise and hurricanes in the Southern Hemisphere to rotate clockwise.

3. Global Wind Patterns

In the days of sailing ships, captains of ships bound for Europe from America might plot a course in the northern latitudes to take advantage of westerly winds. How could they rely solely on wind for such a distance?

Global winds are surface winds that blow in fairly constant, predictable patterns around Earth, as seen in the computer image at the beginning of the lesson. They are also called *prevailing* winds. They are not the same as local winds, such as sea breezes, whose direction is determined by local pressure systems. Instead, global winds represent average large-scale wind patterns over time. The pattern of global winds is caused by the large convection cells and the Coriolis effect.

The three global winds in the Northern and Southern Hemispheres are the trade winds, the westerlies, and the polar easterlies. As seen in Figure 9.3, they blow from high to low pressure belts. The trade winds blow from 30°N or 30°S toward the equator. Their path appears curved from east to west because of the Coriolis effect. Westerlies blow from west to east between 30°N and 60°N and between 30°S and 60°S. The polar easterlies blow away from each pole from east to west.

Global winds affect other aspects of climate because they help to move air masses, along with their moisture and temperature properties, around Earth. Because storms often form where air masses meet, global winds influence where storms occur.

Sailing ships rely on the power of global winds to push their ships across the oceans. Global winds also push air masses, and therefore affect temperature and precipitation patterns.

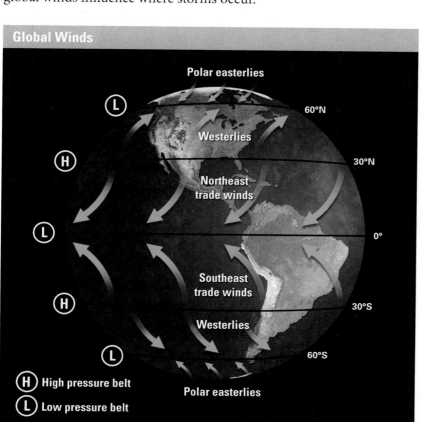

Figure 9.3

Global winds are surface winds that blow in predictable patterns from high pressure belts to low pressure belts. They appear to curve to the west in the Northern Hemisphere or to the east in the Southern Hemisphere because of the Coriolis effect.

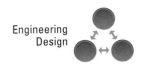

4. Harnessing Global Winds

Sailing ship captains are not the only people who have harnessed the wind as a valuable natural resource. For more than 2,000 years, people built windmills to use wind energy to grind grain. Today, wind turbines are used to convert the energy of the wind into electricity. A wind farm, consisting of multiple turbines, is the wind version of a power plant.

To design a wind farm, engineers must precisely determine the criteria and constraints of building it, including evaluating any impact on the local people and environment. What are some of the considerations they must weigh?

Wind farm engineers need to choose a good location. One of the most important criteria for a wind farm is a reliable source of strong winds throughout the year. Engineers use data gathered by scientists to map wind speeds across the United States. They have also calculated the amounts of power that can be generated by wind turbines at different wind speeds. By analyzing these wind maps, engineers can determine potential places for wind farms. Some likely locations lie in ocean waters near the coast to take advantage of strong global winds blowing across the ocean.

Offshore wind farms use strong global winds that blow over the ocean to generate electricity. Strong winds are a criterion of the wind farm. The impact on people and the environment must be considered when determining constraints.

Block Island, off the coast of Rhode Island, has consistent winds. This is one reason it was chosen as the location for one of the first offshore wind farms in the United States. Built in 2016, the Block Island Wind Farm consists of five turbines that are about 5 km off the shore of the island. It produces enough electricity for about 17,000 homes.

Before building the wind farm, engineers needed to consider any potential impacts it would have on people. When defining constraints, they had to consider both the effects of the wind farm and its construction. Too much noise from operating turbines could reduce the quality of life of people living nearby on Block Island. One constraint was noise from construction should not negatively affect people. Another constraint was that the wind farm could not impact the scenic view from the shoreline of Block Island. Residents and visitors to the island were concerned that the turbines would reduce the natural beauty.

Solutions for Wind Farm Negative Impacts

Constraints	Solutions
Wind farm cables in fish habitat could damage fisheries.	Bury cables under the sea floor to reduce the impact on the environment.
Noise during construction of the wind farm could reach harmful levels.	Reduce onshore construction noise by surrounding the construction site with a wall.
Some residents and tourists think the wind turbines interfere with the natural beauty and scenic view.	Locate the turbines five kilometers from shore and paint them white and light gray to blend with the color of the sky.

When planning the wind farm, engineers also needed to consider the impacts on the environment. Fish are an important part of the marine environment and the fishing industry. An environmental impact study showed that the wind turbines and connecting cables could impact fish habitats as well as marine mammals.

Engineers defined the constraints of the offshore wind farm so they could come up with solutions to reduce possible negative impacts. Before building the wind farm, engineers were required to submit a report that explained these solutions. Figure 9.4 shows some of the constraints of building the wind farm and solutions that engineers developed.

Noise was one of the problems that had to be addressed. While the turbines were being built, engineers planned a wall around the onshore construction area to reduce the construction noise levels. Pile driving occurred during daylight hours starting after dawn and ending prior to dusk. And engineers determined that noise from the operating turbines would not be a problem because the wind turbines were so far offshore.

To minimize the impact on the scenic view and meet this constraint, the turbines were located as far offshore as possible and painted white or light gray to blend well with sea and sky. The number of turbines for the wind farm was also reduced to only five.

Engineers addressed another important constraint by planning the project to avoid directly disturbing fish resources and important fish habitats. Cables were buried under the sea floor to connect the turbines to the existing system that is used to distribute electricity. And one long-term benefit of the wind farm is that it does not produce carbon dioxide or other pollutants. By analyzing the potential impacts of this sustainable energy source, engineers developed ways to responsibly harness the power of the wind.

Figure 9.4

Constraints of the offshore wind farm included construction noise, a reduction in natural beauty, and damage to fish habitats. Engineers needed to find solutions to these potential negative impacts of building the offshore wind farm.

Uneven Heating of Earth Produces Global Winds

The uneven heating of Earth by the sun produces global winds that affect climate. As this model shows, convection cells in the atmosphere, which are global circulation patterns, help to redistribute energy from the warm equator to the cooler poles. How do pressure belts and global winds influence precipitation patterns around the globe?

Wet climates are present near low pressure belts and near the equator. Dry climates are present near high pressure belts.

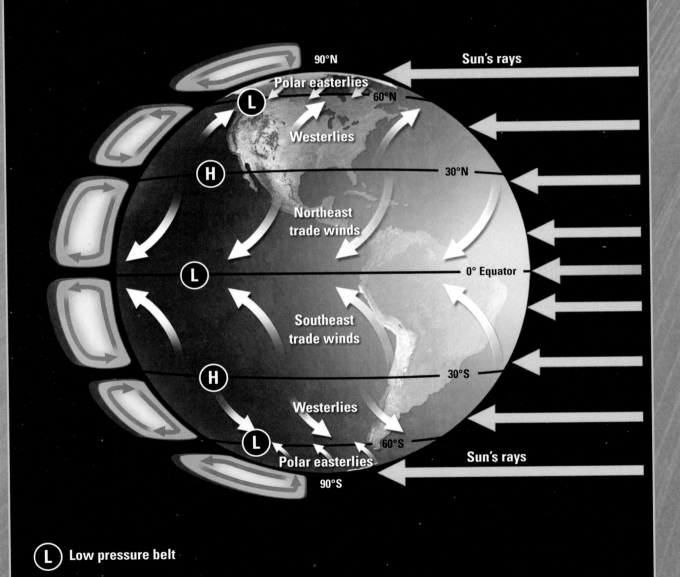

L Low pressure belt

H High pressure belt

5. Jet Streams

You fly from the East Coast to the West Coast of the United States. The flight is over 5 hours long. But when you fly back, the flight is an hour shorter! Why is the flight in one direction shorter than the other?

Pilots traveling eastward can use jet streams to give planes an extra push. **Jet streams** are strong winds in the upper troposphere that are found in relatively narrow bands. Jet streams are like fast-moving rivers of air that follow wavy paths from west to east at about 10 km above Earth's surface. Two major jet streams blow in both hemispheres, as shown in the illustration. They form between masses of warmer air and colder air. Polar jet streams form at about 50°N to 60°N and 50°S to 60°S, where cold polar air meets warm air at the middle latitudes. Subtropical jet streams form around 30°N and 30°S between the warm air at middle latitudes and hot tropical air.

Jet streams vary from season to season and affect weather and climate by moving air masses. The winds are stronger in the winter when the temperature difference between the air masses is greater. The jet streams also tend to move closer to the equator in the winter. In the winter, the polar jet stream in the Northern Hemisphere may dip southward, bringing a cold Arctic air mass to the southern United States.

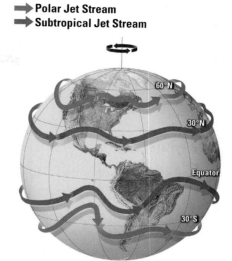

➡ **Polar Jet Stream**
➡ **Subtropical Jet Stream**

A polar jet stream and a subtropical jet stream are found in each hemisphere between masses of warm and cold air. They are narrow bands of fast moving air that travel eastward around the globe in the upper troposphere.

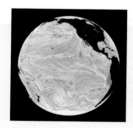

LESSON SUMMARY

Global Circulation of the Atmosphere

Developing a Model of Global Air Circulation George Hadley developed the first model showing how two convention cells circulate air and redistribute heat in the atmosphere. The modern model includes three convection cells in both the Northern and Southern Hemispheres that influence temperature and precipitation patterns.

Curving Air—the Coriolis Effect The Coriolis effect is the apparent curve in the path of an object caused by Earth's rotation from west to east. It causes the paths of winds to appear curved.

Global Wind Patterns The polar easterlies, westerlies, and trade winds are global winds that blow along the surface in predictable patterns between the high and low pressure belts. They affect climate by pushing air masses, which influence temperature and precipitation.

Harnessing Global Winds Offshore wind farms harness global winds that blow across the ocean. Engineers consider the criteria and constraints in building wind farms and their potential impacts on people and the environment.

Jet Streams The polar and subtropical jet streams are narrow bands of strong winds that blow in the upper troposphere. Jet streams affect weather by moving air masses.

Around the World with Global Winds

If you were to attend one of the hot-air balloon festivals that take place each summer, you would see many of these engineless aircraft overhead. You might wonder how the balloons stay aloft and how far they will travel before they land. Or you might even ask, what is the *farthest* they could travel without landing? Could a balloon use global winds to travel all the way around the world?

Hot-air balloons have been used for air travel for over two centuries. The hot-air balloon is made of a large cloth bag (called an *envelope*) attached to a basket that people ride in. Above the basket are burners, which heat the air that fills the envelope.

Hot-air balloons rise in the air because of the density difference between the air inside the balloon and the surrounding air. The density of a gas decreases as its temperature increases, so the hot air inside a balloon's envelope is less dense than the surrounding air. Air is a fluid, and the less-dense air inside the envelope floats in the denser surrounding air and takes the envelope and the basket with it.

When people ride in balloons, they are not completely in control of where they go. Where and how fast a balloon goes depend on the wind. The balloon pilot can control the balloon somewhat by moving the balloon up and down in the atmosphere. Wind direction and speed vary at different altitudes. During a recreational hot-air balloon flight—that is, a flight just for fun—the trip is about an hour long and may cover a distance as far as the wind allows in that hour in altitudes ranging from 305–914 m (1,001 ft–2,999 ft).

A hot-air balloon is one way to travel through the air. It is made of a large cloth bag called an *envelope*, a basket to hold people, and burners that heat the air inside the envelope. How far and how fast a balloon travels depend on wind speed and amount of fuel.

Designed for Distance

Most hot-air balloons tend to fly short distances because they fly at low altitudes where the wind speed is relatively low. Hot-air balloons may travel farther by flying higher in the atmosphere to a level where the winds are stronger and allow balloons to travel a few hundred kilometers over several hours. However, the distance that a hot-air balloon can travel is limited by the amount of fuel that it carries. It can only stay aloft as long has it has fuel to burn and heat the air in the envelope.

Balloonists who want to travel very long distances, such as across a continent or an ocean, use a special kind of balloon called a *Roziere*. The envelope of a Roziere is made up of two separate chambers. An inner chamber is filled with helium, which is a low-density gas. The helium makes the balloon float just like helium makes a child's toy balloon float. An outer chamber is filled with air and is open at the bottom like a hot-air balloon envelope. Burners under the air chamber are used to heat the air inside the bottom chamber.

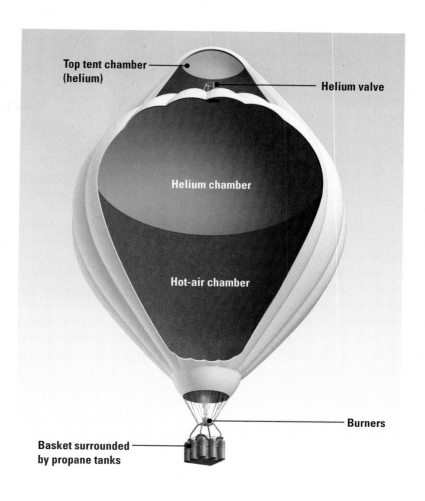

A Roziere balloon is designed to travel farther than a regular hot-air balloon. A Roziere has two chambers in its envelope: an inner chamber filled with helium and an outer chamber filled with hot air.

The dual chambers of the Roziere allow balloonists to partly overcome the fuel limitation of hot-air balloons. The helium keeps the balloon aloft without having to heat it. The balloon can stay at a relatively constant altitude without using any fuel. However, at night, the helium cools and becomes denser, and the balloon will start to descend. To maintain the balloon's altitude, the balloonist fires the burners to heat the air in the outer chamber to give the balloon more lift. (The burners can also be used to adjust the balloon's altitude at any time during the flight.) As a result, some Roziere balloons can stay up for days at a time. And, of course, the longer the balloon stays up, the farther it will travel.

The first flight in a Roziere balloon in 1783 lasted only about four minutes with the balloon launched at the end of a tether. Today, these human-carrying balloons can circumnavigate the planet and have set records for total world distance and duration for aircraft.

The *Breitling Orbiter 3* was the first balloon to travel around the world nonstop. In this photo, Bertrand Piccard and Brian Jones prepare to embark on their historic record-breaking flight.

The *Breitling Orbiter 3* was 55 m (180 ft) tall when the envelope was inflated. The basket, which was actually an enclosed capsule, was a little bigger than a minivan.

Around the World in 19 Days

Because Roziere balloons can stay up for very long periods of time, balloonists began to wonder if they could use a balloon to fly around the world without stopping. There were several attempts at this daring feat, but they failed for various reasons including running out of fuel or being forced down by storms. The first successful trip to circumnavigate the planet didn't take place until 1999.

The first balloon to travel around the world nonstop was called the *Breitling Orbiter 3* and was piloted by Bertrand Piccard (from Switzerland) and Brian Jones (from England). Piccard was inspired by the achievements of his grandfather, Auguste Piccard, who pioneered high-altitude, hot-air balloon flights in the 1930s, as well as his father, Jacques, who was one of the first people to explore the Mariana Trench, the deepest part of the world's ocean. To go around the world, the pilots had to fly their balloon at a high altitude so that they could catch jet streams.

To reach the jet streams, the *Orbiter* had to fly at altitudes of more than 6,000 m (19,685 ft). At one point, it set the altitude record for a Roziere balloon when it flew 11,737 m (38,507 ft) above Earth's surface. To fly that high, the *Orbiter* had to have a huge envelope to carry a huge volume of helium. Fully inflated, the balloon was 55 m tall—that's almost as tall as a 17-story building!

The *Orbiter* took off from a village in Switzerland on March 1, 1999. The jet streams helped the balloon move relatively quickly around the world making the trip in 19 days, 21 hours, and 55 minutes. It still had a day's worth of fuel when it crossed the finish line. The pilots decided to fly a little further before landing in an Egyptian desert.

Going It Alone

Once the *Breitling Orbiter 3* completed its record-breaking trip, the next goal for balloonists was for someone to make a solo trip around the world. A solo trip is harder than a trip with more than one crewmember because the balloonist doesn't have anyone to take over the controls when he or she gets tired. One person must be "on duty" all day for many days in a row.

The first person to fly solo around the world in a balloon was American aviator Steve Fossett. The flight also made him one of the handful of people to fly around the world in a balloon. His flight happened in 2002 and took only 13 days, 8 hours, and 33 minutes to circle Earth. That time shattered the record previously held by the *Breitling Orbiter 3*. Fossett also used jet streams to zip through the atmosphere where he achieved a speed of 322 km/h (200 mph) during the flight.

Fossett's time record stood for 14 years until the next person managed to fly around the world in a balloon. In 2016, a Russian adventurer named Fedor Konyukhov flew around the world in 11 days and 6 hours at speeds of about 240 km/h (149 mph). Like Fossett, Konyukhov used a Roziere balloon similar in design to the *Breitling Orbiter 3*.

The colorful hot-air balloons you see drifting through the air at a festival may be for display or people enjoying a pleasant ride. But if you ever spot a silvery balloon very high up in the sky, you might be looking at a Roziere balloon trying to break a world record. ◆

Fedor Konyukhov's balloon was a Roziere balloon. This photo was taken just after he took off from Australia.

Fedor Konyukhov tries out the gondola that he will live in for the duration of an 11-day flight. Konyukhov holds the world record for flying around the world in a balloon in the shortest amount of time. He completed his journey in July 2016.

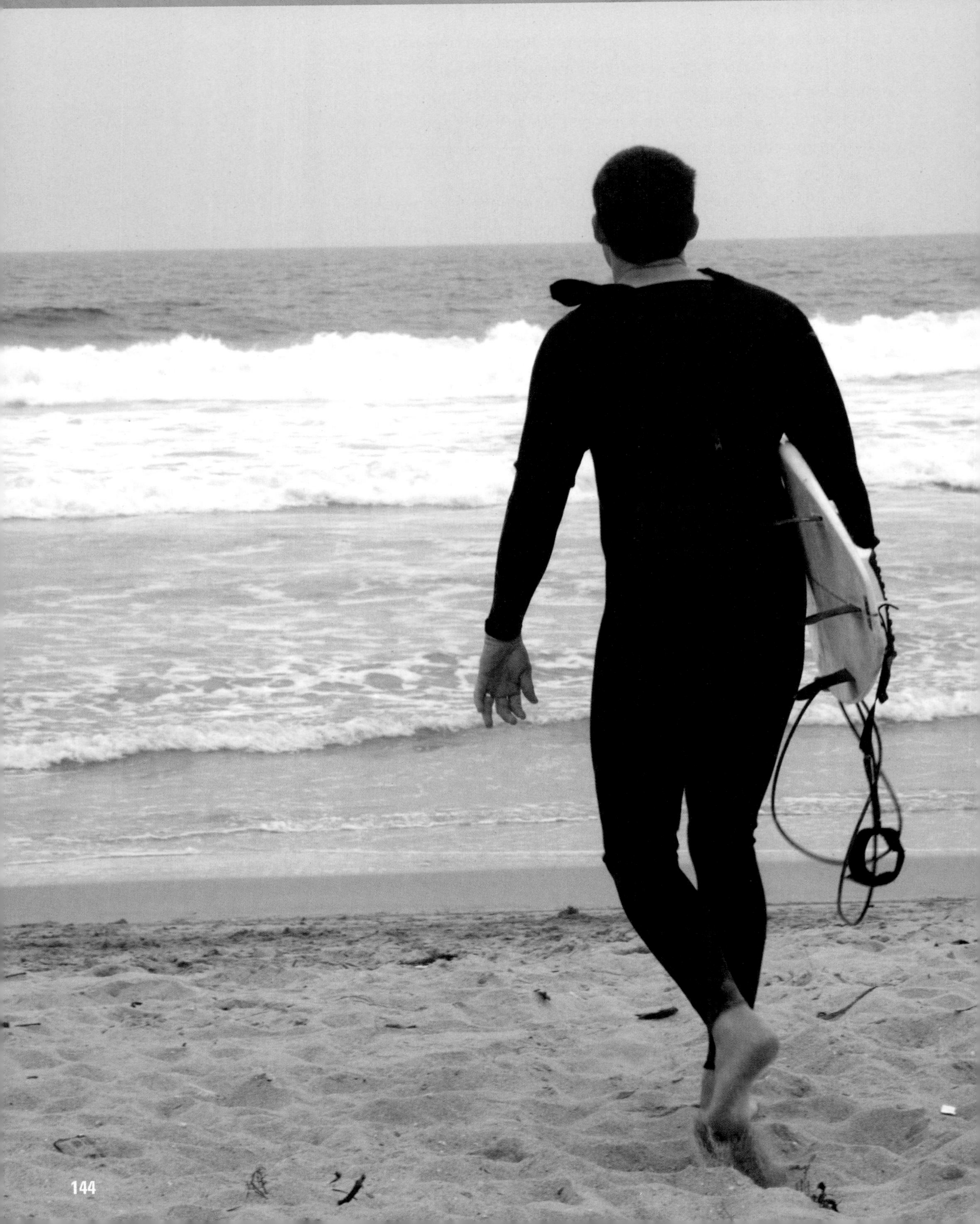

How the Ocean Affects Climate

How does the way ocean water mixes and moves influence climate?

Introduction

On which ocean shore in the United States do you think the surfer in the photo is walking? His wetsuit gives you a clue that the ocean is cool at his location. If it is summer, he might be anywhere on the West Coast, even San Diego. Even though Southern California has a mild climate year round, the Pacific Ocean is chilly. However, the surfer is unlikely to be in the southeast. He could surf in the Atlantic Ocean in board shorts near Charleston, South Carolina. The water there is warmer than in San Diego in the summer. Even though both locations are at the same latitude, why is the water off the California coast so cold compared to the water on the East Coast?

In this lesson, you will learn how the properties of the ocean allow it to store and release energy, and how this energy is distributed around the planet by currents of flowing water. You will also discover how scientists gather data about the temperature and movement of ocean water and use this data to model the system of currents throughout the ocean. You will conclude the lesson by exploring El Niño, a periodic climate pattern produced by winds and currents.

Vocabulary

ocean current the movement of water along a certain path in the ocean

surface current an ocean current, usually in the top 100 m of water, that is driven by global winds

Gulf Stream a warm-water surface current that flows northeast in the North Atlantic Ocean

California Current a cold-water surface current that flows south along the west coast of North America

density currents ocean currents deep in the ocean that flow because of differences in the density of water

global ocean convection cycle an ocean-wide system of surface and density currents that are driven by differences in water temperature and saltiness; also called thermohaline circulation

El Niño part of a climate pattern that occurs when ocean surface temperatures in the Pacific Ocean near the equator are warmer than usual

Next Generation Science Standards

Performance Expectations

MS-ESS2-6. Develop and use a model to describe how unequal heating and rotation of the Earth cause patterns of atmospheric and oceanic circulation that determine regional climates.

Science and Engineering Practices

Developing and Using Models Develop and use a model to describe phenomena.

Crosscutting Concepts

Systems and System Models Models can be used to represent systems and their interactions—

such as inputs, processes, and outputs—and energy, matter, and information flows within systems.

Energy and Matter The transfer of energy can be tracked as energy flows through a designed or natural system.

Disciplinary Core Ideas

ESS2.C. Variations in density due to variations in temperature and salinity drive a global pattern of interconnected ocean currents.

ESS2.D. • Weather and climate are influenced by interactions involving sunlight, the ocean, the

atmosphere, ice, landforms, and living things. These interactions vary with latitude, altitude, and local and regional geography, all of which can affect oceanic and atmospheric flow patterns. • The ocean exerts a major influence on weather and climate by absorbing energy from the sun, releasing it over time, and globally redistributing it through ocean currents.

1. The Ocean Stores Energy

It is summer and you go for an early swim in a pool. Although the morning air is cool, the water is surprisingly warm. Why did the water stay warm during the night while the air cooled down?

The pool water stays warm overnight because it stores energy from the sun and cools slower than the surrounding air. Remember, more energy is needed to change the temperature of water compared to other types of matter, so water heats up and cools down slowly.

The ocean helps to control temperatures on Earth because it changes temperature slowly. Because of its immense size, and the large amount of energy required to change water's temperature, the ocean can absorb and store a massive amount of energy. Compare the temperatures in Figure 10.1. When the ocean is cooler than the atmosphere, it absorbs energy from the air and stores it. As ocean waters flow, the energy stored in the ocean is distributed around Earth.

Figure 10.1

The ocean takes longer to warm up and cool down than the air above it. Because of its immense size and the large amount of energy required to change water's temperature, the ocean can absorb and store a massive amount of energy.

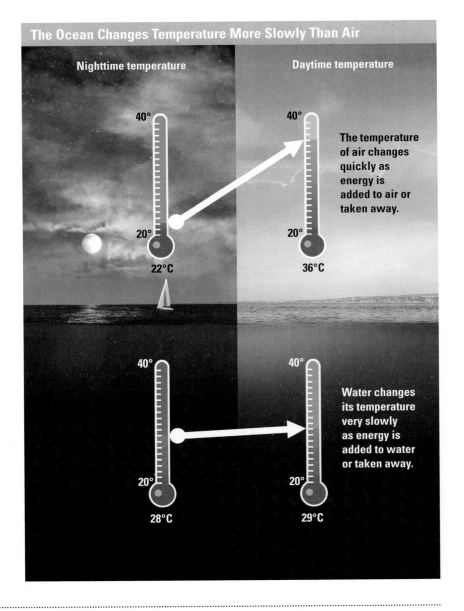

The Ocean Changes Temperature More Slowly Than Air

Nighttime temperature   Daytime temperature

40°   40°

20°   20°

22°C   36°C

The temperature of air changes quickly as energy is added to air or taken away.

40°   40°

20°   20°

28°C   29°C

Water changes its temperature very slowly as energy is added to water or taken away.

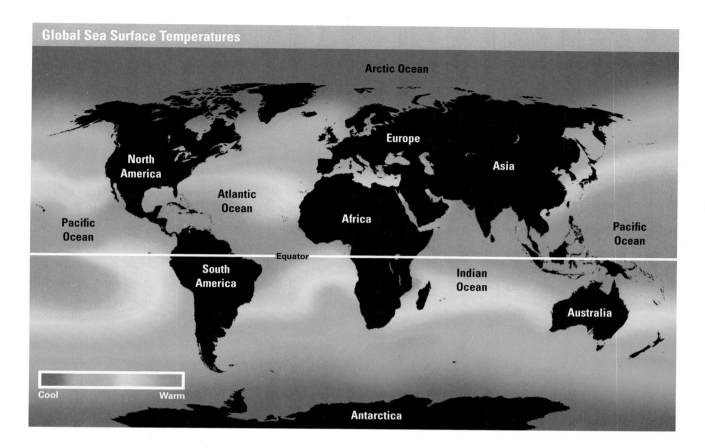

Global Sea Surface Temperatures

Arctic Ocean

Europe

Asia

North America

Atlantic Ocean

Pacific Ocean

Africa

Pacific Ocean

Equator

South America

Indian Ocean

Australia

Cool   Warm

Antarctica

2. The Ocean Distributes Solar Energy

When you add hot water to cold water in a bathtub, the water near the faucet end is warmer. If you made a map of the water temperatures in the tub, what would it look like? How would it change over time?

Figure 10.2 shows the average temperatures of ocean surface water for the entire planet. This map was made using sea surface temperatures that were taken by satellite. The temperature range is about 30°C. Red indicates the warmest temperature and purple is the coldest temperature. What type of temperature pattern do you see? Can you think of an explanation for this pattern?

The temperature of the ocean depends on the amount of direct sunlight it receives. Remember, Earth's curved shape and the tilt of its axis affect the amount of direct sunlight it receives. The ocean temperature map shows that the ocean is warmest near the equator, where it receives the most energy from the sun. The ocean receives less energy from the sun at higher latitudes, so it is cooler toward the poles.

Although the water temperature in a bathtub eventually evens out, ocean temperatures never reach equilibrium. In the ocean, energy moves from the equator to the poles as it circulates from warmer to colder areas. Unlike in a bathtub, energy from the sun continuously affects the temperature of the sea surface near the equator. Like global circulations in the atmosphere, global circulations of water distribute energy in the ocean.

Figure 10.2

This map uses colors to represent the average temperature of the surface of the ocean as measured by satellites. It shows that the ocean is warmest near the equator and coolest near the poles. Energy flows from the equator toward the poles, helping to moderate the sea surface temperatures in each region.

Global Winds and Ocean Surface Currents

Global winds

Global Surface Currents

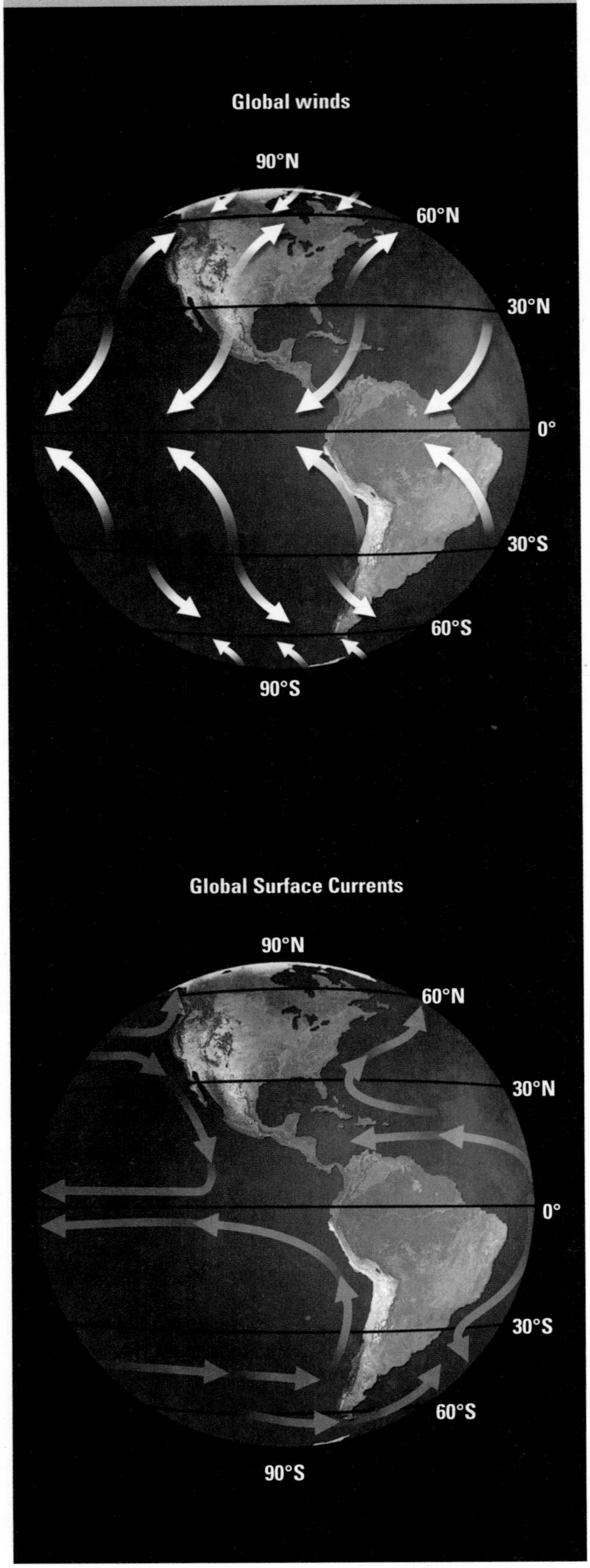

3. Surface Currents

You come upon a bottle nearly buried on a beach on the West Coast of the United States. A piece of paper is rolled up inside. Maybe it is a message. You pull out the paper. The message is in Japanese! How did the bottle float all the way across the Pacific Ocean?

The bottle likely traveled on a current. An **ocean current** is the movement of water along a certain path in the ocean. Currents are like rivers in the ocean and occur globally. There are several types of ocean currents. Some currents occur near the shore, and others are much larger and flow across the oceans. These currents may occur near the surface or deep in the ocean.

Water at the surface of the ocean is also pushed by global winds. A **surface current** is an ocean current, usually in the top 100 m (328 ft) of water, that is driven by global winds. Winds blowing across the ocean drag surface water with them because of friction, a force that opposes the motion between two surfaces that are touching. Compare the models of global winds and surface currents in Figure 10.3A.

The change in the direction of surface currents when they meet continents is called *continental deflection*. While global winds can travel over the top of the land, the ocean cannot and is deflected.

The Coriolis effect determines the direction that global-scale surface currents bend. Note the direction of the surface currents along the west coasts of North and South America in Figure 10.3A. In the Southern Hemisphere, the surface current curves so that it is flowing northward. In the Northern Hemisphere, the surface current curves so that it is traveling southward. Currents are deflected clockwise in the Northern Hemisphere and counterclockwise in the Southern Hemisphere.

Figure 10.3A

Ocean surface currents flow in predictable patterns because they are pushed by global winds. The Coriolis effect and continental deflection affect the currents, causing them to curve.

What shape paths do the currents form in the ocean basins shown in Figure 10.3B? They form when surface currents in different parts of the ocean connect together to form large spiral surface current systems called *gyres*. Gyres form because the Coriolis effect causes surface currents in the open ocean to curve. Five main gyres are found in Earth's oceans: the North Pacific, South Pacific, North Atlantic, South Atlantic, and Indian Ocean gyres. Each gyre is made up of several currents. These systems of currents circulate water and thermal energy around the ocean surface.

Surface currents also help to redistribute energy in the ocean from the equator to the poles. As Figure 10.3B shows, warm surface currents tend to flow toward the poles, although their paths are influenced by the Coriolis effect and continental deflection. On the map, can you locate areas where ocean currents are being deflected by land? As warm water travels away from the equator in warm surface currents, it transfers energy to the cooler water and air that surround the currents. Cold water from the polar regions tends to flow toward the equator. As cold surface currents travel toward the equator, the water absorbs energy from the warmer air and water that surround the currents. Gyres are made up of both warm and cold surface currents.

Surface currents affect the climates of the nearby coastal regions because they affect air temperature and moisture. Winds blowing over warm currents bring warm, moist air to coastal land regions. The air is moist because warm air holds more water vapor. Winds blowing over cold surface currents bring cooler, drier air to coastal regions. The air is drier because cool air can hold less water vapor than warm air. The reach of this effect is not limited to the coastal areas. The climate for areas hundreds of miles away from the shore may be influenced by the effects of surface currents.

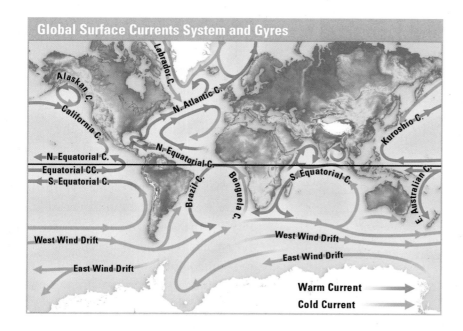

Figure 10.3B
Surface currents redistribute energy away from the equator toward the poles. As the warm and cold currents deflect off continents, they affect the climates of coastal regions.

4. A Warm Surface Current—the Gulf Stream

You want to take advantage of the long winter nights at high latitudes to see the Northern Lights, but you are dreading frigid temperatures. Would you choose to go to northern Alaska or the coast of Norway? Which place would you expect to be warmer to view them?

You might choose to go to Norway because a warm surface current flows by its coast. The **Gulf Stream** is a warm-water surface current that flows northeast in the North Atlantic Ocean. You can see the Gulf Stream in the map of ocean surface temperatures in Figure 10.4. The map was made using temperature measurements that were taken by a satellite. The temperature range is shown by the color scale—red is warmest at about 32°C (89°F) and dark blue is the coolest at about 0°C (32°F). The Gulf Stream appears as a red and orange river of warm water meandering along the coast of the southeast United States. It becomes warmer as it veers eastward away from the coast to cross the North Atlantic Ocean to Europe.

The Gulf Stream carries warm water away from the equator toward the poles and cools as it travels northward. As the water cools, it transfers energy to the air above it and warms the air. This warm air is then transported by winds. Near North America, the global westerly winds blow away from land. Near Europe, these same winds blow the warm air toward land.

The warm water of the Gulf Stream moderates the climates along the East Coast of the United States, especially the Southeast, and in Western Europe. The nearness of the southeastern United States to warm water makes the climate there warmer than it would be otherwise. Warming due to the Gulf Stream is even more striking in Europe, where the warm air blows toward land. This results in warmer winters than other locations at similar latitudes. The average winter temperatures along the coasts of Norway are above 0°C (32°F). In contrast, the average winter temperature in Anchorage at 61°N on the Alaskan coast is −7°C (19°F). The winters along the coasts of Norway are much milder than expected for a region that is at or above 60°N latitude, so Norway is probably the better place to view the Northern Lights in comfort.

Figure 10.4

This temperature map shows the Gulf Stream current as a warm, curving flow along the northeast coast of North America. As the stream transports warm water from the equator northward, it warms the air as it cools. It flows across the Atlantic Ocean to Western Europe, where it moderates the climate there and makes winters warmer.

A Temperature Map of the Gulf Stream

Cool
0°C

Warm
32°C

5. A Cold Surface Current—the California Current

Thanks to the Gulf Stream, the ocean waters are warmer near Charleston, South Carolina, in the summer. However, the ocean at the same latitude near San Diego, California, might be too chilly for a long swim unless you wear a wetsuit like the one the surfer has on in the photo at the beginning of this lesson. Why is the ocean near San Diego so chilly even in the summer?

The **California Current** is a cold-water surface current that flows south along the west coast of North America. It flows from British Columbia to the southernmost tip of Baja California. You can see the California Current on the temperature map in Figure 10.5. The yellow color on the map indicates temperatures of about 30°C (86° F) while the purple color indicates temperatures of about 13°C (55.4°F).

A Temperature Map of the California Current

Cool
13°C

Warm
30°C

The California Current causes a process called *upwelling*. Upwelling happens when surface water is pushed by surface winds and moves away from the coast, and cold, deep water rises up to take its place. Figure 10.5 shows where upwelling is taking place, indicated by the purple color hugging the coast near latitude 40°N. The cold water is full of nutrients, which help support the diverse marine life found along the West Coast.

The California Current causes the coastal areas along the West Coast of the United States to be cooler than along the East Coast. Warm air is cooled when it passes over the cooler current. Westerlies then blow this cool air toward land. Because of the cool air, cities along the California coast are cooler in the summer than inland regions at the same latitude.

The California Current is also part of the reason that coastal cities, including San Diego and San Francisco, have summer fog. As warm, moist air blows across the cold water, it cools. This cooling causes water vapor to condense into water droplets that make up fog.

The Gulf Stream and California Current are only two of the many warm and cold coastal currents that occur in the world's oceans. These numerous currents bring much of the same phenomena of temperature and moisture differences to the coastlines they influence.

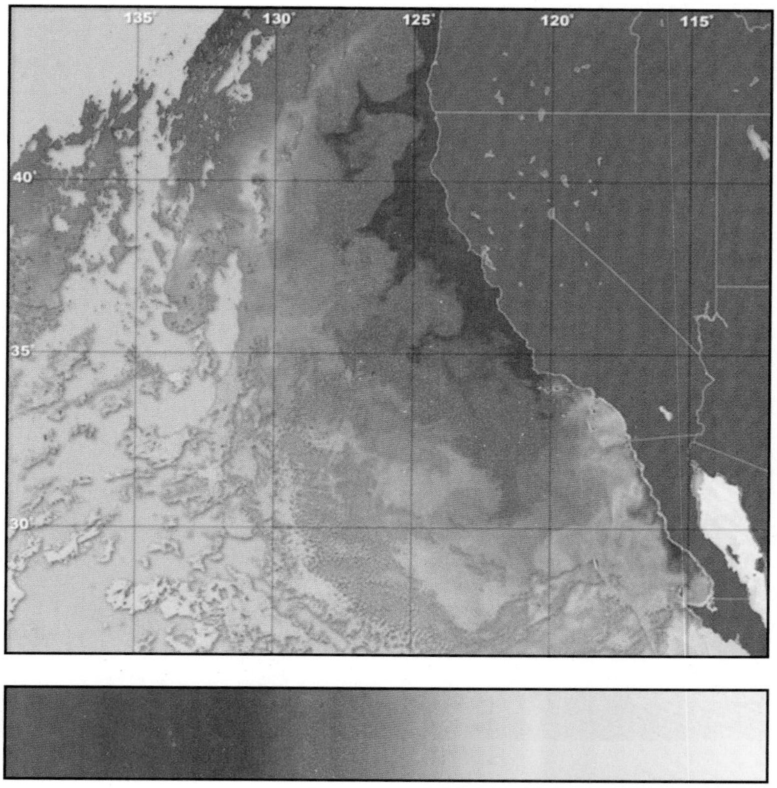

Figure 10.5

In this temperature map, the California Current is dark red, showing a cold surface current that transports water south along the California coastline toward the equator. The purple area along the shoreline indicates upwelling, while the dark gray area indicates the West Coast of the United States.

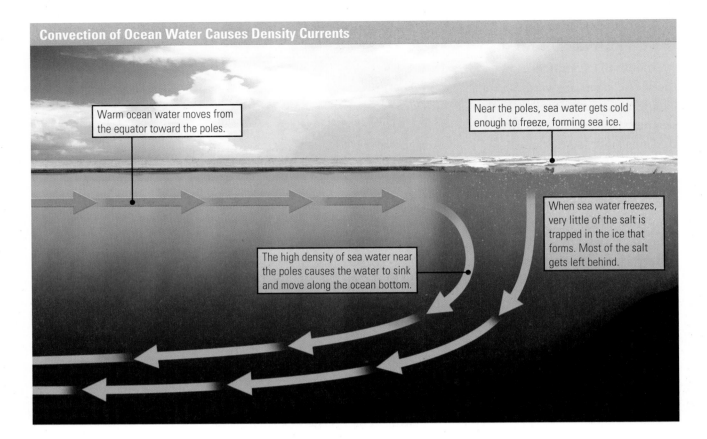

Warm ocean water moves from the equator toward the poles.

Near the poles, sea water gets cold enough to freeze, forming sea ice.

When sea water freezes, very little of the salt is trapped in the ice that forms. Most of the salt gets left behind.

The high density of sea water near the poles causes the water to sink and move along the ocean bottom.

Figure 10.6A

Water cools and becomes denser as energy is transferred from the water to the cold air near the poles. Due to convection, the dense water sinks to the bottom of the ocean in the polar regions. It flows toward the equator, producing a density current. Density currents form because of varying water temperature and saltiness.

6. The Global Ocean Convection Cycle

You can feel the effect of warm or cold surface currents when you are by a seashore. Surface currents move water usually in the upper 100 m of the ocean. But, what forces move water along the ocean floor, thousands of meters below the ocean surface?

Density currents are ocean currents deep in the ocean that flow because of differences in the density of water. These differences are controlled by temperature and salinity. Recall that density is the mass of a given volume. The ocean is denser in places where seawater is colder and saltier. Colder water's particles are closer together. Saltier water has more particles in a given volume. The ocean is also saltier in places where evaporation is greater than precipitation. So, seawater is denser near the poles where it is less rainy and the water is cold and salty. Seawater is less dense near the warm, rainy equator.

The density of the ocean also varies with depth. The coldest, densest water is at the bottom. Like denser air, denser water also sinks. Density currents form because ocean water at the surface becomes cold and salty enough to sink. Figure 10.6A shows how a density current forms. In the polar regions, surface water cools as it transfers energy to cold air. As sea ice forms, salt stays in the liquid water, increasing its density. The resulting denser water sinks due to convection, and a current of warmer surface water replaces it. A current of cold, dense water flows away from the sinking water toward the equator.

The **global ocean convection cycle** is an ocean-wide system of surface and density currents that are driven by differences in water temperature and saltiness. This cycle transfers energy by convection as water sinks, flows deep in the ocean, rises, and flows at the surface of the ocean. It is also called the *thermohaline circulation* to emphasize the role of heat (*thermo-*) and salt (*-haline*). The cycle is sometimes referred to as the *global conveyor belt* because it forms a continuous system of currents that transports water and energy around the world and through the depths of the ocean.

Figure 10.6B shows a simplified model of the system of currents that make up the global ocean convection cycle. The arrows indicate the direction of surface currents as they transport water around the ocean. Density currents that are deep, cold, and dense are represented by the blue paths. Warmer, less dense surface waters are represented by the red paths. Density currents cycle water and energy throughout the ocean, from the cold ocean bottom to its surface and back again. These currents form a conveyor belt, as they twist and turn around continents and flow both near the surface and the bottom of the ocean. Water in the global conveyer belt travels great distances, and it travels very slowly. Scientists estimate that a cubic meter of water would take about 1,000 years to complete the ride. Because the atmospheric and oceanic circulations are closely connected, what might be the effect on climates if these global circulations were to change over time?

Figure 10.6B

This model of the global ocean convection cycle shows the ocean-wide system of currents. This closed-loop system of surface and density currents acts like a conveyor belt transporting water around the oceans. As water moves globally, it also transports energy by the process of convection.

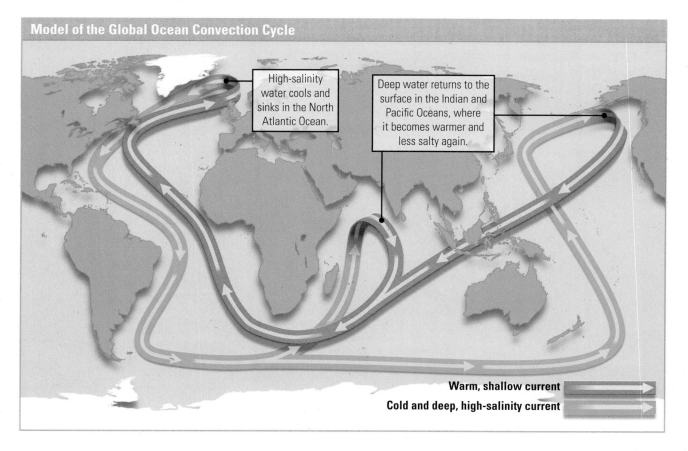

Model of the Global Ocean Convection Cycle

High-salinity water cools and sinks in the North Atlantic Ocean.

Deep water returns to the surface in the Indian and Pacific Oceans, where it becomes warmer and less salty again.

Warm, shallow current

Cold and deep, high-salinity current

Ocean Currents and Climate

Climate is affected by the flow of energy from the equator to the poles through the atmosphere and the global ocean convection cycle driven by density currents. These models represent how the ocean redistributes this energy through complex interactions within two systems: surface currents and the global ocean convection cycle. What could the impact be on climate patterns if the ocean current circulations were to change?

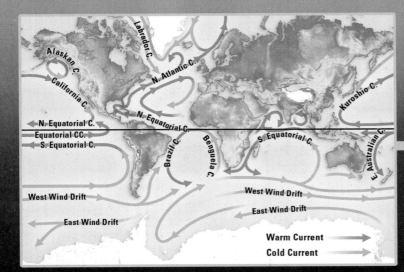

Global Surface Currents

Global Surface Currents

- Driven by winds
- Gulf Stream
- California Current
- Energy flows on ocean surface
- Form gyres
- About 100 m (328 ft) deep

- Redistribute energy from equator to poles
- Deflected by land masses

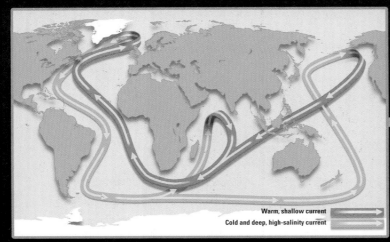

Global Ocean Convection Cycle

Global Ocean Convection Cycle

- Driven by differences in density
- Shallow and deep currents
- Energy flows vertically and horizontally
- Convection cycle
- Slow moving
- Closed-loop system
- Can be thousands of meters deep

7. El Niño

What is El Niño and why does it cause variations in climate? And what might it mean for the weather where you live?

El Niño is part of a climate pattern that occurs when sea surface temperatures in the Pacific Ocean near the equator increase more than 0.5°C (0.9°F) above normal for at least five successive three-month seasons. This happens about every two to seven years. During an El Niño event, the southwest United States may be cooler and rainier, the Pacific Northwest may be drier, and winter in the Northeast might be warmer. *La Niña* is the climate pattern that is opposite of El Niño. This pattern happens when sea surface temperatures in the Equatorial Pacific decrease by more than 0.5°C for at least five successive three-month seasons. The impact from a La Niña event tends to create drier conditions in the southwest United States and cooler-than-normal temperatures in the Northwest. Both of these small changes in ocean temperature can cause big changes in weather patterns because the ocean-atmosphere system is interconnected.

El Niño occurs when the surface waters near the equator in the Pacific Ocean are warmer than usual. During these events, the southwest United States is likely to have a rainier winter than usual dependent upon the strength of El Niño.

LESSON SUMMARY

How the Ocean Affects Climate

The Ocean Stores Energy The ocean helps control temperatures on Earth because it changes temperature slowly and stores energy. Energy that is stored in the ocean is distributed around Earth.

The Ocean Distributes Solar Energy The ocean is warmer near the equator than it is near the poles because it receives more direct sunlight near the equator. Global circulation of water distributes this energy.

Surface Currents Surface currents are driven by global winds and guided by the Coriolis effect and continental deflection. They affect the temperature and moisture of the air that blows over them.

A Warm Surface Current—the Gulf Stream The Gulf Stream carries warm water from the equator towards the poles in the Atlantic Ocean and moderates climates along some U.S. and European coasts.

A Cold Surface Current—the California Current The California Current transports cold water from the northern Pacific Ocean toward the equator along the West Coast of the United States. It can cause upwelling.

The Global Ocean Convection Cycle An ocean-wide system of surface and density currents makes up the global ocean convection cycle. This cycle transfers energy both horizontally and vertically through the ocean.

El Niño El Niño is a climate pattern that occurs when sea surface temperatures in the equatorial Pacific Ocean are warmer than usual. La Niña events have the opposite impact of El Niño.

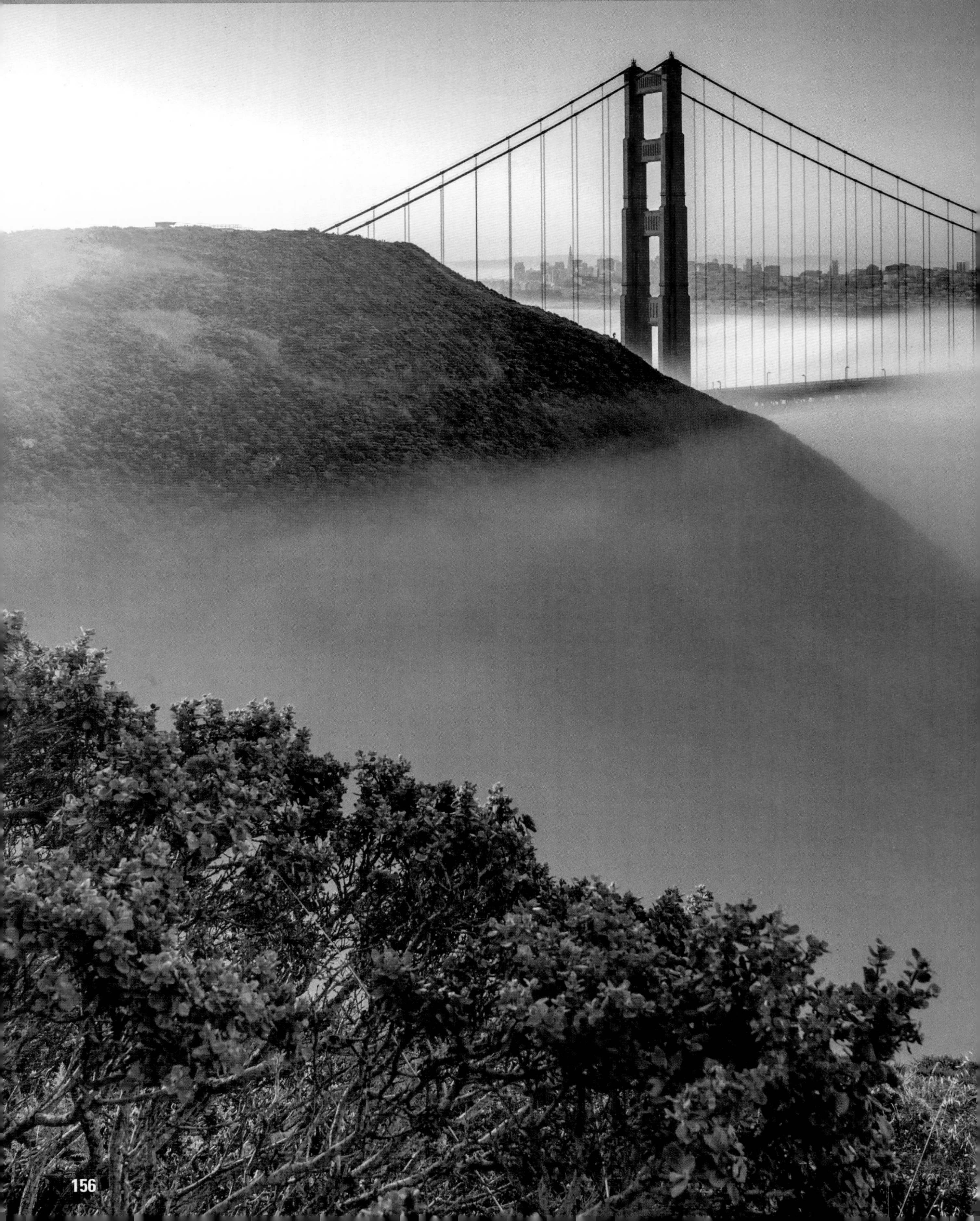

Local Climate

What factors affect climate at the local level?

Introduction

The Golden Gate Bridge in San Francisco is mostly hidden in a blanket of summer fog. Yet, another city only 30 minutes away inland may be sunny without a cloud in the sky. San Francisco and the other land areas near the California coast have a similar climate of mild winters and dry summers. The cool California Current affects climate there. It is one of the reasons that the Golden Gate Bridge in San Francisco and other coastal areas are often blanketed by summer fog. However, even within the city of San Francisco, climate can vary from place to place. Why does climate vary in nearby locations?

Local climate is climate on the scale at which people live. The regional climate is made up of several local climates like those around San Francisco and elsewhere. In this lesson, you will learn about local climate and factors that influence it, including ground surface, vegetation, topography, and urbanization. You will examine models that represent these climate systems and their interactions. Finally, you will learn about microclimates and how they contribute to local climates.

Vocabulary

local climate the climate of a particular area such as a city, town, or portion of a state

albedo the ratio of reflected sunlight to the sunlight that strikes a surface

topography the shape of the natural features of a land surface

urban heat island a city area where the climate is warmer than the surrounding area

microclimate the climate of a small area, such as a neighborhood or backyard, that may be different from nearby climates

---

Next Generation Science Standards

Performance Expectations

MS-ESS2-6. Develop and use a model to describe how unequal heating and rotation of the Earth cause patterns of atmospheric and oceanic circulation that determine regional climates.

Science and Engineering Practices

Developing and Using Models Develop and use a model to describe phenomena.

Crosscutting Concepts

Systems and System Models Models can be used to represent systems and their interactions—such as inputs, processes, and outputs—and energy, matter, and information flows within systems.

Scale, Proportion, and Quantity Time, space, and energy phenomena can be observed at various scales using models to study systems that are too large or too small.

Disciplinary Core Ideas

ESS2.D. Weather and climate are influenced by interactions involving sunlight, the ocean, the atmosphere, ice, landforms, and living things. These interactions vary with latitude, altitude, and local and regional geography, all of which can affect oceanic and atmospheric flow patterns.

1. Climate at the Local Level

It's summer in the northeastern United States. People in New York City are sweltering in the heat. Vacationers at Bethany Beach, Delaware, are enjoying a refreshing ocean breeze. Meanwhile, hikers atop the White Mountains, New Hampshire, need jackets to stay warm. How can the climates of areas in the same region be so different?

Figure 11.1 shows the Northeast region of the United States, which includes New York City, Bethany Beach, and the White Mountains. Regional climate is the climate of a large area with similar precipitation and rainfall patterns. The regional climate of the Northeast tends to be warm and humid in the summer and cold and snowy in the winter.

Local climate is the climate of a particular area such as a city, town, or portion of a state. Although New York City, Bethany Beach, and the White Mountains share the same regional climate, they have different local climates from each other. Summers in New York may be humid while winters may be cold. Bethany Beach can be slightly warmer in the winter than New York City. And the climate on the tallest peak of the White Mountains is very different from both locations. It is much cooler there, and snow may fall in June. Local climates vary because local conditions such as elevation and land cover vary. What is the local climate like in the area where you live? Is it different from other local climates that share the same regional climate as the state where you live?

Figure 11.1

The map shows the northeastern United States, which shares the same regional climate. However, each location in the photos has a different local climate. Local climate is the climate of a particular area such as a city, town, or portion of a state.

Local Climates in the Northeastern United States

ME
White Mountains
VT
NH
NY
MA
CT RI
Atlantic Ocean
PA
New York City
NJ
MD DE
Bethany Beach

White Mountains, New Hampshire
Cold, windy, and snowfall at high elevations into June

Bethany Beach, Delaware
Warmer year round with ocean breezes

New York City, New York
Cold winters and hot summers with high humidity

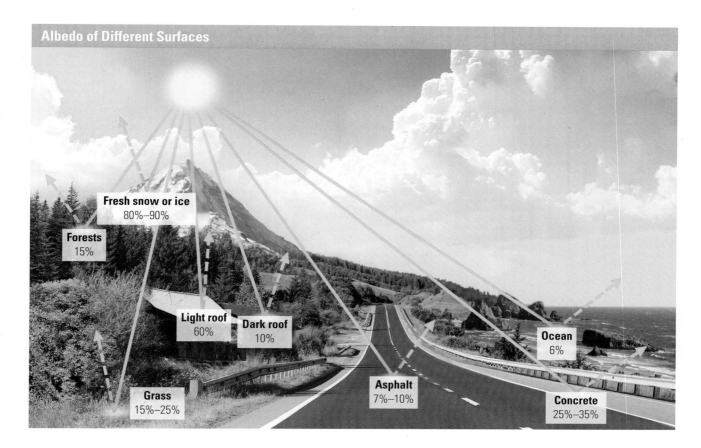

Albedo of Different Surfaces

Fresh snow or ice
80%–90%

Forests
15%

Light roof
60%

Dark roof
10%

Grass
15%–25%

Asphalt
7%–10%

Ocean
6%

Concrete
25%–35%

2. Surface Materials Affect Local Climate

As you cross the road on a hot, sunny day, you feel the heat radiating up from the asphalt. When you step onto some grass, the air around you suddenly feels cooler. Why does the material that you are standing on affect how warm or cool you feel?

Surfaces, such as asphalt and grass, reflect and absorb different amounts of the sunlight that strikes them. **Albedo** is the ratio of reflected sunlight to the sunlight that strikes a surface. It is a measure of how much a surface on Earth reflects sunlight and can be expressed as a percentage. Light-colored surfaces reflect more sunlight than dark surfaces, so they have high albedos. Compare the albedo values in the model in Figure 11.2. How does the albedo of a surface change depending on the type of material and the color? Bright, white snow or ice has a high albedo, up to 90 percent, while asphalt has a low albedo, in the range of 7 percent to 10 percent. These values indicate that snow reflects more sunlight than asphalt.

The albedo of a surface affects local climate because absorbed sunlight heats surfaces unevenly. So, materials with a low albedo absorb most of the sunlight that strikes them. The sunlight heats the material, and the material then transfers the energy to the air above it. Thus, the air temperature increases. So, the air above asphalt surfaces is likely to have a slightly higher average temperature than the air above grass and trees.

Figure 11.2

This model shows how different surface materials affect the amount of sunlight that is reflected. More sunlight is reflected from surfaces with higher albedos than surfaces with lower albedos. A low albedo means that the surface absorbs more sunlight, which heats the material. This raises the air temperature above the surface.

Topography affects local climate, including precipitation and wind patterns. Chinook winds are warm winds that blow down from the mountains, quickly increasing temperatures and melting snow. They can also produce unusual cloud formations like these seen over the Rocky Mountains in Banff National Park in Canada.

3. Topography Affects Local Climate

You might see snow all year round on the top of tall mountains in New Hampshire because temperature decreases as you travel up a mountain. However, one side of the mountain may have more snow than the other side. How do mountains affect local climate?

The shape of the natural features of a land surface is called **topography**. Topography includes the height, shape, number, and arrangement of mountains, hills, and valleys. It can result in the formation of lakes when water flows into large depressions, which is how the Great Lakes formed. The topography of an area affects its local climate by altering temperature, wind, and precipitation patterns.

Mountains affect climate because moving air is forced upwards when it meets a mountain. You have already learned about the rain shadow effect. Because of this effect, the local climate on the windward side of a mountain tends to be much wetter than the local climate on the leeward side.

The air flowing down the leeward side of the mountain may also form strong winds. Wind forms when the dry air sinks and warms quickly. The resulting warm winds are called *Chinook winds*. Strong gusts and high drifts of snow are frequently produced by Chinook winds. These winds, called *snow eaters*, can warm temperatures and quickly melt snow in mountain ranges like the one in the photo. Temperatures may rise 22°C (40°F) in one hour when Chinook winds blow!

Topography affects local wind patterns in other ways. Valley breezes and mountain breezes, modeled in Figure 11.3, form near mountains because of daily temperature differences in the air near the surface of the mountain and farther away. During the day, air near the valley floor heats up, causing the air to expand and rise. The warm air flows up the mountainsides resulting in a valley breeze. After the sun goes down, the air near the slopes cools more than the air in the middle of the valley. The air sinks down the slopes into valleys at night, producing cool mountain breezes. Strong winds may whip across places that are very flat, such as the plains in the photo. The winds are strong because no land features block them or slow them down.

Large lakes moderate the temperature of the local climate. Water takes longer than air to cool. Thus, in regions with cold winters, winter temperatures around large lakes are slightly warmer. The lakes can even extend the growing season for crops in the local area. For example, in western New York, the Great Lakes and the Finger Lakes make air temperatures mild enough to grow grapes.

Large lakes also affect local precipitation patterns. Water evaporating from lakes makes the surrounding air more humid. The water vapor added to the air can also cause snow in the winter. Air masses are warmed and pick up moisture as they pass over warmer lake waters. The water falls as snow when the air passes over the cold land on the other side of the lake. This snow is called *lake effect snow.*

Strong winds blow in places that are very flat, such as the plains in Montana, because winds are not slowed by hills or mountains.

Mountain and Valley Breezes

Valley breeze

During the day, air movement flows upward.

Mountain breeze

At night, air movement slides down the mountainside into the valley.

Figure 11.3
Valley breezes blow up mountain slopes during the day when air close to the valley floor is heated and then expands and rises. At night, the air near the mountain slopes cools more than the air in the valley.

The trees and other plants in the jungle affect the local climate there. The plants increase humidity through transpiration, lower air temperature by providing shade, and decrease wind speed by blocking wind.

4. Vegetation Affects Local Climate

You are hiking through the forest where the air feels damp, cool, and still. As you approach a grassy clearing, the air feels dry and warm, and the wind whips your hair and blows into your face. How do trees and other plants affect local climate?

Much like topography, the vegetation in an area, such as grasses, trees, shrubs, and flowers, affects local climate. Vegetation influences local climate in three major ways: by increasing humidity, decreasing air temperature, and decreasing wind. So, the local climate in a forest will be different from the local climate in an area with grasslands. In return, climate affects which plants grow in an area.

Plants Increase Humidity Recall that plants release water vapor into the atmosphere through the process of transpiration. This process increases the humidity of the air. A large area of thick vegetation, such as a big forest, can increase the humidity so much that the cloud cover and precipitation over the area increases. One of the reasons that the tropical jungle in the photo is so humid is because of all the water vapor the plants release into the atmosphere.

Plants Can Decrease Air Temperatures Plants can also make the air around them cooler. Large plants, such as trees, block some sunlight and prevent it from reaching the ground. You can feel the resulting cooling effect whenever you step under a tree out of direct sunlight. During transpiration, the liquid water on the bottom of leaves absorbs energy, changing the water into water vapor. This cools the plant as well as the surrounding atmosphere.

Forests Can Decrease Wind A large group of trees can affect wind speed and direction. Some wind can flow through the trees, but most is redirected over the top of the trees. As a result, the wind speed under the trees and behind the trees is slower.

5. Urbanization Affects Local Climate

When you turn the corner on a city street, a strong wind might blow in your face. You are less likely to experience such a wind in a small town. As you walk along, you might be shaded from the sun by a tall building instead of a tree. You will see fewer plants in the city than in the country. Trees may be concentrated in some areas such as city parks, but missing in areas where buildings take up a lot of space. How much influence do buildings, sidewalks, and roadways have on climates in urban areas compared to vegetation?

One way tall buildings affect the local climate in cities is through their effects on air temperature and by influencing wind patterns. When the wind blows into the side of a building, it is forced upward and downward. As a result, it can feel very windy for people walking on the sidewalk next to the buildings. Long streets that are lined by tall buildings can act as wind tunnels that produce much stronger winds than winds in rural areas.

The buildings in some downtown areas may be densely packed with little open space for grass and trees between them. Rooftops, sidewalks, and roads make up most of the surfaces in a city. These surfaces affect the temperature of the air because they absorb energy from the sun, store the energy, and transfer the energy to the air. The rooftops of buildings tend to be dark and have a low albedo. So, they absorb most of the sunlight that strikes them and heat up. Asphalt roadways and parking lots also heat up as they absorb sunlight. They slowly release their energy at night.

Concrete, asphalt, and metal also do not absorb much water. Thus, they release very little moisture into the air through evaporation. These surfaces are warmer because they are not cooled by evaporation, so they transfer energy to the air, making air temperature rise as well. And because there are not as many plants in downtown areas, the air is not cooled through transpiration.

The design of urban areas affects the local climate of the city. Gaps between tall buildings cause winds. Surfaces with low albedos, such as building rooftops and asphalt, cause warmer air temperatures because they absorb a lot of sunlight instead of reflecting it. Lack of vegetation means less cooling from evaporation and transpiration.

An urban heat island can form when dense urbanization leads to the warming of an entire city. An **urban heat island** is a city area where the climate is warmer than the surrounding area. For example, a city with 1 million people may be 1°–3°C (33.8°–37.4°F) warmer on average than nearby rural areas. In the profile in Figure 11.5, notice that the temperature is hottest over the downtown area.

Urban heat islands form when asphalt and other building materials heat up during the day and cool off slowly at night. Sunlight strikes buildings, on both the top and sides. So, even though it may be shady on some of their sides, buildings absorb this energy. As a result, less sunlight is reflected and less energy escapes back into the atmosphere. Because the total mass of building materials releases the absorbed energy slowly, urban areas stay much warmer than rural areas at night. In contrast, open land cools down more quickly at night. The energy that is released by the ground in an open area is transferred upward into the atmosphere because nothing absorbs it on its way up.

Urban heat islands can intensify the effects of a heatwave, increase air pollution, and affect human health. Higher temperatures can make certain chemicals, such as ozone, form more quickly. Higher amounts of ozone near the ground can make breathing more difficult for people with asthma. Hotter air temperatures also increase the risk of heat-related illnesses.

People can take steps to reduce the harmful effects of urban heat islands. One way is to plant more vegetation ground cover and trees to provide shade, including rooftop parks. Installing light-colored rooftops and walls that increase the albedo and reduce the absorption of energy is also effective in reducing temperatures.

Figure 11.5

This temperature profile outlines an urban heat island. The city is warmer than the surrounding rural area because building and road surfaces absorb more sunlight during the day and release less energy at night than open areas with many plants.

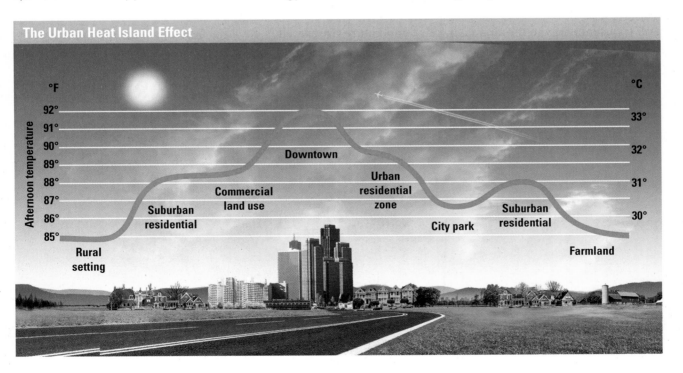

The Urban Heat Island Effect

Postcards from Colorado: Colorado's Local Climates

Colorado's climate is affected by its mountains, overall high elevation, latitude between 37°– 41°N, and location far from oceans. The general climate is cool and dry. However, local climates in Denver, Aspen, Alamosa, and Grand Junction vary due to topography, vegetation, and urbanization. If you sent these postcards, what might you say about the local climates?

Aspen is nestled in a valley among the mountains at an elevation of about 2,400 m. Aspen may be cooler and receives more precipitation than Denver because of its high elevation. It sits in a valley, so nighttime winter temperatures may be very cold.

Denver's high elevation at 1,609 m and location near the mountains create a mild, dry climate. Strong, dry winds may blow down the mountain slopes. Denver is a large city. Its urban heat island effect makes its temperature warmer than surrounding areas in the summer.

Grand Junction is on the western slope of the Rockies at a slightly lower elevation than Denver. Seasonal temperatures here may be extreme and the air, dry. Air masses en route to Grand Junction pass over sparse vegetation, which may not add much moisture to the air.

Alamosa sits in the rain shadow of the mountains near tall sand dunes. Located in a large valley, its elevation is high at about 2,300 m. The climate can be cool, dry, and sunny, but temperatures may be very cold at night because there are no tall buildings to trap in energy.

6. Microclimates

You are in a San Francisco park on a warm sunny day. Your friend texts you from near the Golden Gate Bridge and says, "It's foggy and cold here." How can conditions be so different within the same city?

A **microclimate** is the climate of a small area, such as a neighborhood or backyard, that may be different from nearby climates. It is even smaller than a local climate. Look at how the different scales of climate relate to each other in Figure 11.6. Many microclimates combine to make up the local climate, just as many local climates make up the regional climate. A city may have several microclimates, depending on topography, the amount of urbanization, and variations in vegetation. For example, the sidewalks next to tall buildings may have a windier microclimate than other places in the city. A city park with lots of trees has a cooler microclimate than the surrounding neighborhoods.

San Francisco has a cool, foggy local climate because of the influence of the California Current. In the summer, water particles in warm, moist air condense over the cold water offshore to make fog, as shown in the photo at the beginning of the lesson. However, there are several microclimates within the city, including sunnier climates such as the Mission District located in east-central San Francisco. Winds may push the fog over the downtown area, but tall hills block the fog from this microclimate. People here enjoy sunny skies.

Figure 11.6

A microclimate is a climate of a very small area, such as a neighborhood. The Mission District in San Francisco has a sunnier microclimate than other San Francisco neighborhoods because hills prevent fog from reaching it.

Climate at Different Scales

Global Climate
Earth

Regional Climate
West Coast, USA

Global
Regional
Local
Micro

Microclimate
Mission District

Local Climate
San Francisco

In rural areas, farmers pay close attention to microclimates when growing crops because microclimates are extremely vital for plant growth and development. Strong winds can blow across open fields in the plains. Farmers may try to alter the windy climates in a small area to protect their crops and livestock from high winds. One way they can make a less windy microclimate is by planting trees to create windbreaks to block the wind.

Microclimates exist everywhere, including the desert. For example, oases form where there is a source of water. The plants in an oasis provide shade and make the microclimate cooler than the surrounding desert. A backyard may also be cooler on a hot summer day than the street in front of a house. The microclimate there may be cooler than the front yard if the home shades it from the sun. An asphalt-covered basketball court that sits in the sun all day may be warmer than other areas around your school. The next time you walk through your neighborhood, which microclimates will you encounter? How do they create variety in the local climate of your community?

Microclimates form in many places, including this small oasis in the Sahara Desert.

LESSON SUMMARY

Local Climate

Climate at the Local Level The climate of a particular area such as a city, town, or portion of a state is called *local climate*. Local climates often differ from regional climates.

Surface Materials Affect Local Climate The percentage of sunlight reflected by a surface—its albedo—affects the surface and air temperature. Surface materials with a lower albedo absorb more sunlight, warm up more, and heat the air above them.

Topography Affects Local Climate Local temperatures, wind patterns, and precipitation patterns are affected by topography. The rain shadow effect, Chinook winds, as well as valley and mountain breezes occur in locations near mountains. Large lakes also moderate temperatures and may lead to lake effect snow.

Vegetation Affects Local Climate Plants increase humidity because of transpiration. Transpiration and shade provided by large plants also make the air cooler. Large groups of trees may block wind.

Urbanization Affects Local Climate Buildings in urban areas create wind patterns that differ from those in rural areas. Dark surfaces and tall buildings in cities also produce urban heat islands that are warmer than surrounding areas.

Microclimates A microclimate describes climate conditions on a small scale, such as a backyard. Many microclimates combine to make the local climate.

Urban Farmers

The man in Apartment 7F decides that he's going to make a pizza for his family's dinner. "I'll need some fresh tomatoes and herbs to make a tomato sauce," he says. He leaves his apartment and gets on the elevator, but instead of going down to the street level, he rides it up to the roof. How can he find fresh tomatoes and herbs on the roof?

Urban farming and gardening are gaining popularity. You can now find food growing on balconies, rooftops, and other locations within cities.

The man can find tomatoes and herbs on his apartment building's roof because his family has a rooftop garden. Although this man and his garden are fictional, urban farmers and urban gardens are real. In the past, most food eaten by people in the United States was grown on farms in rural areas. But in the last several years, an increasing number of people are growing their own food, and many of those people are doing so in cities. They grow food on rooftops, balconies, and community gardens located in parks and other public areas.

Just Add Water

When you imagine a farm, you probably picture plants growing in soil in large fields. Such fields do not exist in cities, so today's urban gardeners and farmers use various technologies to adjust the microclimate of their gardens to maximize crop yields in small spaces that have little soil. Sometimes they don't use soil at all.

A common way that urban gardeners adjust microclimates is to increase the availability of water. While plants in most urban gardens get rain, they benefit from receiving extra water supplied by the gardener. This is particularly true when rainwater is collected over only a small area like the surface of the soil in a plant pot. So, urban gardeners use various irrigation systems to provide water to their plants. They might have sprinklers that spray water over plants, or they might have drip systems that put water directly onto the soil.

Some urban gardeners even create microclimates for growing food indoors. They provide water to the plants and use special lights that mimic sunlight. Interestingly, some of these indoor gardens aren't grown in soil. Instead, they are grown in materials such as moss, gravel, or special sponges designed for growing plants. The materials support the plant roots and are filled with water containing nutrients that the plant needs.

Urban gardens are often planted in small containers and need irrigation. Water poured into these pipes can easily reach every plant growing in them.

Some urban gardeners grow their crops in material other than soil. These lettuce seedlings are growing in a special sponge that supports their roots and keeps them moist.

Victory gardens were planted across the country during World War I and World War II. In cities, parks and vacant lots were dug up to plant gardens. Children and young adults helped tend the gardens.

Vegetables for Victory

Although urban gardening has recently become popular, it isn't a new activity. In the United States, widespread urban gardening happened during World War I and World War II.

During the wars, a lot of the food produced by large farms had to be shipped overseas to feed the troops. Furthermore, food that did stay in the country was difficult to move from rural areas to cities because of shortages in transportation and labor. As a result, people in the United States faced food shortages and rationing. To help overcome these shortages, the government encouraged people to grow their own food by planting gardens and provided instruction on how to properly grow and care for vegetables.

People across the country started planting gardens. Those who had yards planted their gardens there. Those who didn't have yards planted in window boxes, pots, and other containers. Gardens were planted in public parks, schoolyards, and vacant lots. These gardens were called *victory gardens* because they were planted to help with the war effort. During World War II, 20 million victory gardens were producing 40 percent of all the vegetables grown in the United States.

Growing for Grades

The current urban gardening trend has even taken hold in schools. Schools at all levels—from elementary schools to colleges—now have gardens that are tended by their students. Food grown in smaller gardens can be taken home by students to share with their families. Schools that have larger gardens may help supply the school cafeteria with herbs, vegetables, and fruit. And some food grown in school gardens is sold to community members at farm stands and farmers' markets.

If your school does not have a garden, you can do research to learn how to set one up. The website of the U.S. Department of Agriculture has information about home gardening and links to other sources of information. Other good sources of information are university extension offices. The information on extension office websites will tell you what kinds of crops are best to grow in your area. To find these websites, do an Internet search with the words "extension office" and the name of your state. If your school does have a garden, you can still do research to find out about different crops to grow and ways to improve the crop yield of the garden.

You can set up a garden almost any place that gets enough sun. If your school doesn't have a yard, consider asking if you can plant a container garden on the roof. Maybe someday you and your classmates will be harvesting vegetables on the roof of your school—with teacher supervision, of course! ◆

Many schools in urban and suburban areas now have gardens. These students are harvesting carrots in their school's garden near downtown Atlanta, Georgia.

Earth's Climate Over Time

How has Earth's climate varied over its history?

Introduction

It's another frigid day at the Halley VI Research Station in Antarctica. At 11 A.M., a climate scientist emerges from her warm shelter to launch a weather balloon. Hanging beneath the helium-filled balloon is a device that will measure conditions in the atmosphere about once a second and transmit the data back to the station. A balloon is launched from the station every day at this same time, along with other weather balloons that are launched from more than 800 locations around the world. What data are the scientists collecting with so many balloons? What can they learn about sudden or gradual changes in Earth's atmosphere with this data?

Earth's climate is changing. Scientists are working hard to understand if it is a natural cycle, an unusual shift in conditions, or some combination of these. How do scientists understand what they know about climate change? And what role do humans play in this change?

In this lesson, you will examine evidence that shows how and why Earth's climate has changed over its long history. You will investigate the rapid climate change that is happening today and understand how it differs from what Earth has experienced before. Then, you will analyze scientific evidence about the factors that are causing the changes in climate today and consider future changes.

Vocabulary

ice age a long period of particularly cool climate when large masses of ice cover large areas of Earth

global warming the long-term increase in the average surface temperature of Earth

climate change a long-term change in climate patterns on Earth, typically including changes in average global temperatures, precipitation, and in the frequency of severe weather

deforestation the permanent removal of forests by humans to make land available for other uses

enhanced greenhouse effect increased warming of the troposphere beyond the natural greenhouse effect due to human activities

Next Generation Science Standards

Performance Expectations
MS-ESS3-5. Ask questions to clarify evidence of the factors that have caused the rise in global temperatures over the past century.

Science and Engineering Practices
Asking Questions and Defining Problems
Ask questions to identify and clarify evidence of an argument.

Crosscutting Concepts
Stability and Change Stability might be disturbed either by sudden events or gradual changes that accumulate over time.

Disciplinary Core Ideas
ESS3.D. Human activities, such as the release of greenhouse gases from burning fossil fuels, are major factors in the current rise in Earth's mean surface temperature (global warming). Reducing the level of climate change and reducing human vulnerability to whatever climate changes do occur depend on the understanding of climate science, engineering capabilities, and other kinds of knowledge, such as understanding of human behavior and on applying that knowledge wisely in decisions and activities.

1. The History of Earth's Climate

What do you think Earth's first climate was like? What do scientists know about prehistoric climate? How can ancient climates be determined?

Throughout its history, Earth's climate has gone through gradual and abrupt changes with long periods of stability. Today, scientists can gather data directly from the atmosphere. However, to learn about Earth's past climate, scientists must gather data from sources other than the atmosphere. They look for evidence in ice cores, rocks, fossils, sediment, and tree rings. Scientists use these sources of data to draw conclusions about past temperatures, precipitation patterns, and atmospheric composition. The evidence shows Earth's climate has gone through huge changes, some of which are shown in Figure 12.1.

Scientists conclude that Earth began to form about 4.6 billion years ago and remained extremely hot for about 200 million years. By about 4.4 billion years ago, Earth cooled enough to form the solid surface and the atmosphere. The ocean then formed as water vapor in the air condensed and came down as precipitation. Another big change was the rise of algae and bacteria that carried out photosynthesis and produced oxygen as a byproduct. In the process, these organisms decreased carbon dioxide levels. Rising and falling carbon dioxide levels have affected Earth's climate throughout its history.

Earth also went through periods of extreme cold, with ice covering much of the planet. An **ice age** is a long period of particularly cool climate when large masses of ice cover vast areas of Earth. There is evidence that there were at least two ice age events between 717 and 630 million years ago, each of which lasted for millions of years. Scientists hypothesize that during these two events, glaciers, or enormous masses of ice, may have covered all of Earth's continents, even those at the equator, to form a "Snowball Earth."

Figure 12.1

Earth's climate has gone through gradual and abrupt changes during its long history. Between these changes, climate was generally stable. Scientists know about Earth's climate history through gathered evidence from various sources.

Climates of Earth's Past

Earth's First Climate: 4.6–4.4 Billion Years Ago	Snowball Earth Periods: 717–630 Million Years Ago	A Warmer Earth: 145–66 Million Years Ago

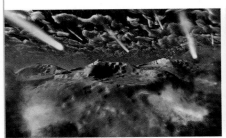

Earth's land, ocean, and atmosphere were beginning to form. Earth was extremely hot.

Earth is thought to have experienced two extreme ice ages, or Snowball Earth periods, when glaciers nearly covered the planet.

When Earth is not experiencing an ice age, the climate is warmer, allowing plants and animals to thrive in places once covered by ice.

Over its history, Earth has experienced very cold and very warm periods caused by changes to the Earth system. Rather than being cold the entire time, during an ice age, Earth's climate cycles between cooler and warmer periods. During *glacial periods*, the climate cools and glaciers grow and cover more land. During *interglacial periods*, the climate warms and glaciers melt. In contrast, when Earth is not experiencing an ice age, most or all of Earth's glaciers melt and temperatures are much warmer, even at the poles.

Changes to Earth's climate have played a major role in the history of life. The largest mass extinction in Earth's history occurred about 252 million years ago at the end of a period of global warming and affected most species on land and in the sea. Some scientists hypothesize the mass extinction was caused by millions of years of unusually high rates of volcanic eruptions. The carbon dioxide and methane from these eruptions may have warmed the climate so much that it was too hot for most species to survive.

By 145 million years ago, after a period of cooling, Earth was again warming up—even the poles were ice-free and warm enough for creatures to survive there. Dinosaurs, flowering plants, and many other living things thrived. However, evidence supports the idea that 66 million years ago, a giant asteroid caused another mass extinction. The asteroid impact would have caused sudden changes to climate. Dust from the impact and smoke from forest fires would have blocked sunlight for a long time, leading to rapid cooling. Eventually, increased levels of carbon dioxide caused the climate to warm again.

The climate from 2.6 million years ago to the present has been dominated by yet another ice age, which we are still in. We have been in an interglacial period for about the last 11,500 years—a small slice of Earth's history. The current climate is just right for humans to thrive.

Warm Periods: **444–252 Million Years Ago**	**Warm and Stable Followed by Abrupt** **Change: 145–66 Million Years Ago**	**The Current Ice Age:** **2.6 Million Years Ago–Present**

The climate was warm and dry. Volcanic eruptions may have caused a mass extinction.	The climate was warm, even at the poles. An asteroid impact may have contributed to changes in climate and a mass extinction.	An ice age with warm and cool periods began. Earth is currently in a warm period of this ice age.

Sun's output changes

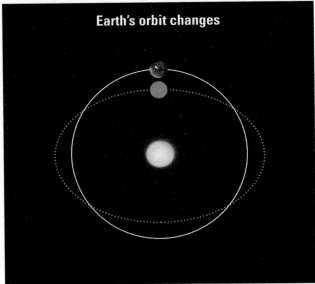

Earth's orbit changes

Falling space objects produce dust and ash

2. Why Climate Changes Naturally Over Time

There are many natural reasons that global climate changes. However, several reasons are the most far-reaching: the amount of energy from sunlight that reaches Earth, the energy Earth radiates back into space, and how energy is distributed around Earth. How do sudden and gradual changes affect climate?

Energy Received from the Sun Climate is affected by how much energy Earth receives from the sun. The sun repeats a pattern in the amount of energy it sends. About every 11 years, the sun goes through a cycle in which the energy it gives off increases and decreases. This variation in the sun's intensity can cause changes in global temperature during each cycle. Through a series of complicated processes, these variations can also alter surface storm paths across the planet.

Periodic changes in the shape of Earth's orbit affect how much energy it receives from the sun. In a cycle that repeats about every 100,000 years, Earth's orbit changes from nearly circular to a more elongated, elliptical shape. When its orbit is more elliptical, Earth receives much more energy when it is closest to the sun than it does when its orbit is more circular.

Some events, such as an asteroid impact, cause rapid changes in climate by blocking sunlight. Evidence indicates that the asteroid impact 66 million years ago led to forest fires around the world, acid rain, and rapid temperature changes. First, the dust and aerosols from the massive collision blocked much sunlight, leading to global cooling. Following this cooling was a period of global warming. Some scientists hypothesize the impact may have added excess greenhouse gases into the atmosphere that caused this warming.

Earth's climate varies naturally because of changes in the intensity of solar radiation and the shape of Earth's orbit. The asteroid impact that led to the extinction of the dinosaurs changed climate abruptly by blocking sunlight.

Volcanoes releasing gases and ash into the atmosphere can also affect global and regional climates by blocking energy from the sun. The amount of change depends on the size and length of the eruption. The volcanic eruptions associated with the largest extinction in Earth's history oozed lava over an area the size of the United States for nearly 1 million years! During that time, the eruptions pumped out massive amounts of carbon dioxide and methane. These greenhouse gases trap heat that caused severe global warming.

Energy Radiated Back to Space
Variations in the percentage of gases and the number of small solid and liquid particles in the atmosphere affect climate by changing the amount of energy Earth radiates back into space. For example, in Earth's early history, living things gradually changed the composition of the atmosphere when primitive life forms in the ocean and then on land used up carbon dioxide. The changing atmosphere led to the changing of Earth's temperatures. As the carbon dioxide levels decreased, the energy that Earth sent back to space increased and Earth's climate grew cooler.

Energy Distributed Around Earth
Changes in the location and shape of Earth's land masses have affected climate throughout Earth's history. The locations of land and water on the planet affect how the planet is heated because land has a higher albedo than the ocean. As continents moved so that more landmass was located over the equator, more energy from the sun was absorbed. The shape of the land masses affect the patterns of ocean currents and circulations in the atmosphere, and therefore, how energy is distributed around Earth.

Global climate changes due to energy received from the sun, energy radiated back to space, and how energy is distributed around Earth. Various conditions such as volcanic eruptions, changes in atmospheric composition due to life forms, and the location and shape of land masses all affect how these processes occur.

Unusually high rates of volcanism

The atmosphere's composition changes

Earth's landmasses change position and shape

3. Earth's Climate Since 1880

Changes in Earth's climate throughout its history have shaped the world you live in. Recent changes in climate today are affecting your future world. What is happening with Earth's climate that affects your future?

Since 1880, scientists like the one featured in the beginning of the lesson have collected surface temperature data from weather stations around the world. Surface temperature is the temperature of the atmosphere near Earth's surface. Scientists have used these data to calculate the average yearly global temperature. Before 1880, there were not enough data to calculate a reliable average temperature. How do scientists use these data to conclude how Earth's temperature has changed in modern times?

In Figure 12.3, the graph compiled with data from NASA shows a pattern of increasing global average temperatures each year. The overall trend illustrates that Earth has warmed by more than 0.9°C (1.6°F) since 1880. The surface temperature increase shown in the graph is evidence that Earth is getting warmer.

Global warming is an important part of a changing climate, but it does not fully describe climate change. **Global warming** is the long-term increase in the average surface temperature of Earth. **Climate change** is a long-term change in climate patterns on Earth. It typically includes changes in average global temperatures, as well as precipitation patterns and the frequency of severe weather. It predicts severe weather events such as heatwaves and an increase in the number of droughts due to increases caused by changing precipitation patterns. Changes to Earth's climate can differ, from variations such as El Niño, that affect regions of North and South America, to changes that affect the entire planet.

Figure 12.3

This graph shows how Earth's yearly global average temperature has increased between 1880 and 2015. The data, from analysis by NASA's Goddard Institute for Space Studies (GISS), is scientific evidence that Earth's climate has changed.

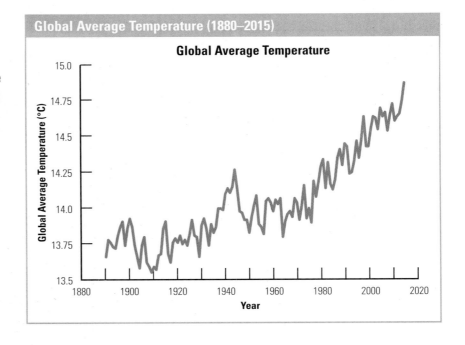

4. Changes to the Atmosphere in Modern Times

If you lived 150 years ago, your life would be very different. A horse-drawn carriage may pass you by on the street instead of a car. How are the ways people live today linked to rising temperatures?

Horse-drawn carriages do not require fossil fuels, but motorized vehicles do. Fossil fuel use has led to an increase in greenhouse gases, especially carbon dioxide, in the atmosphere. Coal, oil, and natural gas are fossil fuels. They formed over hundreds of millions of years from the remains of plants and other living things and are mostly stored carbon. The combustion, or burning, of fossil fuels releases that carbon into the atmosphere.

More and more carbon dioxide has been released into the atmosphere since the beginning of the Industrial Revolution. This sudden event in Earth's history began in Great Britain in 1760 and spread to other countries. The Industrial Revolution generated a period of great advances in technology and manufacturing. However, increased cement production from the rise in construction, as well as new inventions, increased the amount of carbon dioxide released into the atmosphere. Inventions in the late 19th and early 20th centuries included cars with gasoline-powered engines and electricity distribution to homes. Human population has also grown to more than 7 billion people today. Both increases in population and per person use of fossil fuels have led to greater carbon dioxide emissions.

Humans have also increased carbon dioxide in the air by **deforestation,** or the permanent removal of forests by humans to make land available for other uses. Between 2000 and 2010, an area a little larger than the size of Mississippi was deforested worldwide. It occurred mostly in tropical areas where forests were cleared by burning them. This burning released carbon dioxide. Additionally, with the forest gone, it is no longer there to remove carbon dioxide from the atmosphere. Deforestation accounts for between 15 and 30 percent of the carbon dioxide people add to the atmosphere.

Since the Industrial Revolution, humans have been increasing the amount of greenhouse gases. The Industrial Revolution led to more industry like this steel factory (circa 1860). This era was driven by manufacturing and new inventions, many of which burned fossil fuels. Burning fossil fuels releases carbon dioxide into the air.

Carbon Dioxide Concentrations (1880–2015)

Carbon Dioxide Concentrations

Figure 12.4

The graph shows that carbon dioxide levels have been steadily rising since 1880. It uses the Keeling Curve with additional data gathered by NOAA and the Carbon Dioxide Information Analysis Center (CDIAC).

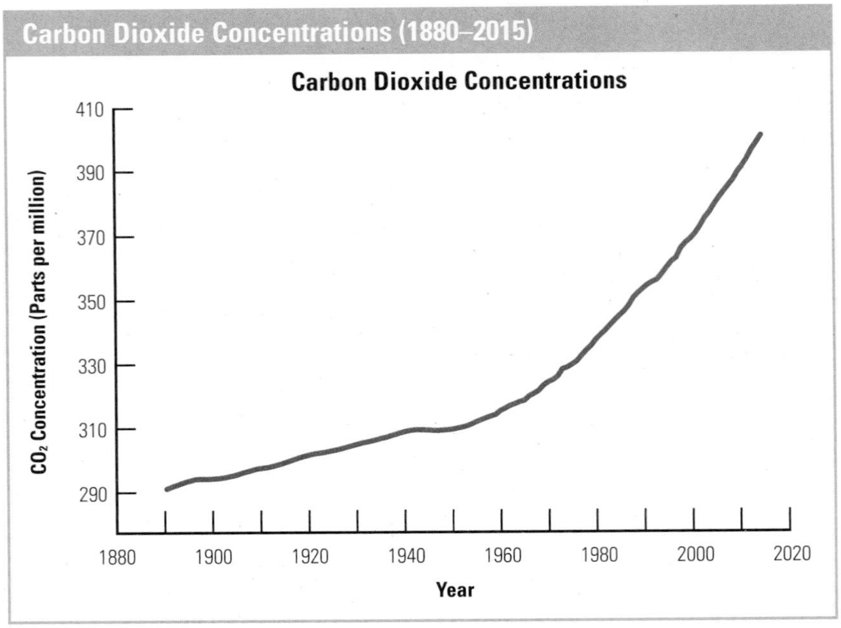

The rise in global average temperatures is directly linked with the rise in carbon dioxide levels. As carbon dioxide levels change, Earth's temperature changes. The graph in Figure 12.4 shows carbon dioxide levels from 1880 to 2015. The portion of the line from 1958 to the present is called the Keeling Curve because the data was collected by scientist Charles Keeling. Keeling developed an accurate and precise way to measure the amount of carbon dioxide in the atmosphere and began recording the data in 1958. Since then, carbon dioxide has been measured daily atop a mountain in Mauna Loa, Hawaii. Other scientists have added carbon dioxide data to Keeling's data based on measurements of air bubbles trapped in ice core samples. These measurements determine the gases in the atmosphere at the time between 1880 and 1950 when the air was trapped. According to the combined data from both sources, you can see on the graph that humans have increased the amount of carbon dioxide by about one-third since 1880. As a result of the increased carbon dioxide, global temperature has risen.

Another greenhouse gas that affects climate is methane. Methane is produced naturally by bacteria as they decompose dead plants and animals. Natural gas is also mostly methane. However, most methane released into the atmosphere—greater than 60 percent—comes from human sources. Methane is released into the air when humans process natural gas and petroleum. The garbage people produce releases methane as it decomposes in landfills. In addition, livestock also releases a large amount of methane. The animals produce methane naturally as they digest food, and their manure releases methane. As more animals are raised to feed a growing human population, more methane is added to the air.

5. The Enhanced Greenhouse Effect

You know Earth's climate has changed in the past due to natural factors, such as changes in solar output, changes in Earth's orbit, and asteroid impacts. But what is causing Earth's recent climate change?

Greenhouse gases have been an important part of Earth's atmosphere for most of its history. Earlier, you learned that greenhouse gases warm the atmosphere by absorbing the infrared light that is given off by Earth's surface after it absorbs sunlight and traps thermal energy in the atmosphere. Without the natural greenhouse effect, Earth's average temperature would be a chilly −18°C (−0.4°F).

The **enhanced greenhouse effect** is the increased warming of the troposphere beyond the natural greenhouse effect due to human activities. Most scientists agree that the evidence shows it is speeding up recent climate change. Compare the enhanced greenhouse effect to the natural greenhouse effect in the model in Figure 12.5. Notice how the processes that warm the atmosphere are the same. However, the enhanced greenhouse effect warms the atmosphere more than the natural greenhouse effect because there is an increased amount of greenhouse gases in the atmosphere. This explains how scientists can predict that temperatures will continue to increase rapidly as human activity adds more greenhouse gases to the atmosphere. However, it is uncertain how much temperatures will increase due to human impact. What risks will humans face if temperatures continue to rise rapidly?

Figure 12.5

The natural greenhouse effect warms Earth and makes it suitable for living things. The enhanced greenhouse effect is caused by humans. It causes Earth to warm at a rapid rate.

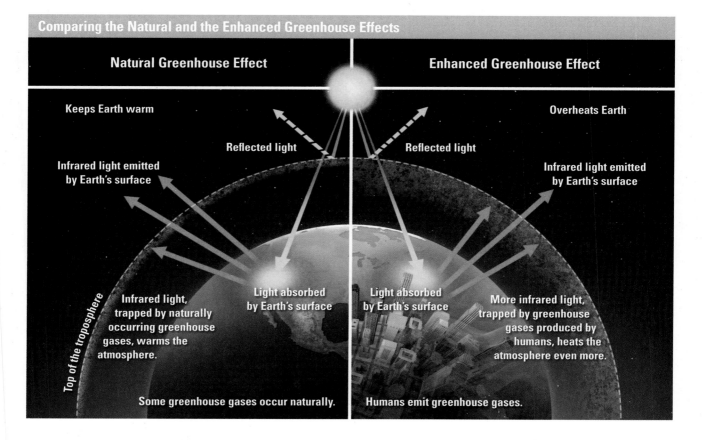

Comparing the Natural and the Enhanced Greenhouse Effects

Natural Greenhouse Effect

Keeps Earth warm

Reflected light

Infrared light emitted by Earth's surface

Light absorbed by Earth's surface

Top of the troposphere

Infrared light, trapped by naturally occurring greenhouse gases, warms the atmosphere.

Some greenhouse gases occur naturally.

Enhanced Greenhouse Effect

Overheats Earth

Reflected light

Infrared light emitted by Earth's surface

Light absorbed by Earth's surface

More infrared light, trapped by greenhouse gases produced by humans, heats the atmosphere even more.

Humans emit greenhouse gases.

Climate Change in Modern Times

A cold snap in the winter makes you doubt that the planet is warming. However, if you look at global data obtained from satellites and weather stations, you will see a clear rise in temperature. Are humans causing this change? Ask yourself questions as you examine this argument.

Claim

Earth's climate is warming due to human activities.

Evidence

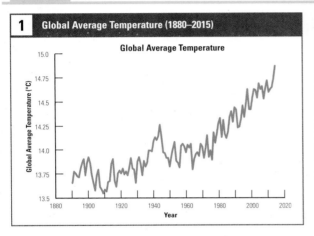

1 Data from NASA show that Earth's average temperature has risen in modern times.

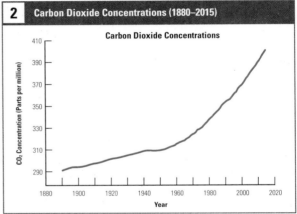

2 Data from NOAA show that atmospheric carbon dioxide, a greenhouse gas, has been increasing in modern times.

3 When the data are compared, Earth's temperature is related to, or correlates with, how much carbon dioxide is in the air. This is because a rise in carbon dioxide causes a rise in air temperature.

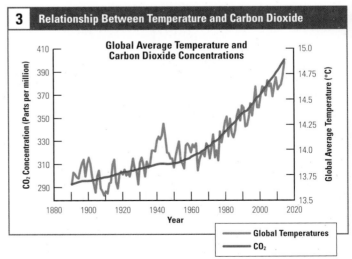

Reasoning

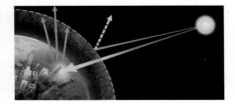

The greenhouse effect explains how greenhouse gases, including carbon dioxide and methane, warm the climate. The natural greenhouse effect keeps Earth's average temperature above freezing—a good thing. However, humans have put so much additional carbon dioxide and methane into the atmosphere that the climate is warming much too fast—a bad thing. This enhanced greenhouse effect is the reason climate is rapidly changing in modern times.

6. Future Climate Change

Climate change affects everyone, including you. As Earth warms, glaciers melt, sea levels rise, and frequent and more severe storms become more likely. Why do scientists predict climate change will continue? Is there anything people can do to limit it?

Scientific evidence supports the argument that Earth is going to continue to warm. Why do nearly all climate scientists accept this evidence? Scientists have published a large amount of climate research in peer-reviewed journals. This means their findings are critiqued by other experts. Also, nearly 200 countries form the Intergovernmental Panel on Climate Change (IPCC). The IPCC evaluates climate change and reviews current findings. In 2016, in the United States, scientists at government agencies such as NASA, NOAA, and the EPA agreed that humans are causing climate change. Climate scientists agree that humans are causing current climate change because reliable evidence and basic scientific ideas support that conclusion.

Humans may be able to limit the future warming of Earth. To do this, they must greatly reduce the amount of carbon dioxide they add to the air. Currently, the amount of greenhouse gases in the atmosphere is the highest it has been in nearly 1 million years. Earth will keep getting warmer as carbon dioxide levels rise. How much temperatures rise depends on the actions of society.

Earth will keep getting warmer as carbon dioxide levels rise. Humans can reduce or limit the amount of carbon dioxide they add to the air. Doing so may affect future climate change caused by rising temperatures.

LESSON SUMMARY

Earth's Climate Over Time

The History of Earth's Climate Earth has gone through extreme warm and cold periods with sudden and gradual changes in climate.

Why Climate Changes Naturally Over Time Earth's climate changes due to how much sunlight reaches Earth, how much energy is radiated back into space, and how energy is distributed around Earth.

Earth's Climate Since 1880 Evidence from historical data shows the average surface temperature of Earth is getting warmer. Climate change is a long-term change in climate patterns on Earth.

Changes to the Atmosphere in Modern Times Since the Industrial Revolution, humans have burned more fossil fuels and removed forests, adding more carbon dioxide to the atmosphere.

The Enhanced Greenhouse Effect The enhanced greenhouse effect explains why Earth is currently warming rapidly as humans add more greenhouse gases to the atmosphere.

Future Climate Change Earth will continue to warm unless humans reduce the amount of carbon dioxide they put into the atmosphere.

The Oldest Ice on Earth

You take a sip of water and decide that you want it colder. You grab ice cubes from the freezer and drop them into your glass. A few minutes later, you take another sip and *yuck!* It stinks! The water smells awful because the ice you added has been in the freezer for several months and has absorbed odors from it. Those ice cubes may be old, but they are extremely young compared to the oldest ice on Earth. How old is the oldest ice on Earth?

Throughout the years, scientists have been trying to discover the oldest ice on Earth. They aren't sure how old that ice is or where exactly they will find it, but one place they tried was in polar glaciers.

A glacier is an enormous mass of ice that does not completely melt, which forms in locations where snow stays on the ground year round. Each year, a new layer of snow covers older layers of snow and compresses the older layers. The older layers gradually turn to glacial ice due to the pressure from the newer layers, and over hundreds of years, thick layers of ice build up and form a glacier. Over the summer months, some of the ice that makes up the glacier does melt. However, as new snow falls on the glacier in winter, new ice is added to it, causing the glacier to grow and shrink according to the season.

Glaciers vary widely in size and thickness. The smallest glaciers are as small as football fields and are less than 100 m (328 ft) thick. The largest glaciers can cover hundreds of square kilometers and can be more than 1,000 m (3,280 ft) thick. Continental ice sheets are even bigger and can cover entire landmasses such as Greenland and Antarctica.

A glacier is a large mass of ice formed when layers of snow compress over time. The kayakers paddling in front of the Holgate Glacier in Alaska can give you an idea of how thick a glacier can be.

At a Glacial Pace

One feature that makes a glacier a glacier is the fact that it moves. Glaciers move because they are so heavy that they flow downhill, similarly to how liquid water in a river flows downhill.

However, the ice of a glacier flows much more slowly than water in a river. Even the speediest glacier moves so slowly that you can't see it move just by looking at it. The fastest glacier in the world moves at about 40 m to 46 m (131–150 ft) per day, which may not seem very slow, but that speed is less than 3 cm/min (1.18 in./min). Meanwhile, the slowest glacier moves about 182 m (597 ft) per year. So, if you hear something described as moving at a glacial pace, you know that it is moving very slowly.

How do scientists figure out how fast a glacier is moving? Not with a stopwatch and meterstick! Originally, scientists drove stakes into a glacier, noted their positions, and then came back weeks or months later and found their new positions. Now, glacier movement is tracked mostly by using satellite images. Overhead images of a glacier are taken at set time intervals and the images are compared.

Sometimes glaciers seem to move backward or uphill over time and are said to be *retreating*. In these cases, the glacier is still moving downhill, but its ice is melting faster than it is being replaced. So, the glacier is getting smaller overall and appears to be moving uphill.

All glaciers move by flowing downhill, but they move very slowly. Some glaciers also retreat because their ice melts faster than it is replaced. This sign marks where the edge of the retreating glacier in the background was in 1908.

Collecting Cores

So far you have learned that glaciers are made of ice and some of the ice is very old. But how do scientists figure out how old the ice in a glacier is? They find out by studying ice cores.

An ice core is a long column of ice that scientists remove from a glacier using a special drill. Samples are typically taken from deep beneath a glacier's surface, at depths up to 3,219 m (2 miles). Each ice core cuts through many layers of ice, which gives the ice cores a striped look. Each stripe is a layer, and, like rings in a tree trunk, each layer in an ice core corresponds to one year. For ice cores taken from young ice near the surface of a glacier, the layers are easy to see. Scientists can simply count the layers to determine the age of the ice.

To find the age of older layers, scientists study substances trapped in the ice, such as gases, dust, and volcanic ash. They use several methods to analyze these substances and find the approximate age of the ice. Scientists thought that ice core samples had an age limit of 800,000 years because ice at the bottom melted from the heat found within Earth.

While ice at this depth was ideal for looking at samples of more recent dates, it was not helpful for finding really ancient ice, say, millions of years old. Scientists started searching in a different kind of ice to find samples that were much older. Blue ice is some of the oldest ice in Antarctica and forms when additional layers of ice form on glaciers and compress older layers of ice over time. Air bubbles trapped in the ice become smaller and smaller as the ice grows denser. Erosion wears away the surface of the compacted ice, and light can enter the ice without the scattering effect from larger air bubbles, making the ice appear blue. Eventually, the bottom ice in blue ice is exposed. In 2017, in an area of blue ice on a glacier in East Antarctica, scientists found a sample that was approximately 2.7 million years old, making it the world's oldest ice to date. To find it, scientists drilled only 205 m (672.57 ft). With this find, scientists set their sights on a new goal: looking for ice up to 5 million years old!

Scientists study ice in glaciers by using special drills to collect ice cores and pull out long, frozen columns. Deep drilling may take months, as the drills cut through many layers of ice.

This photo shows the giant freezer at the National Ice Core Lab in Littleton, Colorado, that stores ice cores taken from glaciers all over the world. Scientists study ice cores to learn about the history of Earth's climate. The assistant curator in the photo is examining a sample taken from Lake Vostok in Antarctica.

Frozen Facts

Although scientists continue to look for the world's oldest ice, the point of their research is not simply to find that ice. Instead, scientists want to study the air and other substances trapped in the ice to learn about the history of Earth's climate to provide clues to its future.

Each tiny bubble of air frozen in the ice is a snapshot of the composition of the atmosphere at the time when the air was trapped. Scientists measure the amounts of different gases in the bubble to learn things about Earth's history. For example, they measure carbon dioxide levels to learn about Earth's temperature. Earth's temperature changes as carbon dioxide levels change. By analyzing ice core samples, scientists know that Earth's temperature has gone up and down many times over its long history.

Scientists can also use the gas bubbles to estimate how much of Earth's surface was covered by wetlands. Methane gas is produced by bacteria as they decompose dead plants and animals in wetlands. High levels of methane gas indicate that bacteria were decomposing at a fast rate, which means that large parts of Earth's surface had to be covered in wetlands for the plants, animals, and bacteria to live.

Scientists can learn a lot more by studying gases and other matter trapped in glacial ice. The ice in your freezer is a lot less interesting. About the only thing you could learn from that ice is whether something smelly was stored the freezer! ◆

Each layer of an ice core sample can tell scientists various things about Earth's climate. The air trapped in the bubbles of this thin ice core slice will be analyzed to determine the composition of the atmosphere at the time when the bubbles were frozen in the ice.

Climate Today and Tomorrow

What are the effects of recent changes in Earth's climate, and how can we address them?

Introduction

The once-lush green branches on the evergreens in the photo are drying and turning brown—symptoms of pine bark beetle infestation. Across the United States and Canada, huge areas of forest are dying because of the infestation. Pine bark beetles are a normal part of forest ecosystems, but in recent years their populations have exploded due to climate change. How can climate change be responsible for things like beetles killing trees and other environmental changes?

Warming temperatures and drought have thrown the Earth system out of balance. Rising temperatures and rising beetle populations do more than just correlate—there is a cause-and-effect relationship between them. The number of beetles has increased tremendously because fewer die in warmer winters. They also grow faster in warmer weather. The trees are weaker because of drought, so they are more vulnerable to attack from beetles.

In this lesson, you will learn how climate change has affected and is predicted to affect the biosphere and hydrosphere. You will explore how changing weather patterns are a part of this change. You will learn how scientists are monitoring climate change and its effects so that humans can minimize and adapt to changes. Finally, you will learn about other problems caused by climate change and how you can be part of their solution.

Vocabulary

ice sheet a huge mass of ice that covers at least 50,000 square kilometers of land; also called *continental glacier*

sea level rise an increase in the average global height of the ocean

permafrost ground that stays frozen throughout the year

climate change mitigation lessening climate change by reducing the amount of greenhouse gases that are added to the atmosphere or by removing them

sustainable the use of natural resources in a way that ensures their availability to future generations of humans

renewable energy energy that is obtained from renewable natural resources such as sunlight, wind, and waves

climate change adaptation any methods humans use to reduce the impacts of climate change

---

Next Generation Science Standards

Performance Expectations

MS-ESS3-5. Ask questions to clarify evidence of the factors that have caused the rise in global temperatures over the past century.

MS-ESS3-3. Apply scientific principles to design a method for monitoring and minimizing a human impact on the environment.

Science and Engineering Practices

Asking Questions and Defining Problems Ask questions to identify and clarify evidence of an argument.

Constructing Explanations and Designing Solutions Apply scientific principles to design an object, tool, process or system.

Crosscutting Concepts

Stability and Change Stability might be disturbed either by sudden events or gradual changes that accumulate over time.

Cause and Effect • Relationships can be classified as causal or correlational, and correlation does not necessarily imply causation. • Cause and effect relationships may be used to predict phenomena in natural or designed systems.

Influence of Science, Engineering, and Technology on Society and the Natural World

Disciplinary Core Ideas

ESS3.D. Human activities, such as the release of greenhouse gases from burning fossil fuels, are major factors in the current rise in Earth's mean surface temperature (global warming). Reducing the level of climate change and reducing human vulnerability to whatever climate changes do occur depend on the understanding of climate science, engineering capabilities, and other kinds of knowledge, such as understanding of human behavior and on applying that knowledge wisely in decisions and activities.

ESS3.C. • Human activities have significantly altered the biosphere, sometimes damaging or destroying natural habitats and causing the extinction of other species. But changes to Earth's environments can have different impacts (negative and positive) for different living things. • Typically as human populations and per capita consumption of natural resources increase, so do the negative impacts on Earth unless the activities and technologies involved are engineered otherwise.

1. Melting Ice and Rising Sea Levels

You are eating a snow cone on a hot summer day. You better eat it fast! Warm air around you is causing the snow cone ice to melt. Can warmer temperatures also be causing Earth's ice to melt in the same way?

There is a causal relationship between rising temperatures and shrinking ice coverage. That is, global warming is causing permanent ice around the world to decrease in size. Permanent ice is an important part of Earth's system that includes ice sheets, glaciers, and sea ice. An **ice sheet,** also called a *continental glacier,* is a huge mass of ice that covers at least 50,000 square kilometers (31,068 square miles) of land. Ice sheets cover most of Greenland and Antarctica. Glaciers are found in mountains around the world. Sea ice floats on the oceans in the polar regions. During warm months, some parts of ice sheets, glaciers, and sea ice melt, but they increase in size again during cold months. Permanent ice is shrinking because it is melting faster than it is growing.

The Greenland ice sheet is about three times the size of Texas, but it is steadily shrinking. Scientists use instruments on planes, satellites, and the ice to gather data to determine how the amount of ice is changing. They have discovered that the Greenland ice sheet is losing about 286 billion metric tons of ice each year. The stream in the photo was formed by water melting on the massive ice sheet.

The thickness and color of snow and ice affect albedo. Melting exposes darker surfaces beneath the snow, which changes the albedo by decreasing it. A lower albedo means more sunlight is absorbed, which in turn leads to faster melting. With rising temperatures and decreasing albedo, the Greenland ice sheet will continue to melt.

This stream of water on the Greenland ice sheet is caused by melting. The ice sheet covers most of Greenland, which is shown on the globe. Global warming is causing permanent ice around the world, such as the Greenland ice sheet, to melt more quickly than it increases in size.

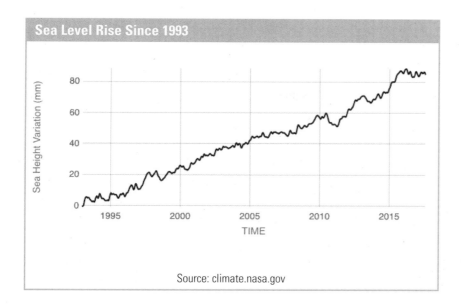

Sea Level Rise Since 1993

Source: climate.nasa.gov

Figure 13.1
This graph from NASA shows sea level data that was collected for more than 20 years. The sea level is rising due to water from melting glaciers and ice sheets, and because of thermal expansion from warmer waters.

Although Greenland is far north between the Arctic and North Atlantic Oceans, the melting ice is contributing to the shrinking land mass of the Maldives, a small nation made up of a group of islands in the Indian Ocean near the equator. How are changes to the Greenland ice sheet affecting tropical islands?

Sea level rise is an increase in the average global height of the ocean. Since 1870, scientists have measured sea level at coastal locations all over the world. Since 1992, scientists have also used satellites to measure sea level. This data, shown in the graph in Figure 13.1, shows that sea level rose about 78.3 mm (3.08 in.) between 1993 and 2015 and is evidence that sea level is continuing to rise.

Sea level rise increases the risk of erosion and flooding caused by high tides and wave surges in coastal areas. Small islands with low elevations, such as the Maldives, are especially vulnerable and, in the future, may completely disappear as a result of sea level rise. As the land near shore erodes, water moves closer to populated areas, forcing people to find a new place to live. Sea level rise also affects coastal areas in the United States, including Florida and New York. This danger increases especially during hurricanes. In 2017, sea level was rising at a rate of 3.4 mm (0.13 in.) per year.

In addition to melting ice, sea level rise is caused by thermal expansion of ocean water. Water expands and takes up more space as it gets warmer. The warming atmosphere causes the ocean to warm, and the warmer water takes up more space causing sea level to rise. According to scientists' best estimates based on many different lines of evidence, roughly two-thirds of sea level rise is due to melting ice, with the remaining third due to thermal expansion. During the next century, the ocean will continue to warm and the melting of ice sheets around the world are expected to increase. Thus, scientists expect that sea level will rise even faster.

Sea level rise increases the risk of erosion and flooding at coastal locations. The Maldives nation, shown in this photo, is at risk of disappearing completely due to sea level rise and its low elevations.

Climate change is affecting ecosystems. Evidence from scientific studies shows that the range of Edith's Checkerspot butterfly is moving northward and to higher elevations. As the climate changes, the range of many plants and animals will change too.

2. Changing Ecosystems

Climate change alters an ecosystem's nonliving parts, and thus affects the living parts. Changes in temperature can give cues to organisms that, in turn, can influence their behavior. For example, the pine bark beetles attacking the trees shown in the photo in the beginning of the lesson are maturing sooner and reproducing quicker as a result of a warming climate. What can happen to living things as the climate changes?

One impact of climate change is that plants and animals seeking cooler temperatures are shifting the range where they live toward the poles and to higher elevations. Scientists expect this trend to continue as Earth warms. One species shifting its range is the Edith's Checkerspot butterfly. In the 1990s, Camille Parmesan investigated whether climate change could be affecting this specific butterfly. It had been studied by other biologists for decades. Dr. Parmesan used their data to find out where the butterflies lived in the past. She visited these places, all the way from Mexico to Canada, at the time of year when the butterflies were expected to be there. She found that many of the butterflies at lower latitudes had disappeared. Her data clearly showed that Edith's Checkerspot butterflies shifted their range northward or to higher elevations. In 2007, Dr. Parmesan shared the Nobel Peace Prize as a lead contributor to the Intergovernmental Panel on Climate Change.

Warmer water is affecting ocean ecosystems, such as coral reefs. Healthy coral is typically very colorful and full of life. Instead, this weakened coral is bleached because the algae that it depends on for food has been expelled.

Changes in ocean ecosystems caused by climate change are similar to those on land. As the average global ocean temperature rises, fish and other animals are moving to higher latitudes. Fishing fleets are seeing changes in the species of fish they catch. However, coral cannot move when the water becomes too warm and respond by expelling helpful algae that live inside of their tissues. The algae give the coral their color and are the coral's primary food source. Without food from the algae, the coral weakens, becomes susceptible to disease, and turns white, or bleaches.

If climate changes too quickly, many plant and animal species will not be able to move their habitats fast enough. But that's not the only problem. Rapid climate change combined with the loss of habitat increases the risk of extinction for many plant and animal species. During ancient climate changes, it was likely that many plants and animals shifted locations successfully, but today they are often prevented by loss of suitable habitat. Species shifting habitats to avoid warmer temperatures may end up in human-influenced areas like cities or farm fields, where they may struggle to survive.

Climate change may promote the spread of certain invasive species. Invasive species are not native and can damage the ecosystems that they move into. For example, the yellow starthistle is an invasive plant in California's grassland ecosystems. Because of climate change, its range has expanded as it competes with and replaces native plants.

Besides making conditions more suitable for invasive species to thrive, climate change also harms ecosystems by changing the timing of seasonal events such as the migrations and hibernation of animals, and blooms of flowers. Some plants, such as lilacs, have begun developing leaves and flowers earlier in the spring due to warmer temperatures. Some birds, such as tree swallows, are also laying their eggs earlier. Shifts in timing can harm an ecosystem because plants and animals that depend on each other may no longer be present together at the same time of year. Migrating birds and marine animals may not find enough food if they arrive too early.

One way to track the effects of climate change in local ecosystems is through the efforts of citizen scientists. These members of the public volunteer to help scientists by carefully observing and recording data. These data may include the number of an animal species in a certain area or dates when a plant species begins to flower. Scientists incorporate and analyze the data, comparing it to past observations to determine how ecosystems are affected by climate change.

Citizen scientists, like this volunteer who is collecting data in Cuyahoga Valley National Park in Ohio, aid scientists in a variety of ways including by conducting animal and plant counts to show how climate change is affecting local ecosystems.

3. Changing Weather Patterns

An important area for local wildlife and migrating birds is the Cheyenne Bottoms Wildlife Wetlands in Kansas. Figure 13.3 shows satellite images of changes to this area during a drought in 2012. Without rain, almost all of the water evaporated. What factors led to the drought that dried up these Kansas wetlands?

Climate change did not necessarily cause the Kansas drought. But it does make droughts more likely. Precipitation patterns are changing because of climate change, and droughts and heavy downpours are expected to increase. Some regions are likely to receive more precipitation in the future while others may get less. Droughts are likely to happen more often because the intervals between rainstorms may increase. Downpours are expected to be more intense with a warmer climate because more water vapor is in the air. Heavy rain combined with dry soil increases the risk of floods. Heavy downpours and floods, such as those after Hurricane Harvey in 2017, have already become more common in parts of the United States.

Scientists expect the strength and frequency of severe weather to increase due to climate change. Heat waves are likely to occur more often, last longer, and become more severe as temperatures rise due to climate change. Meanwhile, the number of days of very cold temperatures is likely to decrease. People who live in cold areas may consider milder winters a positive effect of climate change. However, blizzards may become more common because the air is moister. Already strong hurricanes are likely to become even stronger as ocean temperatures rise. Scientists are still working to understand how the frequency of hurricanes and tornadoes is likely to change.

Droughts, floods, and severe weather have a negative impact on society and ecosystems. They are dangerous to human health and can destroy crops, harm livestock, and reduce fresh water supplies.

Figure 13.3
Almost all the water evaporated from the Cheyenne Bottoms Wildlife Wetlands in Kansas during a drought in 2012. Climate change is affecting precipitation patterns. Fortunately, these wetlands are recovering.

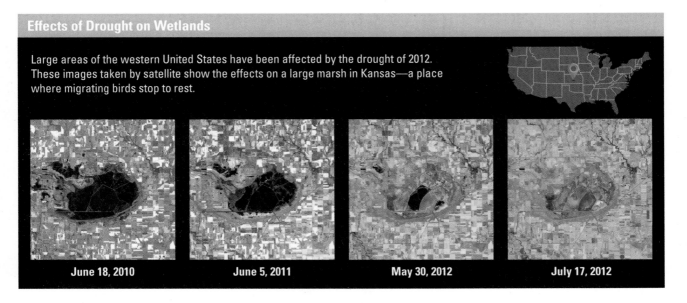

Effects of Drought on Wetlands

Large areas of the western United States have been affected by the drought of 2012. These images taken by satellite show the effects on a large marsh in Kansas—a place where migrating birds stop to rest.

June 18, 2010   June 5, 2011   May 30, 2012   July 17, 2012

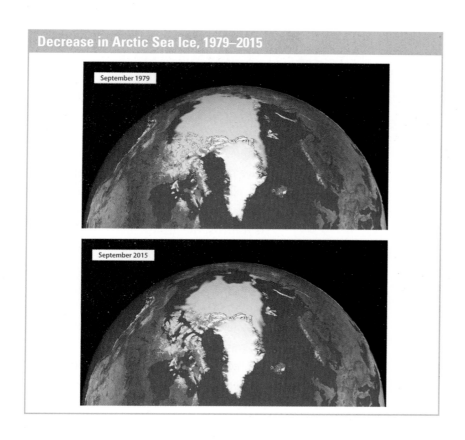

Decrease in Arctic Sea Ice, 1979–2015

September 1979

September 2015

Figure 13.4

These images from NASA show how the Arctic has warmed faster than the rest of world and is seeing big impacts from climate change. The bright white areas in these images from satellite data are permanent ice. How much has the permanent sea ice over the Arctic Ocean decreased?

4. Monitoring Climate Change

The people of Barrow, Alaska, are feeling the effects of a changing climate. Barrow is the northernmost town in the United States, on the edge of the Arctic Ocean. Historically, by late October, sea ice used to cover the ocean around Barrow. However, since 2002, Barrow has been warmer in October and sea ice has remained far from shore. Why is Barrow experiencing the effects of climate change so much more severely than other places where the effects may go unnoticed?

The impacts of climate change are not the same everywhere. You may not notice its current effects where you live. However, climate change is dramatically changing the Arctic and the lives of the people who live there now. The Arctic can serve as a scientific case study for how climate change will affect other areas in the future.

Alaska has warmed twice as fast as the rest of the United States. Snow and ice are starting to melt earlier in the spring. Melting sea ice in the Arctic Ocean and glaciers are part of the reason for the additional warming. Figure 13.4 shows satellite data of how the sea ice cover shrank from 1979 to 2015. The Arctic Ocean sea ice coverage is expected to continue shrinking, and by 2035, it is expected to disappear in the summer. The bright white ice is the permanent ice that stays year round. As more sea ice melts, more ocean water is exposed to the sun. Melting glaciers expose more land. Both water and land have a lower albedo than ice and absorb more sunlight. So, they warm up faster, which leads to even more snow and ice melting.

Permafrost (in this photo, the dirty brown ice) is starting to melt in Arctic locations as temperatures rise. As permafrost under the topsoil melts away, it can cause cracks and damage to the surface.

Scientists track polar bears to determine how their populations are changing. Polar bears are only one part of the Arctic ecosystem affected by climate change. This bear has been temporarily sedated so the biologist can take measurements and gather data about polar bear population size.

Warmer temperatures are also causing permafrost to melt. **Permafrost** is ground that stays frozen throughout the year. Scientists monitor permafrost through fieldwork. They can use radar instruments to measure how far below the surface of the soil permafrost starts and drill holes into it to measure its temperature. These measurements indicate that the permafrost is melting in many locations. As it melts, the ground becomes softer and changes shape. Human communities are being damaged as thawing permafrost is causing the ground below buildings, roads, and trees to sink.

Scientists are monitoring how Arctic ecosystems are being affected by climate change. Animals, such as polar bears and walruses, are threatened by the loss of sea ice. Scientists check the numbers of these animals in different locations to determine how their populations are changing. Polar bears are captured, tranquilized, and tattooed with a number so data can be recorded about the overall health of the bears. After the bears are released, scientists track the animals and compare data from year to year. Scientists estimate the size of the polar bear population by comparing the number of marked to unmarked bears they capture each year.

Scientists also learn about the changing climate and ecosystem from the native peoples who have lived in the Arctic for generations. Because most Arctic locations are very remote, native peoples have relied on hunting for food. They recognize changes that visiting scientists and satellites may not see. Melting ice and changes in animal populations are affecting the native peoples' ability to hunt for food.

Changes in the Arctic due to climate change are only beginning. Land and ocean temperatures will continue to rise. Ecosystems will continue to change as non-native plants and animals move farther north into the Arctic. The Arctic may seem far away, but it is connected to the rest of the Earth system. Changes there affect the rest of the planet. Recall the melting Greenland ice sheet is contributing to sea level rise that is affecting islands near the equator. These changes are a warning sign of the potential impacts of climate change where you live. What can people do to reduce the effects of climate change?

Effects of a Warming Atmosphere

All parts of the Earth system are connected. A change in one part of the system affects the other parts and is a cause-and-effect relationship. How does humans adding more greenhouse gases to the atmosphere start a complex chain of events that affect the Earth system?

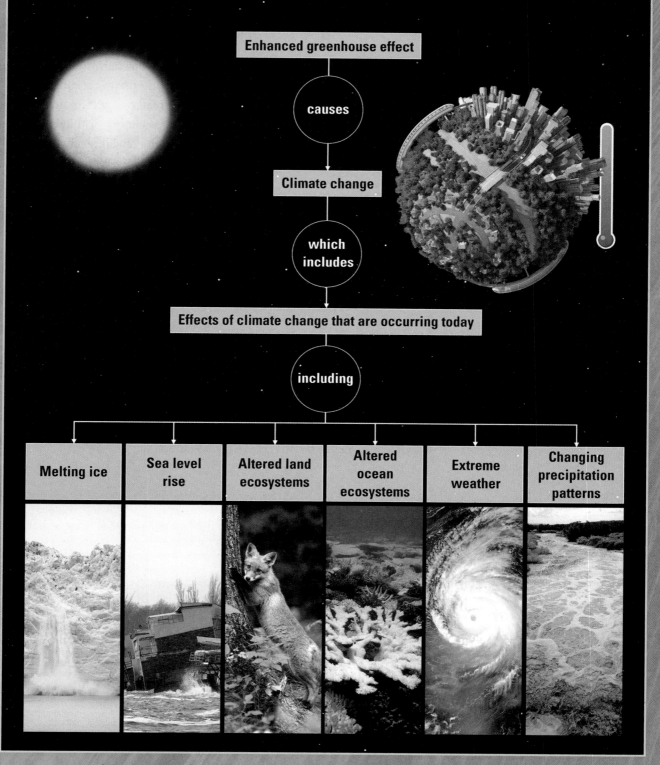

Enhanced greenhouse effect

causes

Climate change

which includes

Effects of climate change that are occurring today

including

| Melting ice | Sea level rise | Altered land ecosystems | Altered ocean ecosystems | Extreme weather | Changing precipitation patterns |

5. Reducing Climate Change

No one knows exactly how much Earth is going to warm. What are some of the ways that human activities produce greenhouse gases? The combustion of fossil fuels for transportation and by industry releases carbon dioxide. Burning trees to clear forests produces it too. Agriculture and garbage dumps produce carbon dioxide and methane.

How might the carbon dioxide that humans continue to emit impact climate change? Climate scientists use computer models to predict how temperature is likely to change over the next century based on possible increases in greenhouse gas emissions. These computer models represent "business-as-usual" scenarios with little to no reduction, to minor and major reduction in human greenhouse gas emissions. The graph in Figure 13.5 shows greater growth in greenhouse gas emissions is likely to cause greater warming. A reduction in emissions due to strict mitigation, shown by the blue line labeled "low growth," is needed to keep warming below 2°C (3.6°F). International policymakers have targeted a 2°C maximum increase above preindustrial levels to try to curb widespread, severe impacts of climate change. You can see that the increase in Earth's average temperature depends on the amount of greenhouse gases that humans add to the atmosphere. How can people manage or reduce the effects of warming over your lifetime?

Figure 13.5

This graph from the Intergovernmental Panel on Climate Change shows the possible increase in temperature over the next century. These changes are predicted by climate models of scenarios for "business as usual," minor, and major reduction in current greenhouse gas emissions. The constant CO_2 line offers an estimate of global warming if greenhouse gas emissions stayed the same at year 2000 levels.

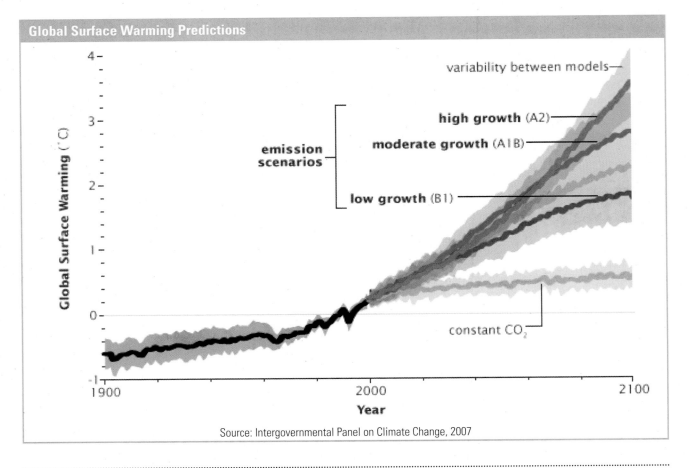

Source: Intergovernmental Panel on Climate Change, 2007

Since we know that adding more greenhouse gases to the atmosphere will increase global warming, and many activities humans perform create such gases, what might be done? Does this mean you should never have a car?

Humans cannot stop global warming, but people can influence how much warming happens. **Climate change mitigation** means lessening climate change by reducing the amount of greenhouse gases that are added to the atmosphere or by removing them. So, people do not need to give up their cars entirely to reduce climate change. Instead, they can choose cars that burn less or no fossil fuels, or alternate with carpooling, mass transit, or bicycling if possible.

To help mitigate climate change, people need to make sustainable choices. **Sustainable** refers to the ability to use natural resources in a way that ensures their availability to future generations of humans. The combustion of fossil fuels is not sustainable. Yet, almost 80 percent of the energy used in the United States is generated by burning fossil fuels. What can people do to reduce this?

Renewable energy is energy that is obtained from renewable natural resources such as sunlight, wind, and waves. Using more renewable energy resources that are sustainable is a way to mitigate climate change because it produces little or no carbon dioxide. Solar power uses energy from the sun that can be converted into electricity. Hydroelectric energy channels water to turn turbines on a generator to produce electricity. Wind turbines convert wind power into electrical energy. Geothermal energy uses heat from rocks and fluids beneath Earth's surface to run heat pumps that can heat or cool buildings, or generate electricity. Each type of energy source may work better in some areas than in others. To reduce carbon dioxide emissions caused by fossil fuels, a combination of these renewable energy sources will be needed.

People may be able to mitigate climate change by reducing their greenhouse gas emissions. Using renewable energy sources such as solar, hydroelectric, wind, and geothermal energy can reduce emissions.

Solar energy

Hydroelectric energy

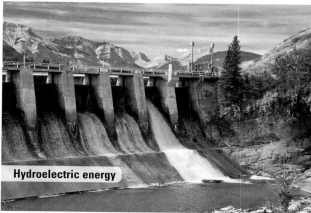
Wind energy

Geothermal energy

6. Adapting to a Changing Climate

Although people may mitigate climate change, Earth is still warming. What do scientists suggest to minimize the impact of a changing climate?

Climate change adaptation is any methods humans use to reduce the impacts of climate change. People in different regions will experience different impacts of climate change. So, the ways they will need to adapt to this depend on where they live. People living in a city's urban heat island may face increased risks of heat waves. In rural areas, farmers may be affected by changes in seasonal temperatures and increased risk of drought. People in coastal areas will be affected by rising sea levels. Each community will need to design its own plan to adapt to a unique set of impacts that may even include relocation, if necessary.

Scientists, engineers, and state and local government officials can determine the specific risks to their area. They can assess how these risks are likely to affect the residents. Then, they can design a climate change adaptation plan to reduce the impacts of climate change. Adaptation plans will include solutions to the specific problems faced by the city or town. Figure 13.6A shows how cities and towns may adapt to climate change. As you can see, some plans may include water collection systems to collect rainwater that, along with reservoirs, can help reduce the impact of droughts. Plans may also include educating people about climate change and how they can change their behaviors. Governments may improve systems to prepare and warn people about severe weather, such as heat waves.

Figure 13.6A

Many cities have designed plans to adapt to climate change. Each community will design a plan suitable for its needs because each region will be impacted by climate change in its own way.

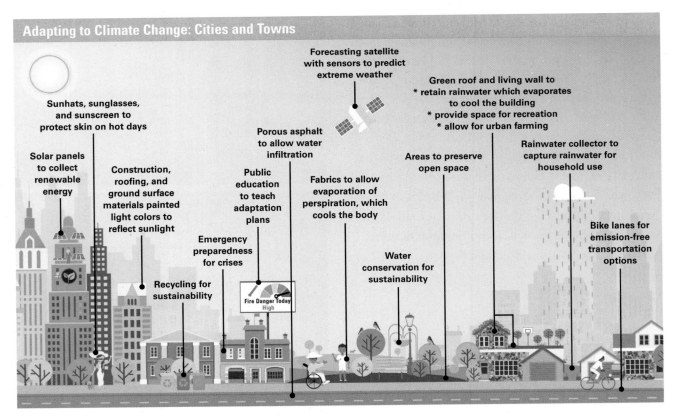

Adapting to Climate Change: Cities and Towns

Forecasting satellite with sensors to predict extreme weather

Green roof and living wall to
* retain rainwater which evaporates to cool the building
* provide space for recreation
* allow for urban farming

Sunhats, sunglasses, and sunscreen to protect skin on hot days

Porous asphalt to allow water infiltration

Areas to preserve open space

Rainwater collector to capture rainwater for household use

Solar panels to collect renewable energy

Public education to teach adaptation plans

Fabrics to allow evaporation of perspiration, which cools the body

Construction, roofing, and ground surface materials painted light colors to reflect sunlight

Emergency preparedness for crises

Bike lanes for emission-free transportation options

Water conservation for sustainability

Recycling for sustainability

Fire Danger Today
High

Figure 13.6B shows how people may adapt in coastal and rural areas. In coastal areas, climate change adaption plans may need to include ways to protect residents from rising sea levels. For example, some cities may build sea walls to keep out rising water. Where there is space, nature preserves may be developed to allow beaches and wetlands to gradually move inland as the ocean rises. Communities may plan to build in areas farther away from the ocean. That way, buildings will not be affected by sea level rise.

In rural areas, farmers need to consider how climate change will affect their crops. In some areas, farmers may benefit from a longer growing season, which will allow them to produce more crops. In other areas, they may be affected by drought or flooding. They may need to plant new crops that use less water and can withstand hotter, drier conditions. They also need to plan to protect their livestock from warmer temperatures, such as by providing the animals with shade.

People can also help wildlife adapt by improving habitats. When scientists monitor animal populations, often they use computer models to predict how animals are likely to be affected by climate change. These models help them identify animals that are at high risk because of climate change. Climate models can show which animals' habitats are likely to shrink and which animals may shift to new areas.

Adaptation can reduce the impact of climate change. However, our ability to adapt depends on how much Earth warms and how quickly it warms. What other strategies can you think of?

Figure 13.6B
Coastal areas need to make changes that reduce the effects of sea level rise. Farmers in rural areas need to make changes because climate change may affect how well their crops grow. People everywhere need to consider how they can help wildlife adapt to climate change.

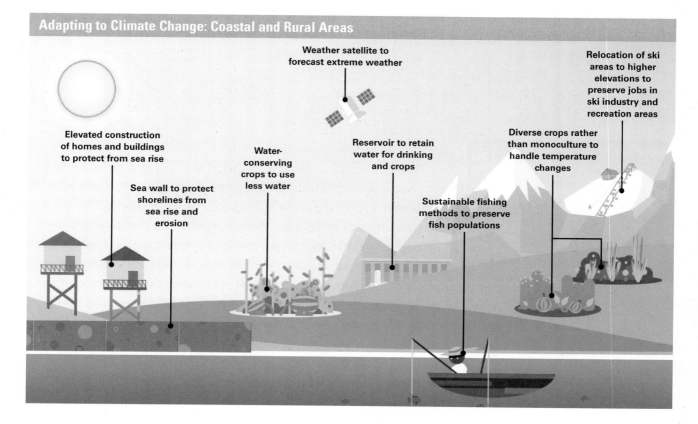

Adapting to Climate Change: Coastal and Rural Areas

Weather satellite to forecast extreme weather

Relocation of ski areas to higher elevations to preserve jobs in ski industry and recreation areas

Elevated construction of homes and buildings to protect from sea rise

Water-conserving crops to use less water

Reservoir to retain water for drinking and crops

Diverse crops rather than monoculture to handle temperature changes

Sea wall to protect shorelines from sea rise and erosion

Sustainable fishing methods to preserve fish populations

Figure 13.7

Humans depend on technologies that burn fossil fuels and emit carbon dioxide. Even with a growing population, humans can minimize warming by reducing greenhouse gas emissions in each of these areas.

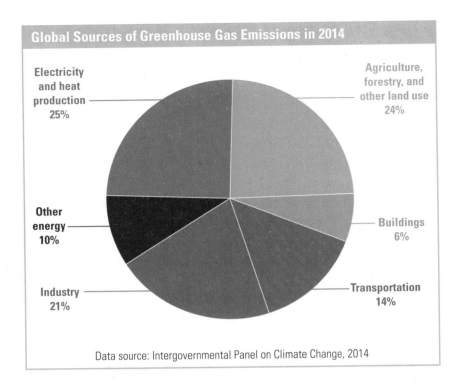

Global Sources of Greenhouse Gas Emissions in 2014

Electricity and heat production 25%

Agriculture, forestry, and other land use 24%

Other energy 10%

Buildings 6%

Industry 21%

Transportation 14%

Data source: Intergovernmental Panel on Climate Change, 2014

The challenges of climate change require individuals, industry, and governments to work together on solutions. In 2015, representatives from countries around the world met in Paris. Formulating effective plans for global actions that address global problems is the goal at these conferences.

7. Designing Solutions to a Complex Problem

Because climate change is such a complex problem, it will require the extensive cooperation of many people to design acceptable solutions. Scientists are gathering data and making models, engineers are inventing new technologies, and governments are making plans to adapt to the impacts.

Reducing greenhouse gas emissions will be challenging as the human population continues to grow and requires more energy. As more countries become developed, more and more people will use electricity, cars, and other technologies. Thus, more greenhouse gases will be produced if technologies are based on fossil fuels. Sustainable choices and new technologies that do not depend on fossil fuels are needed. Otherwise, Earth may warm by more than 2°C.

How can communities agree on what needs to be done and how to accomplish it? Individuals, industry, and governments will need to work together to reduce the impact of climate change. Figure 13.7 shows the percentage of greenhouse gases from different human activities in 2014. People can reduce these emissions by changing their behaviors to find ways to use less energy. Many companies in various industries are adopting green practices, which are strategies to help protect the environment and sustain its natural resources. Cities can also choose renewable energy sources. Many already have. Burlington, Vermont, was one of the first United States cities to use 100 percent renewable energy. State and federal governments can create policies that promote the use of renewable energy over the use of fossil fuels. All these actions drive the use of technologies that reduce carbon dioxide emissions.

8. Earth's Climate and You

As you have learned, climate change is a global problem that does not have a single solution. It will require the effort of many people coming together to develop strategies. What can people do to find ways to foster cooperation towards a sustainable world?

You can have an impact on climate change by understanding the causes and effects of climate change and by basing your lifestyle and future career choices on your knowledge. You can take actions to practice sustainability or use renewable resources. You can expand your knowledge to help craft your community's climate adaption plan. You can also use your understanding of the scientific evidence that explains the causes of climate change to make informed decisions about technologies and public policies. The choices that you make to meet your needs reflect your values, or what you think is important.

The choices you make can have a positive impact on climate change.

LESSON SUMMARY

Climate Today and Tomorrow

Melting Ice and Rising Sea Levels Global warming is causing permanent ice around the world to melt, causing sea levels to rise.

Changing Ecosystems Climate change is altering ecosystems on land and in the ocean. The ranges of some species are changing as a result. Climate change increases the risk of extinction.

Changing Weather Patterns Climate change is affecting precipitation patterns, increasing the likelihood of both droughts and downpours. It is also increasing the risk of heat waves and blizzards.

Monitoring Climate Change The effects of climate change are not the same everywhere. The Arctic is experiencing more impacts from climate change than many other areas.

Reducing Climate Change Earth's temperature depends on the amount of greenhouse gases humans add to the atmosphere. Climate change can be mitigated by reducing the amount of added greenhouse gases.

Adapting to a Changing Climate People will need to adapt to reduce the effects of future climate change. Many state and local governments are developing plans to adapt to climate change.

Designing Solutions to a Complex Problem Greenhouse gases are likely to increase as the world population increases. Reducing and adapting to climate change requires multiple solutions including new technologies and cooperation between groups.

Earth's Climate and You You can have an impact on climate change by knowing the causes and effects of climate change and using your understanding of scientific evidence to make informed decisions.

Learning Resources

The whole Earth and everything beyond it is the subject of science. This set of learning resources includes some essential thinking tools you need in order to explore, investigate, and explain how the world works.

Laboratory Safety

To think like a scientist, you have to act like one. This means making observations, experimenting, and carrying out other types of investigations. The same goes for solving engineering problems. You have to propose, build, test, and improve your designed solutions. All of these things are fun and interesting, but there can be risks involved in handling equipment and materials. What do you have to be aware of to stay safe when practicing science and engineering?

Your teacher may ask you to sign a Science Safety Contract and discuss it with your parents. This is an important first step towards science safety. Before working in the science lab, review these rules.

- ☑ Understand the hazards and rules for a particular investigation before you begin.

- ☑ Make sure your personal clothing is safe for the lab. Do not wear loose clothing, especially long sleeves.

- ☑ Wear closed shoes to protect your feet.

- ☑ If you have long hair, tie it back.

- ☑ Wear safety goggles, protective aprons, and gloves when required by your teacher.

- ☑ Transport and handle all equipment and chemicals as directed by your teacher.

- ☑ Report breaks, spills, or other accidents to your teacher right away.

- ☑ Report injuries to your teacher right away, and follow your school's first aid procedures.

- ☑ Know where safety equipment is in the lab you use and when or how to use it.

- ☑ Dispose of materials in the designated containers at the end of the investigation.

- ☑ Clean up your work area and wash your hands at the conclusion of the investigation.

- ☑ Know what to do in case of a hazardous event such as a power failure, earthquake, or emergency evacuation.

- ☑ Be aware of safety for everyone in your group.

Planning Investigations

Designing your own investigations is a chance to act like a real scientist—and that includes keeping yourself and others safe.

☑ Choose equipment and materials that your teacher tells you are safe to use.

☑ Plan how you will handle the materials safely, including how you will dispose of materials that cannot be used again.

☑ Include safety steps when writing your procedure.

☑ Always obtain permission from your teacher before carrying out your investigation plan.

Field Trip Safety

Some of the most important thigs you can do to stay safe on a field trip is to be prepared in advance.

- ☑ Return a signed parental permission form to your teacher before a field trip.

- ☑ Check the weather forecast so that you can choose appropriate clothing. If there is any possibility of severe weather, make sure there is a plan for taking shelter.

- ☑ No matter the weather, wear footwear that encloses and protects your feet.

- ☑ Wear clothing, hats, or sunscreen to protect yourself from sunburn. Remember, you can get burned on a cloudy day as well as on a sunny one.

- ☑ Learn in advance the types of organisms you may encounter that are dangerous and should be avoided.

- ☑ During the field trip, don't touch plants unless instructed by your teacher or guide.

- ☑ Know how to get first aid for poisonous plants and animal stings and bites.

- ☑ Never eat or put in your mouth anything you find outdoors without permission.

- ☑ Wash up carefully after an outdoor science activity.

- ☑ If the area you visited has ticks, inspect your clothing and body for ticks at the end of the field trip.

Safety for Living Things in the Classroom

When you investigate living things, you can't just think about yourself. You have to think about the organisms in your care, too.

☑ Understand appropriate and humane treatment of animals. This includes selecting a suitable container to house the animals and making sure the temperature is within the proper range for that species.

☑ Help make sure that animals kept in the science classroom are provided with adequate water, food, and that their containers are kept clean.

☑ Keep handling of animals to a minimum and never disturb sleeping animals.

☑ Plan for appropriate care of living things over weekends, holidays, and vacations.

☑ Don't bring personal pets or unknown plants or animals into school, as they may be poisonous, venomous, or negatively affect the other living things in your science classroom.

☑ Never carry out investigations that will cause discomfort, pain, or disease to animals.

☑ Return native wild species to their natural environment.

☑ Never release non-native species into the natural environment.

☑ Wash your hands and surfaces after handling living things.

Asking Questions

Asking questions is central to science. Scientists learn about the natural world by asking questions and trying to answer them. As scientists learn about the natural world, they come up with more questions to answer. What kinds of questions do scientists ask, and how can you learn to ask them?

Questions drive the scientific process. Scientists ask testable questions to guide their research and gain scientific knowledge. This knowledge can lead to new questions to be answered.

Questions Scientists ask questions about the natural world and about current scientific ideas. The types of questions scientists might ask include: What causes a particular phenomenon? How do different factors affect observations? Why did an event occur?

Testability Science can only answer questions that are testable, which means that a scientist must be able to gather evidence to answer the question. To determine if a question is testable, ask yourself: How can the answer to this question be determined? Would the answer be a fact or an opinion? Can I design an investigation to answer this question?

Phenomena or theories

Testability

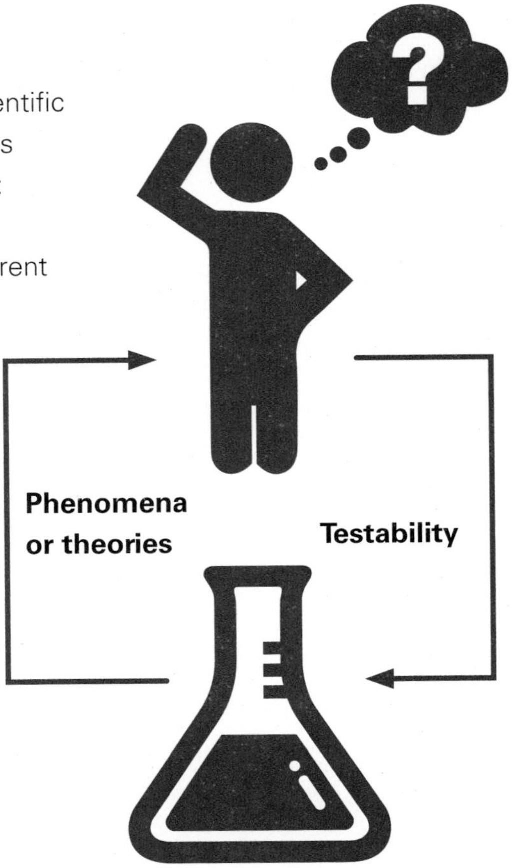

Science Testable questions can lead to new scientific knowledge, which can lead to new questions. Ask yourself: How can I gather data to answer this question? How well does this data support the answer? Are there other possible answers that this data could support?

Phenomena and Theories Scientists ask questions based on observed phenomena and scientific theories. The questions may be asked to clarify ideas or to introduce new ideas. Ask yourself: What other questions does this new understanding raise? How does this explanation relate to other scientific ideas or theories?

If you go to cities around the world, you will probably see a couple of pigeons or maybe a couple of hundreds of pigeons. Unlike many other wild animals, pigeons do not seem to mind living around people. How might you research pigeons to find out why that is?

Asking Questions You can start your research by asking questions. These questions might include: Why are pigeons more common in cities than other species of birds? What birds lived in an area before an area was developed? How does the diet of a city pigeon compare with the diet of a pigeon living in the country?

You can ask testable questions to learn about the natural environment. For example, if you are studying pigeons, you might ask questions to compare the diet of city pigeons with the diet of country pigeons.

Determining Testability After scientists come up with questions, they pick at least one question to investigate further. Suppose that you wanted to find the answer to the question "How does the diet of a city pigeon compare with the diet of a pigeon living in the country?" The question you are trying to answer must be testable. To determine this, you might ask: What kind of investigation will help answer the question? What evidence do I have to gather to answer the question?

Conducting Science You may want to start your investigation on pigeon diets by reviewing research done by other scientists. Some questions you may consider are: What other research has been done on pigeon diets? What methods did other scientists use? How will my investigation differ or improve on previous investigations?

Coming Up with Phenomena and Theories While investigating pigeon diets, you may try to connect your observations with known phenomena and theories. Ask yourself: What do my observations say about pigeon nutrition? How does a pigeon's diet compare with that of other species of birds? How do my results relate to phenomena like the adaptation of pigeons to their environment?

The fact that asking questions in science often leads to new questions may seem frustrating, but it is actually a good thing. The cycle of questions leading to more questions means that science will always grow and improve.

Defining Problems

Before engineers can begin designing a solution, they have to define the problem they are trying to solve. By thoroughly defining the problem, engineers know exactly what qualities the solution must have and what obstacles they may need to work around to achieve the solution. What do engineers have to do to define a problem?

Defining problems involves clearly identifying the problem, the boundaries and components of the problem, and the criteria and constraints of the problem's solution.

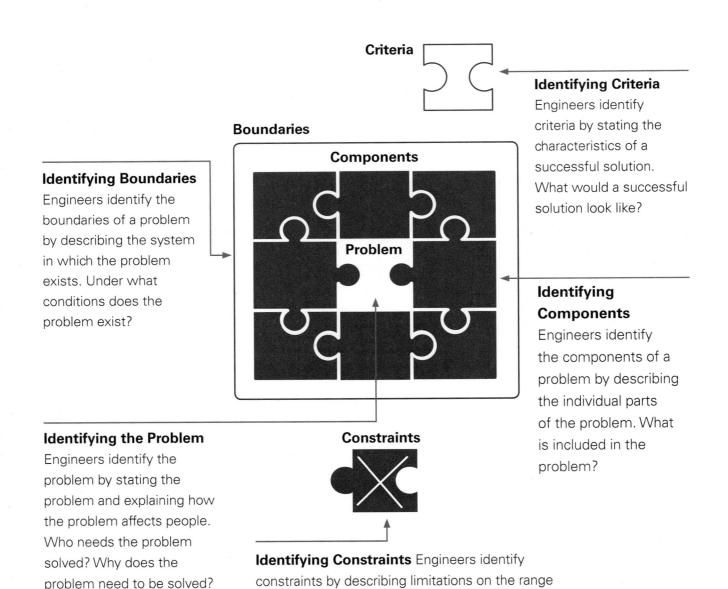

Identifying Criteria
Engineers identify criteria by stating the characteristics of a successful solution. What would a successful solution look like?

Identifying Boundaries
Engineers identify the boundaries of a problem by describing the system in which the problem exists. Under what conditions does the problem exist?

Identifying Components
Engineers identify the components of a problem by describing the individual parts of the problem. What is included in the problem?

Identifying the Problem
Engineers identify the problem by stating the problem and explaining how the problem affects people. Who needs the problem solved? Why does the problem need to be solved?

Identifying Constraints Engineers identify constraints by describing limitations on the range of possible solutions to a design problem. What would make a solution impractical or unusable?

Defining a problem by identifying boundaries, components, criteria, and constraints is the first step in finding a good solution. Making healthy lunches that students will eat is a problem that many schools struggle with.

If you could buy anything to eat at your school cafeteria, what would you get? You probably want foods like pizza and cake. But pizza, cake, and other popular foods tend not to be healthy. What can school cafeterias do to encourage students to eat better foods?

Identifying the Problem Kids across the country eat most of their lunches at school. School cafeterias try to provide nutritious meals, but often the healthy parts of the meals end up in the trash. So, the problem is providing healthy foods that students will eat.

Identifying the Boundaries and Components The boundaries of this problem surround the school and the people in it. The components of the problem include the food, the students, school kitchen, kitchen staff, and administrators. The students eat the food that is prepared by the kitchen staff, while the administrators purchase the food and approve the meals. However, many things are not important to the problem, such as the color of the walls and whether lunch tables have chairs or benches to sit on.

Identifying Criteria and Constraints The criteria and constraints of a successful solution can be organized in a table.

Criteria	Constraints
• meals are nutritious	• budget (need to afford food)
• at least 85% of students eat the meal	• kitchen (need right equipment to prepare food)
• meal plan has variety	• time to prepare food

Solving the problem of serving healthy school lunches is not easy, but understanding the problem will help find a solution. If the solution is successful, it will be good and delicious.

Developing and Using Models

Scientists use models to explain and understand natural phenomena. Scientific models can be physical models such as a globe or a drawing of a cell. Scientific models can also be conceptual models, which means that they are collections of related ideas. For example, the big bang theory is a conceptual model to describe how the universe began. How can you learn to develop models the way a scientist would?

When scientists develop a model, they identify the components of the model, describe the relationship between the components, and explain the connections between the model and the real world.

Model

Real World

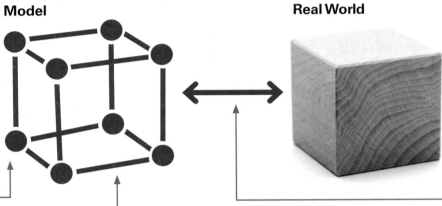

Components Components are the parts that make up the model. Each component represents something in the real world. When you develop a model, you have to decide which parts of the real word are important to represent and which are not.

Relationships The relationships in a model describe how the components interact. When you develop a model, the relationships you describe help you understand how the components of the model work together and make predictions about the model.

Connections The connections between a model and the natural phenomenon it represents make the model useful. Models simplify the phenomenon to make it easier to observe, understand, predict, or quantify.

Scientists develop some models by combining what they have learned about a particular phenomenon. However, sometimes scientists use a simple, common object as a model to help explain something in nature. For example, lasagna could be used as a model for sedimentary rock. The common object used as a model has some similar features to the phenomenon it is modeling, but it generally cannot explain everything about the phenomenon. How is lasagna a good model for sedimentary rock formation, and how does it fall short?

Components The layers of lasagna represent the layers of rock in sedimentary rock. The different layers in lasagna—noodle, cheese, and meat—can represent different kinds of rock.

Relationships Lasagna layers are distinct, so you can see each layer. One relationship in this model is the order of the layers. Using this relationship, you can see how the lasagna was built even if you did not see it being assembled. You know the lasagna was built up so that the first layer is at the bottom and the last layer is at the top.

Scientists develop models to explain or describe natural phenomena. Lasagna is a useful model for describing the structure and formation of sedimentary rock, but it cannot compare in terms of timescale.

Connections The structure of the lasagna and the way it was built are similar to the structure and the formation of sedimentary rock. The layers in sedimentary rock are distinct and easy to see. Sedimentary rock is also built up with the oldest rock layers at the bottom and the newest rock layers at the top.

However, lasagna and sedimentary rock have important differences. A person can build a lasagna in about 15 minutes, but sedimentary rock may take millions of years to build up. Studying the layers in sedimentary rock can tell you about the environments in which the layers formed. Studying lasagna layers cannot tell you much of anything, except for which layer you like the best!

Planning and Carrying Out Investigations

Scientific research involves conducting investigations. Scientists use many different methods for planning investigations, but every method has common elements. One method is outlined here. The elements in this method are common to other methods that a scientist might use. What things should you consider when planning an investigation, and what might happen when carrying out an investigation?

The steps in planning and carrying out an investigation can happen in any order and can be repeated multiple times.

Identifying Evidence Identify what evidence you need to answer your question; only some evidence will be useful. If you were investigating why birds sing in the morning, you might observe birds in the morning and also at other times of the day to see what else they do.

Identifying the Phenomenon

The subject of your investigation might be a phenomenon to be explained, a question to be answered, or a design to be tested. You might try to answer the question, "Why do birds sing in the morning?"

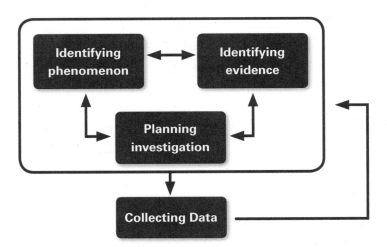

Planning the Investigation

Describe how you will gather data that will serve as evidence toward a claim. Create a specific list of steps to follow. For example, you could set up a camera in a park. Then, you could watch the video, marking down bird activity such as singing, feeding, and flying.

Collecting Data Collect your data by following the steps outlined in your investigation plan. Be sure to keep your data organized. For an investigation about birds singing, you could make a table with rows marked with time of day and columns marked with various bird behaviors.

Refining the Plan Refining your investigation plan means making changes to improve it. Ask yourself questions such as: Was the data accurately and precisely collected? Does the data support a claim about the phenomenon that I am investigating? If the answers are "no," then you need to change the investigation's plan.

Your science class is having a toy car race to investigate forces and motion. Each team of students is given a kit with which to build a toy car, but the design of each car is up to the team members. What plan do you come up with for your investigation?

Identifying the Phenomenon Together your class brainstorms factors that may affect the speed of a toy car. The class decides to investigate how a car's shape affects the car's speed.

Identifying Evidence Your class identifies the data to collect: which car shape wins each race. These data can then be analyzed to find evidence for which shape is best for a fast car.

Specifying the Steps The class comes up with the following steps:

1. Each of the 15 teams will make a car, and each car will have a different shape.

2. Cars will race on a track that has five lanes.

3. In preliminary rounds, five cars will race at least two times. The first car to win twice will advance to the final round.

4. In the final round, the preliminary round winners will race. The first car to win twice will be declared the best shape.

Collecting Data The winners of the preliminary rounds include your wedge-shaped car, a minivan-shaped car, and a car shaped like a cone. However, you notice that the car in the leftmost lane always finishes last.

Refining the Plan Because the leftmost car always loses, the answer to the question, "Were the data accurately collected?" is "no." The class runs trial races, which show that cars run slower in the outside lanes. The class revises the investigation plan. Instead of racing five cars, you race three cars using only the center lanes. Then you will have two semifinal rounds and one final round.

Your wedge-shaped car wins its preliminary round and its semifinal before barely losing to the cone-shaped car in the final round. The race is so close that some classmates think the investigation may need more revision to be sure of the winning design. What other revisions could you make?

Scientists plan and carry out investigations to gather evidence to support their explanations. You can gather evidence about which toy car design is fastest by holding a series of races and recording which design wins each race.

Analyzing and Interpreting Data

Scientists and engineers collect data in many different ways. In order to connect data to their investigation, scientists and engineers have to analyze and interpret the data. How can you think like a scientist or an engineer to make sense of data you collect?

Analyzing and interpreting data involves organizing the data, identifying relationships within the data, and then interpreting the data based on the relationships found.

Organizing Data Scientists and engineers organize their data in tables or graphs to help them make sense of it. Data that include written descriptions might be organized in data tables, while data that show changes over time might be organized in a line graph, bar graph, or pie chart.

Identifying Relationships Scientists and engineers identify relationships by looking for patterns in the organized data. They ask themselves questions such as: What parts of the data show changes? Are there data that change in regular ways? Do two different kinds of data change in similar ways?

Interpreting Data Scientists and engineers interpret data by drawing conclusions from the relationships identified. They may ask: What could be causing the patterns in the data? What could happen if the patterns continue? Could the patterns have more than one explanation?

Your science class is studying a nearby lake. You collect measurements of air and water temperature at the same place at the same time every day for a year.

Organizing Data You divide the measurements into air temperatures and water temperatures for each month. Then you find the average air temperature and water temperature for each month. Finally, you organize the average temperatures into a data table.

Both air temperature and water temperature change throughout the year. But you are not sure how the temperature changes are related. So, you graph the temperatures over time.

Identifying Relationships You can see a relationship between air and water temperature in the graph. The changes in temperatures follow similar patterns, but the patterns do not line up. The water graph is about a month behind the air graph. The air graph reaches its highest temperature in July, but the water graph does not reach its highest temperature until August.

Interpreting Data After studying your graph, you propose an explanation for why air and water temperatures follow a similar pattern. You propose that the changing air temperatures cause changes in water temperature. That is why the temperature changes follow similar patterns. Furthermore, you suggest the patterns do not line up because water changes temperature slower than air does.

The data in this table are organized using a line graph. You can see a relationship in the data on the graph; the changes in air and water temperature follow a similar pattern. How would you interpret this relationship?

Average Lake Air and Water Temperatures

Month	Air Temp. (°C)	Water Temp. (°C)
Jan (1)	-5.6	6.1
Feb (2)	-4.4	3.3
Mar (3)	-1.1	1.7
Apr (4)	7.2	2.2
May (5)	12.2	3.3
June (6)	18.3	6.7
July (7)	21.1	10.0
Aug (8)	17.8	16.7
Sept (9)	12.8	15.6
Oct (10)	4.4	13.9
Nov (11)	-0.6	10.0
Dec (12)	-2.2	7.8

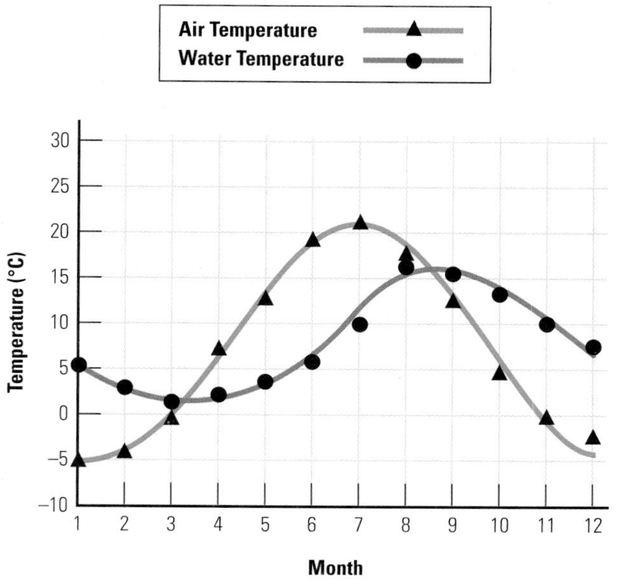

Using Mathematical and Computational Thinking

Scientists use mathematical and computational thinking in many ways. They might use math to analyze data, make predictions, or build scientific models. Furthermore, some scientific laws and principles can be expressed as equations. For example, Newton's second law of motion can be expressed as force = mass × acceleration. In each of these situations, scientists use math to represent observed systems. How can you use math to represent systems you encounter in science and your everyday life?

When scientists use math to describe a system, they state what parts of the system are represented, describe how numbers and symbols are used to model the system, and then use math to analyze the system.

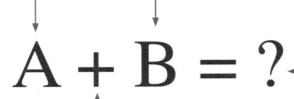

Representation In math, representation means to use symbols (such as letters) to stand in for variables in a system. For example, Newton's law describes the relationship between three variables: force, mass, and acceleration. These variables are represented by the letters F, m, and a, respectively.

Mathematical Modeling Mathematical modeling means to find how the variables in a system are related mathematically. For example, the relationship between the variables in Newton's second law is represented mathematically by the equation $F = m \times a$. You could use graphs to find relationships or you could see if the variables are related by an equation. Scientists sometimes build computer simulations that connect many different variables.

Analysis Analyzing a mathematical system means to find patterns in the system. The pattern can be used to make predictions or support claims. Analyzing a system might involve solving equations, finding trends in graphs, or using a computer simulation. For example, you can use the equation for Newton's second law to analyze how a change in force affects acceleration. If a force on an object is doubled, the acceleration of the object will also double.

The equation for Newton's second law of motion, like many equations in science, can be applied in many situations. However, scientists sometimes develop equations that describe only the situation that they are studying. How can you develop an equation to describe the change in a rabbit population in an ecosystem?

Representation The first step in developing a rabbit population equation is to identify and represent the variables in the system. You might pick the following variables and representations:

- b represents the number of rabbits born

- e represents the number of rabbits eaten by predators

- d represents the number of rabbits that died of natural causes

- Δp represents the change in rabbit population (The Greek letter delta (Δ) often means "change in," so Δp means change in p, the rabbit population.)

Mathematical Modeling To mathematically model the change in rabbit population, you have to decide how each variable affects the population. Does the variable increase or decrease the population? What mathematical operations are the equivalents to increasing and decreasing a value? An increase in population would add to the population, and a decrease would subtract from the population. Births increase the population and deaths decrease the population. So an equation for the change in population would be:

$$\Delta p = b - e - d$$

Scientists often use math to represent the systems they are studying. An equation can be used to find the change in a rabbit population in an ecosystem. The equation can be analyzed to predict how the rabbit population might change under various conditions.

Analysis To analyze the accuracy of your equation, you might solve the equation to see how the number of rabbits changes each month. Then you might draw conclusions, such as the rabbit population increases in the summer months due to a rise in births. You could also analyze the equation by using it to make predictions. What would happen if the predators in the ecosystem died? What would happen if a disease spread throughout the rabbit population?

Constructing Explanations

As they work, scientists construct explanations of phenomena. Constructing explanations is similar to engaging in argument from evidence but has key differences. When scientists engage in argument, they are using evidence to defend an idea. When scientists construct explanations, they are using evidence and reasoning to build an idea. How can you learn to think like a scientist when constructing explanations for the phenomena you experience?

Scientists construct explanations by using reasoning to describe the connections between phenomena and evidence.

Phenomenon When scientists construct explanations, the phenomenon is the event or observation that they are explaining. For example, scientists might try to explain why honeybees are dying off.

Arguments for the Explanation Scientists use arguments to support their explanation. An argument is made up of a claim, evidence for that claim, and reasons why the evidence supports the claim. For example, scientists might claim that more flowering plants are sprayed with pesticides now than ever before. Evidence supporting that claim may include data about historic and present day sales of pesticides.

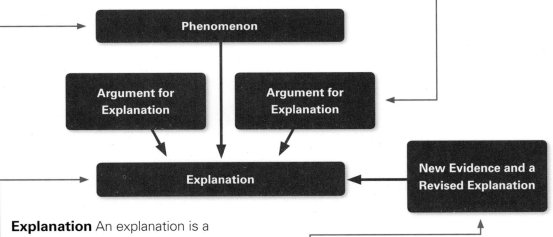

Explanation An explanation is a statement composed of one or more arguments that describe how or why the phenomenon happens. An example explanation might be: Honeybees are dying off because of the use of pesticides on flowering plants.

New Evidence and a Revised Explanation After scientists have proposed an explanation, new evidence may arise that makes the scientists change their explanation. Perhaps scientists studying honeybees learn that a disease is spreading throughout honeybee populations. They may revise their explanation to include the disease as a reason why the bees are dying off.

You can construct explanations for phenomena that you observe in your everyday life. For example, suppose you have a banana bread recipe that you make successfully all the time. Your friend who lives in Denver, Colorado tries to make the bread, but the batter overflows and the bread is gummy. What causes the differences?

Phenomenon Your friend says that he followed your recipe exactly. You determine that the only variable that changed between your loaf and his loaf was where the loaves were made. So, the phenomenon that you are trying to explain is why the same recipe produces a nice loaf at your home but makes a mess at your friend's.

Explanation You and your friend talk to figure out the differences between your homes. You know some differences, such as the number of bedrooms in the homes, will not cause changes in how bread bakes. You rule out those differences as factors. Eventually, you come up with an explanation. The recipe failed because your friend in Denver lives at a higher altitude than you do.

Arguments for the Explanation The main argument for your explanation is that the higher altitude in Denver causes the banana bread batter to rise too much during the baking process. You learned that the air pressure at higher altitudes is lower. When the air pressure that is pushing down on the batter is lower, the air bubbles produced by the baking soda in the batter can get bigger. The bigger bubbles cause the batter to rise too much and overflow the pan.

New Evidence and a Revised Explanation You tell your friend your explanation, and he has another idea. He explains that the lower pressure in Denver allows liquids to evaporate more quickly. This new evidence causes you to rethink your explanation.

Your explanation is not completely wrong, but it needs to be improved. Your explanation accounts for the batter overflowing but does not explain why the loaf was gummy. You cut yourself a piece of banana bread while you think about how quicker evaporation of liquid in the batter might affect the bread's texture. Hopefully, the snack will help you come up with a more complete explanation!

Scientists construct explanations of phenomena and use arguments to support their explanations. An explanation as to why a banana bread recipe fails in Denver is that the city is at a higher altitude. Therefore, Denver has a lower air pressure.

Designing Solutions

An engineer's primary job is to design solutions to problems. You use these solutions all the time. For example, an engineer designed the calculator you use in math class. Engineers have also designed bus routes, airplane seats, and water treatment plants. How do engineers come up with their solutions? And how do they know which solution is best?

Engineers generate a lot of ideas for solutions. They then narrow down those solutions to find the best one to a given problem.

Possible Solutions Engineers think of many different solutions to a single problem. All the possible solutions should be based on scientific knowledge. They may ask themselves: What scientific ideas are related to the problem? What scientific ideas will help or hinder finding a solution to this problem?

Evaluating Solutions Evaluating solutions is the process of comparing the solutions to the criteria and the constraints. In this step, engineers determine how well each solution meets the criteria and fits within the constraints.

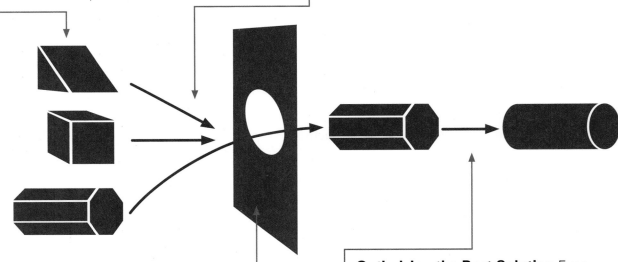

Criteria and Constraints Criteria are the requirements that must be met for an engineering solution to be successful. Constraints are limitations on an engineering solution. Criteria and constraints describe which possible solutions are good and which are not as good. Criteria and constraints may be redefined based on things learned during the designing process.

Optimizing the Best Solution Even after picking the best solution to a problem, engineers need to refine the solution. During this step, engineers test their solution and make changes based on the results of the tests. The solution may need to go through several iterations to make it the best possible solution.

Suppose that your class is having a fundraiser, and the class decides to sell cookie cutters in the shape of the school's logo. Before you can sell the cutters, you have to make them. And before you make the cutters, you have to decide what material to use.

Criteria and Constraints The criteria for the material include that it has to have the ability to be shaped in the form of your school's logo, and it has to hold its shape. Other criteria are that the material has to be able to cut cookie dough and last a long time.

Some of the constraints for the material are that the students in your class have to be able to make the cutter from the material and that the material is not too expensive.

Possible Solutions Science can help you come up with possible materials to use for the cookie cutters. Copper is a possible material because it is a malleable metal. It can be bent into the right shape. Stainless steel is another malleable metal.

Evaluating Solutions You use the criteria and constraints to evaluate the solutions. Copper fits the following criteria: It can be shaped, it can hold its shape, and it will last a long time. It fits the constraint that students can shape it, but it is relatively expensive. So, it does not fit within the inexpensive constraint. Stainless steel fits the following criteria: It can be shaped, it can hold its shape, and it will last a long time. It fits within the constraints that students can shape it, and it is inexpensive. You decide to use stainless steel.

Optimizing the Best Solution Using stainless steel, you make a prototype cookie cutter. The prototype is made out of a 1-cm wide strip of steel. You make cookies using the prototype and find that it does not hold its shape. The narrow strip bends too easily.

You make a second prototype that is made out of a 2.5-cm wide strip of steel. You test the second prototype and find that it holds its shape well. This prototype is determined to have the best design.

You and your classmates make 200 cookie cutters that are identical to the second prototype. You sell the cutters and raise enough money for a field trip to a science museum.

Engineers compare solutions to the criteria and constraints to determine which solution is most likely to solve the problem. The best solution is then optimized through testing and refining. You can use a similar process when designing your own solutions.

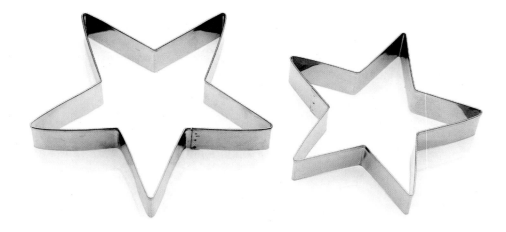

Engaging in Argument from Evidence

Engaging in argument is a key element of scientific practice. However, the arguments that scientists and engineers have with each other are not like typical arguments. They are not trying just to prove each other wrong. Rather, they are trying to collaboratively find the best explanation or model, or design the best solution. What kinds of thinking and statements are needed for a strong argument?

Strong scientific arguments have three key components—a claim, evidence for that claim, and reasoning as to why the evidence supports the claim.

Claim The claim is the statement that the argument is attempting to convince people to believe. Scientists might make claims about an explanation of a phenomenon, such as why snowflakes are always symmetrical. Or, they may make claims about a model, such as a food web. Engineers might make claims about which material is best for their design.

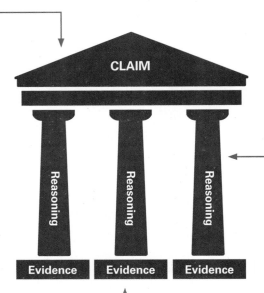

Reasoning Evidence alone is not enough to convince people of a claim. Reasoning shows how the evidence is connected to the claim, using logic or scientific concepts. The reasoning might, for example, explain why a diagram of the structure of water molecules supports the claim that all snowflakes are symmetric.

Evidence Evidence is the data or observations that support a claim. Relevant measurements, tables, and graphs can often be used as strong evidence for a claim. Generally, the more evidence there is for a claim, the stronger the argument is.

Refutation Of course, no argument is one sided. There is often an opportunity for someone to refute an argument. A refutation provides new evidence, which, along with reasoning, shows that the claim is incorrect. A refutation may also provide a different interpretation of the evidence, showing that it does not support the original claim.

Your friend Jerome sent you a photo with his phone. "Check out this great rainbow!" Look at Jerome's photo, and make an argument about the weather Jerome is experiencing. Try asking yourself questions as you develop your argument.

To make your claim, ask yourself, "What kind of weather is in this photo?" Next, identify your evidence by asking, "What specific things do I see in this photo that support my claim?" Then develop your reasoning by asking, "How do the things I pointed out as evidence support my claim?" Your argument might look something like this:

Claim Jerome took the photo while weather was clearing up after a rainstorm.

Evidence There are no visible raindrops in the photo, and the ground does not look wet. However, there is a rainbow in the sky. There are also dark clouds on the right side of the sky, but not on the left side of the sky.

Reasoning Since there are no visible raindrops in the photo and the ground does not look wet, it was probably not raining right when the photo was taken. However, rainbows only form when there are water drops in the sky, and usually form immediately after it has been raining. Also, dark clouds like the ones in the photo usually produce rain. But since the clouds only cover half of the sky in the photograph, the storm seems to be moving away from the place the photograph was taken.

Do you agree with this argument? If not, come up with a refutation. Then, the next time you make a claim, do it like a scientist or engineer—back it up with evidence and reasoning.

Your friend sends you a photo of a rainbow. You can develop an argument of what the weather was like at the moment the photo was taken by asking yourself a set of questions.

Obtaining, Evaluating, and Communicating Information

Scientists spend a lot of time obtaining, evaluating, and communicating information. In fact, most people use this process every day. For example, when you read, you are obtaining information. You then evaluate the information you read by determining if it is accurate and important. You also might communicate this information by talking about it with a friend. How does obtaining, evaluating, and communicating information help scientists do their work?

A scientist may obtain, evaluate, and communicate information during any point in an investigation.

Obtaining Information
When scientists gather information, they may ask: Where can we find information about this topic? What different kinds of information are available?

Evaluating Information
Scientists evaluate information by asking questions like these: What does this information mean? Is this information reliable? Is this information relevant?

Communicating Information Before scientists share information, they must decide how to communicate it. They may ask themselves: What is the best way to communicate this information? Should we give lectures, or should we write about it? Should we make a video? Or will a graph, photo, or mathematical equation better communicate the information?

Although scientific research is generally thought of as being a good thing, it can be controversial. One controversial topic in astronomy is the placement of telescopes on a dormant volcano in Hawaii named Mauna Kea. Some of the world's best telescopes are already on Mauna Kea. Astronomers consider the volcano to be one of the best places in the world for telescopes, and they would like to build additional ones there. However, some Hawaiians consider the volcano to be sacred and do not want any more telescopes built on it. Do you think astronomers should put more telescopes on Mauna Kea? How would you decide?

Obtaining Information *Where can you find information about this topic?* Probably the easiest place for you to get information is the Internet. You can also check specialized resources at the library. *What different kinds of information are available?* Scientists, the Hawaiian government, and Hawaiian residents are some of the groups that provide information on this topic.

Evaluating Information *What does this information mean?* Some information will tell you why Mauna Kea is such a great place for telescopes, while other information will explain the negative impact of telescopes on the volcano. *Is this information reliable?* Consider where the information is from. Websites from universities, the government, and major media outlets tend to be reliable sources. *Is this information relevant?* Once you have information from reliable sources, think about whether the information supports either side of the Mauna Kea controversy. If the information does not help one side or the other, the information is probably not relevant.

Communicating Information *What is the best way to communicate this information?* If you are communicating your opinion about telescopes on Mauna Kea to your class, you might make a poster or explain your reasoning in a class discussion. But if you are a Hawaiian citizen, you might want to write a letter to the state governor that could influence the future of Mauna Kea.

People obtain, evaluate, and communicate information all the time. Scientists and the public need to obtain and evaluate reliable information when making decisions on controversial topics, such as the placement of telescopes on Mauna Kea.

Patterns

Patterns play a key role in many scientific investigations. Scientists make sense of data they have collected by trying to recognize and analyze patterns. Often, noticing a pattern in nature will spark a series of questions. All patterns have an underlying cause, which can be uncovered by a scientific investigation. What patterns can you recognize in the following natural phenomena?

How can the different patterns in finches' beaks help you understand how a species can adapt to its environment? When Charles Darwin discovered different species of finches on the Galapagos Islands, he noticed that each species had a beak that was well-suited to its diet. The differently shaped beaks led Darwin to discover the pattern that exists between the shape of a finch's beak and its individual diet. This pattern seemed to point to a species' ability to adapt to its environment.

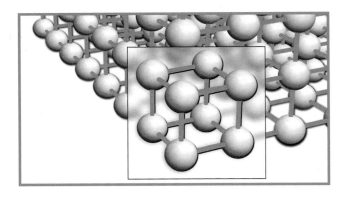

How is the microscopic pattern of table salt related to the macroscopic, or easily visible, shape of a salt crystal? You can see that each individual crystal has a cube-like structure. On the atomic level, sodium and chlorine atoms are arranged in a regular, repeating pattern that is shaped like a cube. The way a substance appears to the human eye is often determined by its atomic level structure.

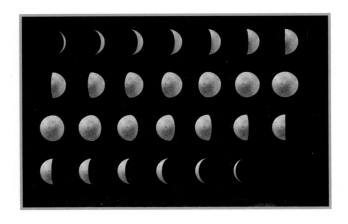

How can understanding patterns help you predict the different shapes of lunar phases? The apparent shape of the moon from Earth is determined by the positions of Earth, the moon, and the sun. Over the course of about a month, the moon transitions from a new moon to a full moon and back to a new moon in a repeating pattern. Because the apparent change in the moon's shape always follows the same pattern, you can predict when the next full moon will take place!

Cause and Effect

Looking for cause-and-effect relationships can help immensely when you are designing experiments to answer scientific questions or testing engineering solutions. Think about these three questions from different areas of science. What experiments might people design to test them?

Do magnetic fields cause compass needles to rotate? Suppose you measure the direction a compass needle points under normal conditions. Then you could add a magnetic field and look at the change in the behavior of the needle. Identifying cause-and-effect relationships allows you to make predictions about related situations. You could predict that a compass needle will always point north because Earth's magnetic field prompts the needle to point in a consistent direction.

Does the introduction of wolves cause elk populations to decrease? Biologists might measure the size of the elk population before and after wolves settled in an area. While cause-and-effect relationships may seem obvious, they are not always true. For example, climate change could have resulted in the loss of nutrient rich grasses for elk to eat, leading to a decrease in the elk population.

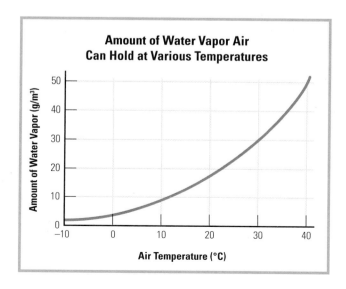

Does an increase in temperature indoors cause humidity to rise? First, you could measure the current humidity in a room. Then you could increase the air temperature of the room and measure if there was a change in humidity. It is important to only change the air temperature so there is only one cause to observe the effects of.

Scale, Proportion, and Quantity

Systems occur at different measures of size, time, and energy. Part of science is recognizing that different objects and situations occur at different scales, in different proportions, and in different amounts. Something that can be observed at one scale may not be observable at another scale. How can scale, proportion, and quantity help you understand phenomena in science?

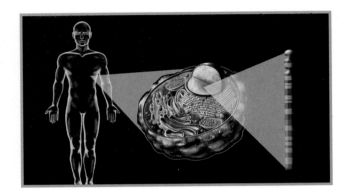

How can you describe the functions of the human body at different scales? Your whole body functions to eat, breathe, and move. At a smaller scale, cells, which can only be seen with a microscope, are the building parts for tissues and organs. Inside these cells is a nucleus, which contains chromosomes on an even smaller scale. Chromosomes are structures that contain instructions for how your body should grow.

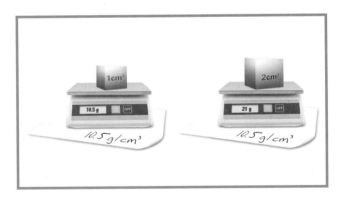

How can proportions be used to identify materials? Density is a proportion that can be used to identify materials. Here, there are two different cubes on a scale. The mass of each cube is different, just as the volume of each cube is different. However, the density of the two cubes is the same. Though the cubes are a different mass and volume, their density allows you to identify them as the same material.

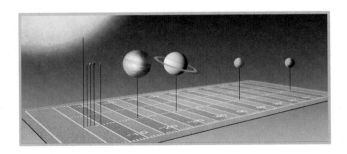

Why are different measurement units used to measure quantities in space? Within the solar system, scientists use astronomical units (AU) in which 1 AU is the average distance between the sun and Earth. However, the distances between stars are so far apart that scientists use a different unit of measurement—light years.

Systems and System Models

Systems occur in the natural world and in objects that are engineered by humans. Many systems interact with other ones, are parts of a larger complex one, or have subsystems of their own. How can you use the concept of systems to understand different phenomena such as the human body, a motor, and the motion of planets in the solar system?

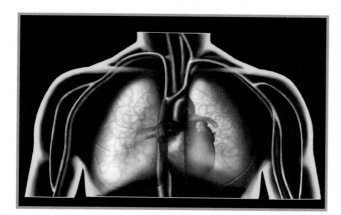

How do subsystems interact within the human body? Your whole body is composed of subsystems that work together to allow you to function. As your respiratory system draws in oxygen through your lungs, it sends oxygen to your bloodstream that is then carried through your body by the circulatory system. Both of these systems work together to help fulfill the body's needs. This is an example of two naturally occurring subsystems interacting as part of a complex whole.

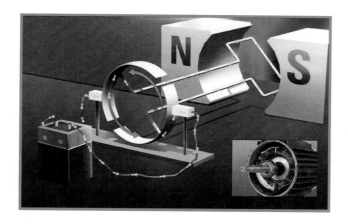

How does a model of a motor represent the way energy and matter flow through a system? This model of an electric motor shows that there is an energy input into the system from the battery. The energy is transferred to electrically charged particles in the motor's wires. The particles begin to flow, forming an electric current that flows past a magnet. The forces between the wires and the magnet cause the motor's shaft to spin, outputting energy.

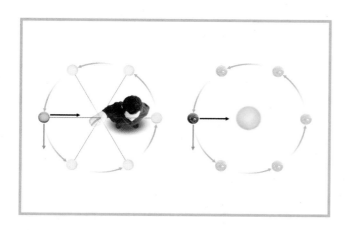

How can you use a model to represent the Earth-sun system? Suppose you swing a ball tied to a string around your head, causing it to move in a circle around your head. The string exerts a force on the ball, but the ball is moving fast enough to keep it from falling back into your hand. In this model, the string represents the gravitational force between the sun and Earth. Using a model allows you to understand how gravitational force functions in the Earth-sun system.

Energy and Matter

Systems can be described in term of energy and matter. Matter is anything that has mass and volume. Energy is the ability to cause motion or change. Energy takes two forms—kinetic energy, which is energy due to motion, and potential energy, which is stored energy. If you can track the energy in a system, you can use it to explain or predict motion and other changes. How does the transfer of energy drive motion or changes in each of the following systems?

How does a food web describe the transfer of energy and matter in an ecosystem? Energy can come from different places and is introduced into the food web when producers, such as plants, absorb energy from sunlight. Other organisms, called consumers, eat producers and other consumers to obtain their energy. Organisms use the energy they obtain to do things like move and stay warm. When they use this energy, they transfer energy to the environment.

Matter follows a path similar to energy in the food web. A consumer will eat an organism lower in the food web, consuming that organism's matter. However, unlike other organisms in the food web, producers get their matter from a different place than where they get their energy. Producers get matter from air, soil, and water, rather than sunlight. The matter from the air, soil, and water comes from decomposers that get their matter from the dead matter and wastes left behind by other organisms in the food web.

Matter and energy follow similar, but different paths. Matter is constantly being cycled through the ecosystem, while energy will flow in one direction.

How does a snowboarder transform potential energy into kinetic energy? Suppose a snowboarder was at the top of a hill, waiting to glide down to the bottom. A chairlift used energy from electricity to lift her up the mountain. That energy is stored by the snowboarder as potential energy. Since the mountain is so tall, she has a large amount of potential energy stored up.

Once the snowboarder tips over the ledge and glides down the hill, her potential energy begins to transform into kinetic energy. Kinetic energy is the energy an object has due to its motion. As the snowboarder is moving down the hill, not only is she moving herself, she is also moving the snow beneath her board. So, she is transferring some of her energy to the snow, giving it kinetic energy.

After the snowboarder glides to the bottom of the hill, nearly all of her potential energy has become kinetic energy. In order to stop, she must transfer all of her kinetic energy to her surroundings. Her board slides across the snow, spraying some of the snow forward and heating it up.

How does the transfer of energy drive the motion of matter in the water cycle?
Water particles are always moving, so they always have some kinetic energy. Water particles near the surface of water with a lot of kinetic energy evaporate off of the surface. When they do, they carry energy away from the water.

Since the particles that escaped the surface of the water have a lot of kinetic energy, they also have a high temperature. Their high temperature causes them to rise into the atmosphere. As they rise, their kinetic energy is converted into potential energy. Since the particles are losing kinetic energy, they also cool.

High in the atmosphere, slow-moving particles condense to form water droplets and clouds. These droplets are held high in the atmosphere due to updrafts of air.

During the precipitation stage, the water particles become too heavy to be held in the atmosphere by updrafts. They begin to fall, and their potential energy is converted back into kinetic energy. Even after reaching the ground, they continue to convert potential energy into kinetic energy as water flows down rivers and into the ocean.

Structure and Function

The structure and properties of a natural or engineered material often determine how that material will function. If a scientist or engineer can understand the structure of that material, then they can also determine how it should function and what may cause it to function improperly. How can you use the concept of structure and function to understand the behavior of natural and engineered materials?

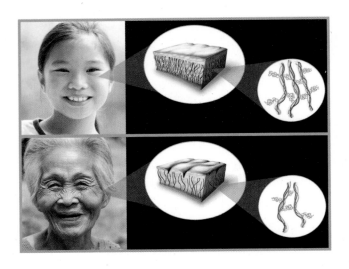

How do changes in the structure of skin tissue affect its function? Two of the proteins made by skin cells, collagen and elastin, help determine the skin's traits. When you are young, your skin continually replaces its collagen and elastin, which keeps your skin strong but flexible. Young skin is very good at protecting the underlying tissues of the body. Over time your body produces less of these proteins, resulting in more wrinkles and reduced protection, strength, and flexibility. The skin's functioning is directly related to the structural components that make it up.

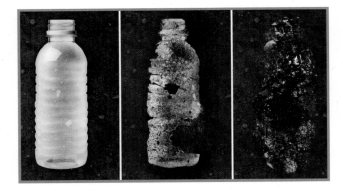

How does the molecular structure of plastic affect its function? Plastics, such as the ones that make up water bottles, are polymers that are made of long flexible chains of molecules. Their structure allows them to retain their shape while remaining flexible. Biodegradable plastics are made of polymers that easily break down into smaller molecules over time. This allows the plastics to break down when buried in a landfill.

How do engineers use the properties of light and glass to design camera lenses? The structure and shape of the glass lens determines how well it functions as a medium for light waves. Glass can be shaped to refract the right amount of light, minimize absorption and reflection, and transmit light to the camera sensor. Once the structure is designed to be just right, the camera can get the perfect shot.

Stability and Change

Scientists can measure the behavior of systems by their stability, or resistance to change, and how they respond to change. Systems, whether small or large, will respond to any amount of change in different ways. How can you observe the way that systems respond when different amounts of change are introduced on different scales?

How can an ecosystem adjust to a change and reestablish its stability? When beavers construct a dam on a stream, they cause changes in the nonliving parts of the ecosystem. These changes in the nonliving parts of the ecosystem do not destroy the system but instead change which species can live there. The ecosystem adapts to changes over long time scales so that it is not completely disrupted. The ecosystem is able to reach a new state of stability.

How do stability and changes in your motion affect you when you ride in a car? If you are moving, you will continue moving at the same speed and in the same direction unless unbalanced forces are acting on you. In a car crash, this stable motion can be very dangerous. Unbalanced forces on the car cause the car to stop suddenly. If you are not wearing a seatbelt, there is no force pushing you back, so your motion will remain stable. You will keep moving forward.

How do different amounts of change over time effect the stability of Earth's system? The amount of carbon dioxide in Earth's atmosphere took millions of years to slowly reach a level that supports animal life on land. But starting about 150 years ago, people have been adding large amounts of carbon dioxide in the air. This fast change caused many destabilizing effects to Earth's system, which causes changes in stability to subsystems such as weather and climate systems.

Analyzing Text Structure

After watching a television program about space, you decide to do some reading about our solar system. You have already found a long online article and a couple of books at the library, but there is a lot of information to read through. How can you get the most out of your reading in the least amount of time?

Reading scientific texts can seem like a difficult task, but when you identify the structure and organization of the text, it becomes much easier to understand the topic you are reading about.

Identifying the Purpose of the Text One way to make sense of a text is to identify the author's purpose. An author may be writing for many different purposes, including any one of these three:

- **Persuasive Argument** The author tries to convince the reader that his or her argument is correct.

- **Tell a Story** The author informs the reader about a process or explains why something came to be.

- **Explanation of Facts** The author informs or teaches the reader about a subject or topic.

Identifying Text Structures Another way to analyze text is to figure out how the information is organized, or structured. Authors may use many different text structures, including the following:

- **Cause and Effect Structure** The author attempts to answer a question about what causes something to happen.

- **Chronological Structure** The author explains a series of events in order.

- **Compare and Contrast Structure** The author compares two or more subjects to argue or clarify facts.

Identifying Organizing Elements Look for specific features of the text that you can use to preview or review the text. A piece of text may have one or more of these organizing elements.

- **Table of Contents** The table of contents helps you identify where information is located in certain lessons or sections.

- **Introductions and Summaries** An introduction can provide previews of the text and explain the structure, while a summary can provide main ideas and a conclusion statement.

- **Headings** Reading headings provides information about the topic of a particular section of text.

- **Graphic Organizers** Visual aids organize large amounts of data into charts and graphs that are easy to understand.

Common Roots, Prefixes, and Suffixes in Science

While reading, you come across the word *exoskeleton*. You know what *skeleton* means, but you wonder what *exo-* means. Knowing common roots, prefixes, and suffixes, and how they combine, can make unfamiliar science words easier to understand! Here is a list of some of the common roots, prefixes, and suffixes you may encounter when you are reading science related texts:

Root, Prefix, or Suffix	Meaning	Examples
astro-	pertaining to stars or celestial bodies	astronaut, astrophysics
bio-	life	biofuel, biomass, biome, biosphere
chem-, chemo-	chemical	chemical, chemistry, chemotherapy
eco-	environment, nature	ecology, ecosystem
endo-	within, inside	endoskeleton, endothermic
exo-	without, outside	exoskeleton, exothermic
gene-	pertaining to heredity	genes, genetics, mutagen
geo-	the earth, pertaining to Earth	geography, geology, geosphere
hyper-	over, above	hyperthermia
hypo-	under, below	hypothermia, hypodermic
macro-	very large in scale, scope, or capability	macroscopic
micro-	extremely small	microscope, microscopic
-ology	a science or branch of knowledge, the study of something	archaeology, biology, geology
poly-	many, several, more than one	polymer
-sphere	spherical shape, supporting life	atmosphere, biosphere, hydrosphere
therm-, thermo-	heat, hot	hypothermia, thermodynamics, thermometer

If you can recognize a common root, prefix, or suffix, you can identify the meaning of unfamiliar words. Insects commonly have exoskeletons. The prefix *exo-* means "without" or "outside."

Writing Scientific Arguments and Explanations

After making observations and conducting an experiment, your teacher gives you an assignment to write a scientific argument about your experiment. It may sound simple, but where do you start?

Scientists do a lot of hands-on experimentation, but they also write arguments that convince people their claims are true. Writing is very important to the scientific process—well-written observations and notes will help you write a strong argument.

Claim The claim is where you introduce your hypothesis or the answer to a question you are trying to solve by gathering data. This is also where you would establish a formal style. You can do this by using full sentences and scientific terms you may have learned in class.

When writing scientific arguments, it is useful to organize your data into charts or graphs and ask a peer to review your work. Doing these simple things will help to make your argument stronger and more convincing.

Evidence Your evidence is specific scientific data that supports your claim. You can also use charts and graphs to communicate your findings. They make it easy to see and compare evidence, which can make your argument stronger.

Reasoning After providing your evidence, you need to convince the reader that the evidence supports the claim. If your classmates have different claims, you can point these out and use evidence to tell the reader why your claim is correct. You may also write a concluding statement to refresh the reader's memory and summarize the evidence and related reasoning.

Before you finish writing a scientific argument, read it for any spelling and grammatical errors. It also helps to have a peer read your argument. If your peer does not understand your argument, you may need to rewrite it until how you came to your conclusion is clearer.

Writing Investigation Procedures

The steps needed to carry out an investigation are called a procedure. Scientists write a procedure as part of the process of designing an investigation and use the procedure as a guide during the investigation. Scientists also record a procedure so that their fellow scientists can follow the investigation easily and confirm results. How can you write a good investigation procedure?

A good procedure organizes steps and data easily so you can complete your experiment without running into problems or danger. A procedure should also be written so anybody can repeat your experiment and obtain an identical result. Use this checklist as a guide when writing your procedure and to evaluate your writing when you are done:

☑ All of the necessary steps are included and clearly labeled.

☑ The tools and materials for each step are listed.

☑ Each step is clearly written using precise language and vocabulary so that a classmate or any stranger can follow it.

☑ The steps are in the correct order.

☑ Safety notes are included for any steps that require them.

☑ The type of data you will collect in each step is clearly described.

☑ If necessary, a data table is prepared to record data in.

☑ The language of the procedure is unbiased and something a fellow scientist would be comfortable reading.

Once your teacher has reviewed your procedure, you are ready to conduct your investigation!

When writing an investigation procedure, it is important that the steps are clearly written, are in the right order, include the materials needed, and have identified safety precautions.

Communicating with Graphic Organizers

Your teacher divides the class into teams and gives you all an assignment to build a protective structure for an egg out of simple materials. Afterwards, you work together as a class to create a graphic organizer to explain all the information and see why different teams got different results.

Scientists use graphic organizers to visually communicate complex ideas or large amounts of data. If you can read a graphic organizer, you can explain the results you see. When gathering data, it is useful to take the information you have and sketch a graphic organizer by hand. Once you decide how to present the information on paper, you can create your graphic organizer on the computer. Many software programs have the tools you need to create graphic organizers, like flow charts, Venn diagrams, and tables.

Flow Chart Flow charts are useful for displaying processes. In this case, the flowchart is explaining the process your team used to build your egg protector. You can add more detailed information to each box, but the chart should be a step-by-step explanation of each stage of your work. Computers have many applications that can be used to create flowcharts, including word processors or paint applications. The flowchart you see here is a good reference for the process you should follow when designing a solution to a problem.

Defining the Engineering Problem
- Clearly state the problem to be solved
- Define criteria for egg container
- Define constraints of egg container

Optimizing the Design Solution
- Optimize design of egg container
- Retest egg container
- Optimize container more if needed

Developing Possible Solutions
- Develop egg container designs
- Narrow down egg container designs
- Design egg container
- Test egg container

Tables Tables group information into various categories by columns and rows and are useful for displaying large amounts of data. Scientists use tables to help them observe patterns in their data. In this case, the table displays the different materials used by the teams in your class to create their egg protectors. You can create a table by using spreadsheet software and inputting information into cells or by hand-drawing rows and columns on a sheet of paper. Look at the table below. Can you see any patterns in the materials used by the teams to create their egg protectors?

Team 1	Team 2	Team 3
Tissue Paper	Tissue Paper	Tissue Paper
Wooden sticks	Cotton Balls	Paper cup
Tape	Plastic Bag	Tape

Venn Diagram Like flowcharts, computers have applications that can be used to create Venn diagrams. Venn diagrams are used to show similarities and differences; each circle lists the traits of an object, and the overlap is used to list similarities. They are useful when comparing the traits of two or three different objects or ideas. Consider the Venn diagram below. Which material was used by all teams? Which materials were only used by one team? What conclusions would you be able to draw from this based on the results of the experiment?

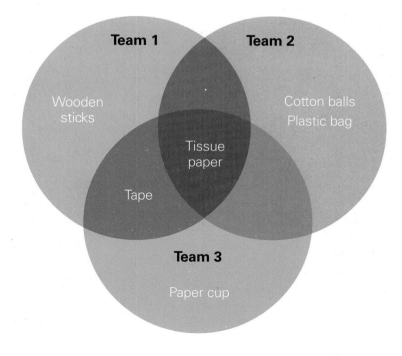

Research Project Tips

After reading about the periodic table, you decide you want to research it as a research project topic for your science class. One of the first things you need to do is find sources. With so many different places to look, including online and print sources, how do you even know where to begin?

How to Find Sources

- **First, go to the library.** The reference librarian will be able to point you in the right direction and teach you how to use the online catalog to find books, magazines, and journal subscriptions.

- **Find reliable sources.** Government and university websites, scientific magazines and journals, and other major magazines can be valuable sources of information that are easy to access.

- **Start general with search engines.** When using search engines, use words you would expect to find in your source. You do not need to worry about capitalization. Most search engines are able to understand what you are trying to find.

- **Try an advanced search tool.** Many search engines have a button for an "advanced search." Here, you can tell the search engine which kinds of websites you are looking for. If you want to find a government website, you can type "site:.gov" into one of the search fields.

The library is one of your best resources for research. Not only does it have books, it also has subscriptions for online magazines and journals that have current information on scientific advancements.

How to Evaluate Sources

- **Evaluate whether a source has bias.** Consider whether the source has arguments that are either supported by widely accepted facts or available data. If you find information on a website that is very different from some of your other sources, you may want to reconsider using that source.

- **Evaluate the source of your source.** Unofficial websites that are not supported by scientific, government, or academic institutions are probably not good sources to use. Check the URL for clues. Websites that end in .gov or .edu tend to be more reliable than general .com sites. You can also read a source's "About" page to see what their intention is for the information they provide.

- **Evaluate the quality of your source.** One source that has a lot of information about one topic can be more useful than several sources that have a little information about one topic.

How to Cite Sources

- **Keep track of which sources you use.** Keep notes as to which sources you use and where you use them in your own work. It helps to use bookmarks that you can label to mark which pages you draw information from. Another easy way to keep track of your sources is to make a copy of the first page of a book or article, or take a screenshot of a webpage. You may also want to create a spreadsheet or document that keeps track of the name of a source, its title or URL, and the information you took from the site.

- **Use a style manual.** There are several guides that teach you how to cite sources. The APA Style Manual, MLA Handbook, and Chicago Manual of Style are good places to start.

- **Avoid plagiarism.** When you quote a source or use information you got from a source, you need to give the source credit. The style manuals will have instructions on how to give credit for different kinds of sources.

As you gather information from sources, it is very important to keep track of which sources you use. Keep organized notes for online sources by creating a document or spreadsheet. Label paper bookmarks or sticky notes for print sources.

Positive and Negative Numbers

Positive and negative numbers are used together to describe quantities having opposite directions or values. Positive numbers represent values greater than zero, while negative numbers represent values less than zero. How can you use positive and negative numbers to describe changes in temperature?

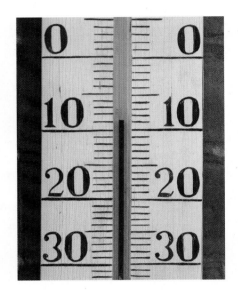

Thermometers display temperatures on a vertical number line. Numbers below zero on the number line are negative temperatures, while numbers above zero are positive temperatures.

A weather report says the temperature is –5°C. A negative number is a number that is less than zero. A number line represents numbers in relation to zero. On a horizontal number line, negative numbers are to the left of zero and positive numbers are to the right of zero. So, –5°C is five degrees below zero, which is five degrees to the left of zero. Likewise, 5°C would be five degrees above zero which is 5 degrees to the right of zero on a number line diagram.

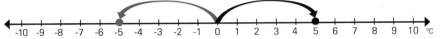

During the afternoon, the temperature rises. The weather report says that the temperature increased by 7°C. What is the temperature now? To add a positive number, move right along the number line.

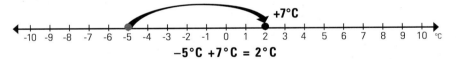

$$-5°C + 7°C = 2°C$$

After sunset, the temperature drops, or decreases in value. The weather report says the temperature dropped 10°C after sunset. What is the temperature now? When you subtract a positive number, you move left along the number line.

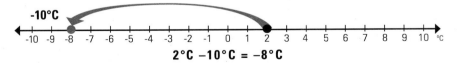

$$2°C - 10°C = -8°C$$

What is the difference between the temperature in the morning (–5°C) and the temperature after sunset (–8°C)? To find the difference, subtract the morning temperature from the current temperature. To subtract a negative number means to add the positive of that number, so move right on the number line, just like adding a positive number.

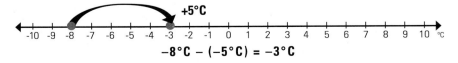

$$-8°C - (-5°C) = -3°C$$

Exponents and Scientific Notation

Scientists often need to represent very small numbers and very large numbers, which have many digits. These numbers can be so long that they are difficult to read. So, scientists developed a simpler method to represent these numbers, called scientific notation.

Scientific notation requires the use of exponents. An exponent is a number or symbol indicating how many times a base number should be multiplied by itself. For example, the "5" in 8^5 is an exponent, and 8^5 can also be expressed as "eight to the power of five" or $8 \times 8 \times 8 \times 8 \times 8$.

When you write numbers using scientific notation, 10 is the always the base number. Each time you multiply by 10, you move the decimal point one place to the right. So, multiplying by 10^6 moves the decimal point six places to the right. Scientific notation takes a number between 0 and 10 and multiplies it by a power of 10. This calculation moves the decimal point to the left or right the correct number of places.

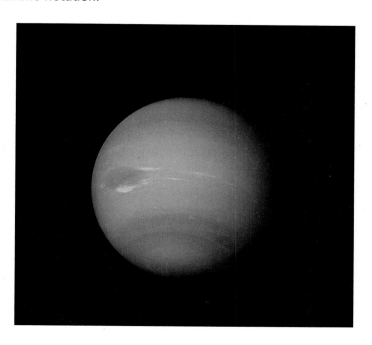

Scientists use scientific notation to represent very small and very large numbers using powers of 10. Neptune is approximately 4,700,000,000 km from Earth, which can be written in scientific notation as 4.7×10^9 km.

Scientific notation is useful for writing very large numbers that represent distances in space. For example, engineers designing a probe to send to Neptune would often need to refer to the distance between Earth and Neptune, which is 4,700,000,000.0 kilometers. 4,700,000,000.0 can be expressed as 4.7 with the decimal point moved to the right nine places.

$$4.7 \times 10^9 \text{ km} = 4,700,000,000.0 \text{ km}$$

Very small numbers can also be written using scientific notation. For example, the diameter of a hydrogen atom is approximately 0.000000000106 meters. To write small numbers, you divide by 10 instead of multiplying by 10. You can represent this in scientific notation using negative exponents. 0.000000000106 meters is 1.06 meters with the decimal point moved to the left 10 times.

$$1.06 \times 10^{-10} \text{ m} = 0.0000000000106 \text{ m}$$

Dependent and Independent Variables

Scientists use dependent and independent variables to describe the relationships they measure in their investigations. Independent and dependent variables are used in equations to represent two different quantities that change in relationship to one another.

A commercial airplane has a cruising air speed for long-distance flights of 900 km/hr. In this relationship, the distance the plane travels depends on how long the plane has been flying. However, the time it has been flying does not depend on the distance it has traveled. So, time is the independent variable (x), and distance is the dependent variable (y). The relationship between kilometers traveled and the time in hours can be represented between two variables using an equation, a table, or a graph.

An equation that represents the relationship between the distance the airplane has traveled and how long it has traveled is:

$$y = 900x$$

The letter x represents the independent variable, which is the time the plane has been flying. The letter y is the dependent variable, which is the distance the plane has traveled.

The second way to represent the relationship between variables is with a table. The table on this page uses the equation $y = 900x$ to calculate the dependent y value that matches each independent x value in the table. It represents the relationship between x and y.

The third way to represent the relationship between two variables is with a graph. You can use either the equation or the table of values to represent the relationship in a graph. The graph both shows the equation and plots the points from the data table.

Equations, tables, and graphs are three ways to represent the relationship between an independent variable x and a dependent variable y. For a plane flying at 900 km/hr, the independent variable is flying time, and the dependent variable is distance traveled.

Airplane Distance Traveled Compared to Time

Time (hours) x	Distance (km) y
0	0
1	900
2	1,800
3	2,700
4	3,600

Chance and Probability

Some events scientists study involve things that definitely will happen or will not happen. However, most events might happen but will not happen for sure. How can understanding probability help predict how likely events are to happen?

Every year, sugar maple trees produce many seeds, which are carried away from the trees by wind. Many of the seeds germinate, or sprout into a seedling that can grow into a new tree, but not every seed does. A scientist decides to study how likely it is that a maple seed will sprout. That is, she will study the probability that a seed will germinate.

The scientist randomly collects a sample of 1,000 seeds from trees in a 1 km × 1 km area. She and her team plant the seeds in a large field. They return in the spring to determine how many of the seeds germinated into new maple trees. She might find that 910 of the seeds germinated. The proportion of seeds that germinated was $\frac{910}{1,000}$, or 91%.

Her team repeats the experiment several more times in different years and finds that in one year, 97% of the seeds germinated. In the second year, 94% germinated, and 95% germinated in the third year. From this data, she finds the average proportion of seeds that germinate and concludes that the chance of a maple seed germinating is about 95%.

Sugar maple trees produce many seeds, but some seeds do not germinate. By collecting data on how many seeds germinate, a scientist can estimate the probability that each individual seed will germinate.

A 95% probability means that each seed has a 95 in 100 chance of germinating. If you looked at 100 seeds, you would expect 95 of them to germinate. If you looked at 1,000 seeds, you would expect 950 to germinate. However, 950 seeds would not germinate every time. For example, sometimes 962 seeds would germinate, or 935 seeds, or 900 seeds, or even all 1,000 seeds. A probability describes the chance that something will happen, but it does not predict exactly what will happen every time.

Representing and Interpreting Data

Scientific investigations produce a lot of data, but it is often difficult to make sense of the data the way it is recorded during the investigation. Scientists carefully choose how they will represent data to make it easy to analyze, interpret, and communicate its meaning to others.

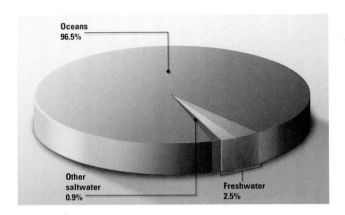

Pie Graphs A comparison between the amount of freshwater and saltwater on Earth is best represented using a pie graph. Scientists use pie graphs to display data with percentages. A pie graph, also known as a pie chart, divides a circle into sections to show the relative sizes of data and how a part relates to the whole. A pie graph can effectively show how one variable is divided between different categories. They often show the percentage of a variable in each category. For instance, the wedges on this pie graph show how the water on Earth is divided into three categories: water from oceans, fresh water, and other saltwater.

Scatter Plots Scientists use scatter plots to show repeated measurements of a similar phenomenon, such as the relationship between the waiting time between eruptions of the geyser Old Faithful and the length of the eruptions. Each measurement of an eruption is one point on the graph. The x coordinate of the point shows the duration of the eruption. The y coordinate shows the waiting time before the eruption. Scatter plots are effective for comparing two variables that do not fall into specific categories. There are many patterns in data that scatter plots can reveal.

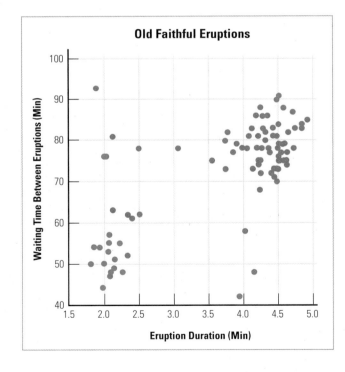

The scatter plot shows that Old Faithful eruptions fall into two main groups: a short wait between eruptions (45–60 minutes) followed by a short eruption (2 minutes), or a long wait between eruptions (70–90 minutes) followed by a long eruption (4–5 minutes).

A scatter plot that compares shoe size to height would probably form a line, indicating that people who are taller usually wear larger shoes.

Bar Graphs This bar graph of earthquakes in Oklahoma shows how many earthquakes occurred in Oklahoma in each year between 2000 and 2015. Scientists use bar graphs, or bar charts, to represent the relative sizes of data values in different categories, such as years, months, colors, or cities. They use horizontal or vertical bars to represent the size of the value in each category. Larger bars represent a higher value, and smaller bars represent a lower value. The bar graph of earthquakes in Oklahoma shows a huge increase in earthquakes in 2014 from previous years since the bar for 2014 is much larger than any of the previous bars.

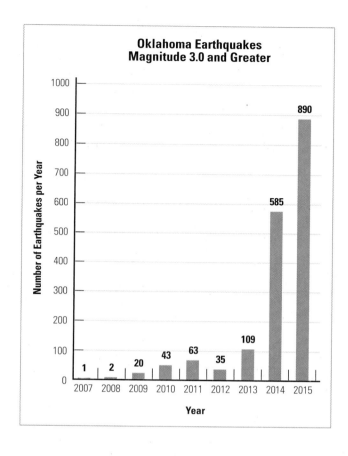

Line Graphs Scientists use line graphs to show how a dependent variable changes as an independent variable is increased. In many cases, the independent variable is a measure of time, so the graph shows how a dependent variable changes over time. For example, the average global temperature over time can be shown using a line graph. Like in a scatter plot, each data point has an x coordinate (time) and a y coordinate (average temperature). Unlike a scatter plot, each data point is connected to the last one with a straight line. Following the line shows how the average temperature changed over time.

This line graph shows many patterns about how the global average temperature changed between 1880 and 2000. The temperature was lowest between 1900 and 1920 and highest after 2000. What other patterns do you see in the graph?

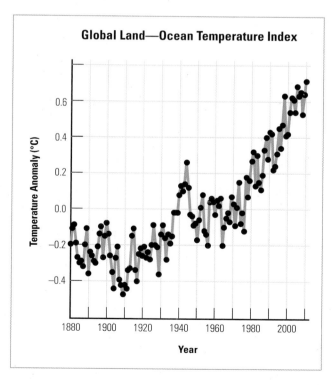

Ratios, Rates, Percents, and Proportional Relationships

When scientists collect data involving numbers, quantities are often compared. You can compare quantities using ratios, percentages, and unit rates. How are these mathematical concepts useful in understanding one of the most important scientific investigations related to changes in species?

Scientists have been observing and studying dark peppered moths near Manchester, England, since 1848. More than 70 species of moths in England have undergone a change from light to dark, with similar observations in the United States.

Expressing Ratios as Percentages To study this change, a scientist named Henry Bernard Davis Kettlewell released light and dark colored moths in polluted and unpolluted woods. He then recaptured as many of the moths as he could over the next week. In the unpolluted woods, he released 496 light colored moths and captured back 62 of them. So, the ratio of captured moths to released moths is 62:496. By finding an equivalent ratio with 100 as the number of moths released, you can find what percentage 62:496 equals.

$$62:496 = 12.5:100$$

Kettlewell recaptured 12.5% of the light moths he released. Similarly, he released 488 dark moths into the unpolluted woods and only recaptured 34. That is 34:488 as a ratio, or 7.0% as a percentage.

Kettlewell released light and dark colored moths and then recaptured them to study how well each type of moth survived in polluted and unpolluted woods. He used the ratio of moths captured to moths released, expressed as a percentage, to support his findings.

Using Unit Rates Scientists often compare quantities using unit rates. A unit rate is the number of one quantity there is for every one unit of another quantity. If Kettlewell wanted to know how many moths he needed to release in order to capture one moth, he would calculate the unit rate. He would do so by starting with the ratio of moths released to moths captured (496:62 for light colored moths). Then he would find an equivalent ratio where the number of moths captured is one. Unit rates are usually written as fractions.

$$\text{Unit rate} = \frac{8 \text{ moths released}}{1 \text{ moth captured}}$$

So, for every eight light colored moths Kettlewell released, he captured one light colored moth back.

Graphing and Interpreting Proportional Relationships

Scientists and engineers look for proportional relationships to better understand and predict how two variables are related. In a proportional relationship, the ratio of one variable to the other is always the same. How can using proportional reasoning make someone a better bowler?

An engineer wants to improve her bowling score, so she decides to study the relationship between the mass of the bowling ball she uses and the kinetic energy of the ball. She builds a machine that throws a bowling ball down the lane at exactly 8 m/s. Then she tests a variety of bowling balls. She makes a table of her data and finds the ratio of energy to mass of the balls. She sees that the ratio is the same for every ball moving at 8 m/s. She discovered a proportional relationship between the bowling ball's energy and mass.

She makes a graph of the data in her table and sees that the data points form a straight line. The line passes through the origin (0, 0). She calculates that the slope of the line is 32 J/kg. The line's slope is the same as the ratio of energy per unit mass in her table.

To make predictions, the engineer writes an equation to describe her data. The equation of a straight line is $y = mx + b$. The y-intercept (b) of her line is 0 J. The slope (m) of her line is 32 J/kg. So, the equation for her line is:

$$y = 32x$$

In this equation, y is energy of the ball, and x is mass of the ball. The engineer now knows how the energy of the ball depends on its mass. But she still has more questions. How does the energy depend on the speed of the ball? And how much energy should the ball have to knock down all the pins?

Mass versus Kinetic Energy With Constant Velocity

Mass (kg)	Energy (J)	Ratio: energy/mass (J/kg)
4	128	$\frac{128}{4} = 32$
5	160	$\frac{160}{5} = 32$
6	192	$\frac{192}{6} = 32$
7	224	$\frac{224}{7} = 32$

Angles, Perpendicular and Parallel Lines

Scientists use angles as well as parallel and perpendicular lines to describe how objects are oriented relative to each other. How can using these mathematical ideas help when explaining how light rays interact with a glass slide?

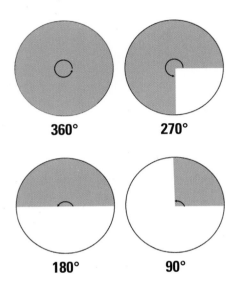

360°   270°

180°   90°

Angles Light travels in a straight line until it passes from one material, or medium, to another material. When a beam of light enters a glass slide, it bends. The amount that the beam bends depends on the angle between the slide and the beam of light. An angle is a shape formed by two rays that begin at the same endpoint, and the size of the angle can be changed by rotating the two rays. Angles are measured in degrees (°). Rotating 360° is rotating in a full circle, returning the object back to where it started. Rotating by 180° is rotating through half a circle, and rotating by 90° is rotating a quarter circle.

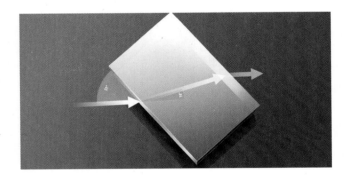

Parallel Lines The beam of light meets the glass at a 51° angle. As it enters the glass, it changes direction, turning 14° counterclockwise. When the beam of light leaves the glass, it rotates back, turning 14° clockwise. The beam of light leaving the glass is parallel to the beam of light entering the glass. Parallel lines are lines that, if you extend them out infinitely in both directions, will never cross.

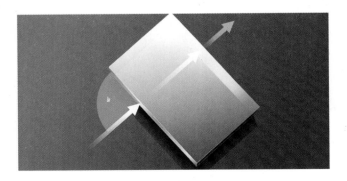

Perpendicular Lines A beam of light will not always bend when it enters a glass slide. If the beam of light is perpendicular to the edge of the slide, the light will pass straight through without bending. Two lines are perpendicular if they meet at a 90° angle.

Area, Surface Area, and Volume

Scientists use area, surface area, and volume to describe the sizes of various objects they study. Area describes the size of a two-dimensional surface. Surface area describes the total size of the surface of a three-dimensional object. Volume describes the amount of space a three-dimensional object takes up. How could a scientist who wanted to explain why cells are so small use the concepts of area, surface area, and volume? He investigates simple cube-shaped cells in the human body.

Area The scientist knows that for a cell to survive, enough nutrients have to pass through its cell membrane to supply the needs of the cell. The larger the area of the membrane, the more nutrients can pass through it. So, the scientist calculates the area of one square-shaped side of the cell.

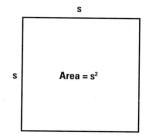

$$\text{Area} = s^2$$

Surface Area But the scientist knows that nutrients can pass through any side of the cube, not just one side. So, he needs to calculate the surface area of the cube. The surface area is the total area of the surface of the cube. The cube has six sides, so its surface area is six times the area of one side.

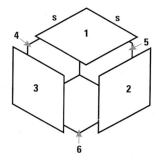

$$\text{Surface Area} = 6s^2$$

Volume However, the scientist knows that volume of the cube is important too. The volume is the total amount of space that the cube takes up. Generally, the larger the volume is, the more nutrients the cell needs to stay alive and the farther the nutrients have to go after entering the cell. The volume of a cube is the side length cubed.

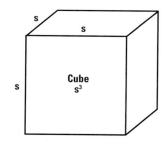

$$\text{Volume} = s^3$$

The scientist sees that as the cube gets larger, the volume grows much faster than the surface area grows. So, he decides that the cells he is studying are all very small because a large cell would not be able to take in enough nutrients through its membrane to support its volume. Cells need a large surface-area-to-volume ratio to survive.

Metric System Units

Throughout history, people around the world used different measurement units for trading goods and building objects and structures. Body parts were used to measure length. Grains of wheat were poured into containers to measure volume. Notches on a burning candle measured time. What problems did these customs cause, and how were they solved?

Traditional measurement units were awkward. It was difficult to compare one unit to another. Even when the same unit was used, there were often variations in how the unit was applied from place to place. In the late 1700s, that all changed. Scientists began to develop new units that were easy to use and accepted by scientists everywhere. Many of those units are part of the metric system.

The units you choose are determined by the goal of your investigation. If you want to measure the amount of matter in a rock, you would choose grams, a measure of mass, as your unit. If you want to measure how warm water is, you would use degrees Celsius. Other metric units are a combination of two units. For example, to describe the speed of a toy car rolling down a ramp, you would record the speed as meters per second.

Some Common Units of the Metric System

Measurement	Unit Name	Symbol
length	meter	m
mass	gram	g
time	second	s
temperature	degrees Celsius	°C
area	meter squared	m^2
frequency	hertz	Hz
force	newton	N
volume	meter cubed	m^3
density	kilogram per meter cubed	kg/m^3
speed, velocity	meter per second	m/s
acceleration	meter per second squared	m/s^2
energy	joule	J
power (energy per second)	watt	W
energy	watt hour	Wh
electric charge	coulomb	C

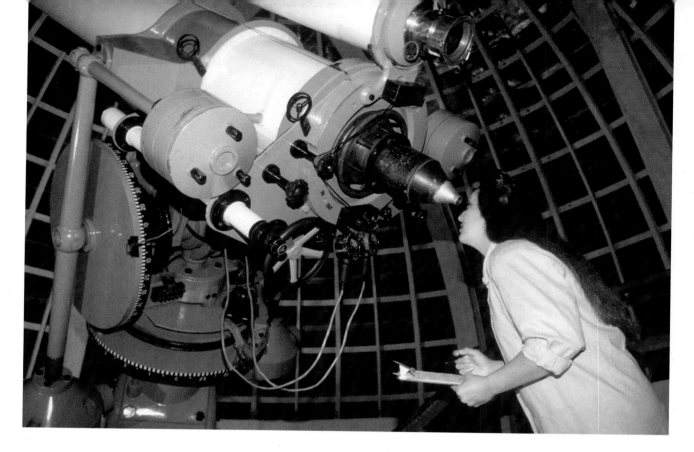

Some units were not developed as part of the metric system, but are still used by many scientists and engineers around the world. For example, if you want to compare distances of objects in the solar system, meters or even kilometers make the numbers difficult to communicate. Astronomers prefer to use astronomical units for this purpose. Similarly, when you need to describe distances between two stars or two galaxies, astronomical units are difficult. The distances are so great that astronomers use a unit called a light year, which is the distance that light travels in one Earth year.

Several measurement units are not part of the metric system, yet they are widely used by scientists and engineers. Two of these units, astronomical units and light years, are essential for communicating data to scientists such as this astronomer.

Some Common Units Outside the Metric System

Measurement	Unit Name	Symbol
time	minute	min
time	hour	h
time	day	d
angle size	degree	°
liquid volume	liter	L
distances inside the solar system	astronomical unit	AU
distances between stars	light year	ly
energy	calorie	cal
digital information	byte	B

Metric System Prefixes

A base unit can be modified using prefixes that indicate different amounts of each unit. Let's say you are investigating plant species to determine how much variation there is among their flower sizes. Some plant species have flowers that are so tiny that they can only be seen with magnification. Others have flowers as wide as a human's arm length. How can understanding measurement prefixes help you?

This flower is produced by plants called *Rafflesia* and is about 1 m across. Most plants have flowers that are much smaller, so smaller units are more useful for describing them.

Using prefixes with base units allows you to choose the unit that is simplest to communicate. Adding a prefix to a base unit makes a new unit. The new unit is made larger or smaller than the base unit by multiplying the base unit by a certain factor of 10. Each prefix represents a different factor of 10.

Here is how it works when measuring length. Meters are the base unit for length and are suitable for describing the size of the largest flowers in the plant kingdom. Millimeters have the prefix *milli*, which is 0.001. So a millimeter is 0.001, or 1/1,000, times the amount of one meter. There are 1,000 millimeters in one meter. Millimeters is a suitable unit for measuring the smallest flowers in the world. Now, suppose you were to travel around the world touring exotic flowers. A larger unit for length would be helpful to describe the distance you traveled. There are 1,000 meters in a kilometer. The prefix *kilo* means 10^3, or 1,000. So a kilometer is 1,000 times the size of a meter.

Many base units can be changed to easier-to-use units by adding a prefix. Start by choosing a base unit. Move up to get larger units and move down to get smaller units.

Some Common Units of the Metric System

Prefix	Symbol	Word	Decimal	Factor of 10
tera	T	trillion	1,000,000,000,000	10^{12}
giga	G	billion	1,000,000,000	10^9
mega	M	million	1,000,000	10^6
kilo	k	thousand	1,000	10^3
hecto	h	hundred	100	10^2
deka	da	ten	10	10^1
Choose a base unit.		one	1	10^0
deci	d	tenth	0.1	10^{-1}
centi	c	hundredth	0.01	10^{-2}
milli	m	thousandth	0.001	10^{-3}
micro	µ	millionth	0.000001	10^{-6}
nano	n	billionth	0.000000001	10^{-9}
pico	p	trillionth	0.000000000001	10^{-12}

Converting Measurement Units

You can also find equivalents of measurements that have the same base unit but different prefixes. One method is to divide or multiply by the number of one unit in the other unit. Another method is to use a metric "staircase" to decide how many places, and in what direction, to move the decimal point.

You can convert a larger unit to a smaller unit using multiplication. To do so, multiply the original measurement by the amount that the new unit differs from it. For example, to convert 9 kilometers to centimeters, you would multiply 9 (the number of kilometers) times 100,000 (the number of centimeters in one kilometer). So, 900,000 cm is equivalent to 9 km.

A smaller unit can be converted to a larger unit by using division. To do so, divide the original measurement by the amount that the new unit differs from it. For example, to use division to convert 900,000 centimeters to kilometers, divide 900,000 (the number of centimeters) by 100,000 (the number of centimeters in one kilometer). As before, 9 km is equivalent to 900,000 cm.

Another way to convert units is by picturing the metric "staircase" shown here to decide how many places to move the decimal point. For example, to convert 1.1 kilograms to milligrams, take six steps down the staircase and move the decimal point six places to the right. There are 1,100,000 milligrams in 1.1 kilograms.

In the United States, certain non-metric units are used in everyday situations. For this reason, you may sometimes need to convert non-metric units into metric units. Luckily, there are many websites and apps that will do conversions for you!

To convert to a larger unit, move the decimal point to the left for each step up the staircase. To convert to a smaller unit, move the decimal point to the right for each step you take down the staircase.

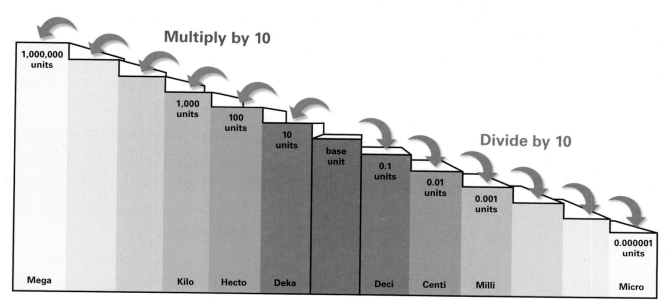

GLOSSARY

A

absolute humidity   the amount of water vapor in a given volume of air, usually expressed as grams per cubic meter (g/m³)

aerosol   tiny liquid and solid particles suspended in the atmosphere

air mass   a huge volume of air that has a uniform temperature and humidity at a given altitude

albedo   the ratio of reflected sunlight to the sunlight that strikes a surface

anemometer   a tool used to measure wind speed

atmosphere   the envelope of air that surrounds the solid Earth, including gases and aerosols

atmospheric pressure   the weight of the air pushing down on an area; the force exerted over an area by all of the air above that area

B

barometer   a tool used to measure atmospheric pressure

biosphere   the parts of Earth in which organisms are able to live, along with all of Earth's living things

blizzard   a winter storm that lasts for at least three hours with winds greater than 56 km/h and large amounts of blowing snow

C

California Current   a cold-water surface current that flows south along the west coast of North America

climate   the long-term weather pattern for a given area

climate change   a long-term change in climate patterns on Earth, typically including changes in average global temperatures, precipitation, and in the frequency of severe weather

climate change adaptation   any methods humans use to reduce the impacts of climate change

climate change mitigation   lessening climate change by reducing the amount of greenhouse gases that are added to the atmosphere or by removing them

climate zone   a region on Earth that has a particular average temperature because of its latitude

cold front   a weather front in which a cold air mass advances to replace a warm air mass

condensation   the change of state of particles from a gas to a liquid

conduction   the transfer of energy from one part of a material to another or between two objects that are in physical contact with each other

constraints   the limitations on an engineering solution

convection   the transfer of energy caused by the circulation of matter due to differences in density

convection cell   a circulation of matter, such as air, caused by constantly rising warm matter and falling cool matter

Coriolis effect   the apparent curve in the path of an object caused by Earth's rotation

criteria   the requirements that must be met for an engineering solution to be successful

crystallization   the formation of a solid structure whose atoms or molecules are arranged in a repeating, three-dimensional pattern

D

deforestation   the permanent removal of forests by humans to make land available for other uses

density   a property of matter that is equal to the amount of mass in a certain volume of matter

density currents   ocean currents deep in the ocean that flow because of differences in the density of water

dew   water droplets that form on surfaces due to condensation of water vapor

dew point   the temperature at which air is saturated with water vapor

E

El Niño   part of a climate pattern that occurs when ocean surface temperatures in the Pacific Ocean near the equator are warmer than usual

enhanced greenhouse effect   increased warming of the troposphere beyond the natural greenhouse effect due to human activities

evaporation   the change of state of particles from a liquid to a gas at the surface of the liquid

G

geosphere   all of the rock, sand, and soil on Earth including at Earth's surface and deep underground

global ocean convection cycle   an ocean-wide system of surface and density currents that are driven by differences in water temperature and saltiness; also called thermohaline circulation

global warming   the long-term increase in the average surface temperature of Earth

global winds   prevailing wind patterns that blow in fairly constant, predictable patterns around Earth

greenhouse effect   the warming of the troposphere by energy trapped by greenhouse gases

greenhouse gas   a gas in the atmosphere that absorbs the energy of infrared light

groundwater   water located underground that fills pore spaces in soil and rock layers

Gulf Stream   a warm-water surface current that flows northeast in the North Atlantic Ocean

H

heat   energy transferred from a hotter object to a cooler object

heat index   the temperature that the air feels like to people when humidity is combined with the actual air temperature

heat wave   a period of unusually hot, and often more humid, weather than is typical for a region

high pressure system   an area within the atmosphere where air is sinking and winds blow away from the center

hurricane a huge, rotating, low pressure storm system that forms over warm water near the equator and has sustained wind speeds of 119 km/h or higher

hydrosphere all of the water on Earth including ice, liquid water in the ocean, rivers, and lakes, and water vapor

I

ice age a long period of particularly cool climate when large masses of ice cover large areas of Earth

ice sheet a huge mass of ice that covers at least 50,000 square kilometers of land; also called continental glacier

isobar a line on a weather map that connects places that have the same air pressure

J

jet stream strong winds in the upper troposphere that exist in relatively narrow bands

K

kinetic energy the energy an object has due to its motion

L

latitude a unit in degrees that describes a position on Earth relative to the equator

local climate the climate of a particular area such as a city, town, or portion of a state

low pressure system an area within the atmosphere where air is rising and winds blow toward the center

M

microclimate the climate of a small area, such as a neighborhood or backyard, that may be different from nearby climates

O

occluded front a boundary between one warm air mass and two cold air masses, in which the warm air mass is pushed above the two cold air masses

ocean current the movement of water along a certain path in the ocean

P

permafrost ground that stays frozen throughout the year

polar refers to the climate zones closest to the North Pole and South Pole, where the average temperatures are cold all year

precipitation solid or liquid water that falls from clouds to the ground

pressure a force applied to a certain area

proportional describes two quantities that are related by a simple ratio

prototype a working model of a design solution that can be used for testing and refining the design

R

radiation the transfer of energy by light

relative humidity the ratio, usually expressed as a percentage, of the actual amount of water vapor in air to the maximum amount of water vapor air can hold at the same temperature

renewable energy energy that is obtained from renewable natural resources such as sunlight, wind, and waves

S

sea level the elevation of the land surface where the atmosphere meets the ocean

sea level rise an increase in the average global height of the ocean

severe thunderstorm a thunderstorm that has wind speeds of 93 km/h, hail that is at least 2.5 cm wide, or a tornado

severe weather weather, such as blizzards, heat waves, severe thunderstorms, tornadoes, and hurricanes, that can damage buildings or cause loss of life

stationary front a boundary between a cold air mass and a warm air mass that are not moving

stratosphere the layer of the atmosphere above the troposphere

surface current an ocean current, usually in the top 100 m of water, that is driven by global winds

surface winds winds that blow near Earth's surface

sustainable the use of natural resources in a way that ensures their availability to future generations of humans

system a group of interacting parts, with each piece influencing the behavior of the whole

T

temperate refers to the climate zone between the tropical and polar zones, with warm summers and cool winters

temperature a measure of the average kinetic energy of the particles of a substance

topography the shape of the natural features of a land surface

tornado a rotating column of air with extremely high wind speeds of 117 km/h or higher that touches the ground

transpiration the evaporation of water from the leaves of plants

tropical refers to the climate zone centered at the equator, where the average temperatures are warm all year

troposphere the relatively thin layer of the atmosphere that is closest to Earth's surface and the layer where weather occurs

U

urban heat island a city area where the climate is warmer than the surrounding area

W

warm front a weather front in which a warm air mass advances to replace a cold air mass

water cycle the movement of water through the Earth system

weather the condition of the atmosphere and its phenomena in a certain place at a specific time

weather front the boundary where two air masses meet

wind air that is moving from a region of higher pressure to a region of lower pressure

Front Matter

Cover/Title page: Shutterstock **iii:** Shutterstock **xxivT:** iStockphoto **xxivB:** Thinkstock **xxvT:** iStockphoto **xxvB:** iStockphoto **xxviiT:** Shutterstock **xxviiC:** Shutterstock **xxviiB:** Shutterstock **xxviii:** Thinkstock **xxix:** Thinkstock **xxx:** Getty Images **xxxi:** Getty Images **xxxii:** iStockphoto **xxxiii:** Getty Images **xxxvL:** Getty Images **xxxvR:** Hero Images Inc./Alamy **xxxvi:** iStockphoto **xxxvii:** iStockphoto

Unit 1 Opener

2: Getty Images **5TL:** Getty Images **5TR:** NASA **5B:** Thinkstock

Lesson 1

6: NOAA **8TL:** Thinkstock **8TR:** Thinkstock **8BL:** Thinkstock **8BR:** Thinkstock **9T:** Thinkstock **9B:** Thinkstock **10T:** NASA **10C:** Thinkstock **10B:** Thinkstock **11T:** Thinkstock **11TC:** Getty Images **11C:** Thinkstock **11BC:** Thinkstock **11B:** Thinkstock **12B:** Thinkstock **13:** Thinkstock **14:** Take 27 Ltd/Science Source **15T:** NASA **15B:** NASA **16:** NASA **17T:** Shutterstock **17B:** NASA

Lesson 2

18: Frans Lanting/MINT Images/ Science Source **20T:** Shutterstock **20B:** Thinkstock **21L:** Shutterstock **21R:** Shutterstock **24T:** Shutterstock **24C:** Shutterstock **24B:** Shutterstock **25T:** Thinkstock **25B:** Jinga80/ Dreamstime **26C:** Thinkstock **26L:** Thinkstock **27T:** Shutterstock **27B:** Shutterstock **29:** NOAA

Lesson 3

30: NASA **32L:** Thinkstock **32C:** Thinkstock **32R:** Thinkstock **33B:** Getty Images **34B:** Thinkstock **39:** Getty Images **40:** NASA **41T:** NASA **41B:** Shutterstock **42T:** Shutterstock

Unit 2 Opener

44: nagelestock.com/Alamy **47TL:** Thinkstock **47TR:** Thinkstock **47B:** Shutterstock

Lesson 4

48: Thinkstock **50T:** Thinkstock **50BL:** Thinkstock **50BR:** Thinkstock **52L:** Wikimedia **53B:** Thinkstock **55T:** Thinkstock **55TC:** Thinkstock **55C:** Shutterstock **55BC:** Thinkstock **55B:** Thinkstock **57:** Thinkstock **58:** Sueddeutsche Zeitung Photo/ Alamy **59:** Shutterstock **60:** Getty Images **61:** Shutterstock **62T:** Shutterstock **62B:** Rapt.Tv/Alamy **63:** Shutterstock

Lesson 5

64: Thinkstock **68T:** Thinkstock **68C:** Thinkstock **69:** Shutterstock **70:** Thinkstock **71:** Thinkstock **72TL:** Shutterstock **72TR:** NewLife Reportage/Alamy **72BL:** blickwinkel/Alamy **72BR:** Shutterstock **74:** Thinkstock **74:** Thinkstock **74:** Thinkstock **74:** Thinkstock **74:** Thinkstock **74:** Thinkstock **74:** Thinkstock **74:** Thinkstock **76:** Gary Crabbe/ Enlightened Images/Alamy **77:** Thinkstock **78:** NASA **79:** Getty Images **80:** NASA **81:** Shutterstock

Lesson 6

82: Thinkstock **85T:** Shutterstock **85C:** Shutterstock **85B:** Thinkstock **88T:** Shutterstock **91TL:** Thinkstock **91TLC:** Thinkstock **91TRC:** Getty Images **91TR:** Thinkstock **91C:** Thinkstock **91C:** Thinkstock **91BL:** Shutterstock **91BLC:** Thinkstock **91BRC:** Thinkstock **91BR:** Thinkstock **92:** Thinkstock **93:** Thinkstock

Lesson 7

94: Mike Hollingshead/Science Source **96T:** Lane Erickson/ Dreamstime **96B:** NOAA **97:** Thinkstock **98:** Thinkstock **100T:** NOAA **101TL:** Thinkstock **101TR:** Thinkstock **101B:** NOAA **102:** Wikimedia **103TL:** Shutterstock **103TL:** Thinkstock **103TR:** Shutterstock **103TR:** Thinkstock **103BL:** Shutterstock **103BL:** Thinkstock **103BR:** Shutterstock **103BR:** Thinkstock **104:** robertharding/Alamy **105:** Thinkstock **106:** Thinkstock **107:** Capt. Martha Nigrelle **108T:** Associated Press **108B:** US Air Force Photo/Alamy **109:** Pluto/ Alamy

Unit 3 Opener

110: Creative Images/Alamy **113TL:** Arterra Picture Library/ Alamy **113TR:** NatPar Collection/ Alamy **113B:** British Antarctic Survey/Science Source

Lesson 8

114: Jodielee/Dreamstime **116T:** Shutterstock **116TC:** Shutterstock **116BC:** Mike Finn-Kelcey/Alamy **116B:** Daniel J. Rao/Alamy **119T:**

Thinkstock **119C:** Thinkstock **119B:** Thinkstock **120T:** Shutterstock **122:** Thinkstock **123T:** Shutterstock **123B:** Shutterstock **124TL:** Thinkstock **124TR:** Vaclav Mach/Alamy **124CL:** Shutterstock **124CC:** Shutterstock **124CR:** Thinkstock **124BL:** Thinkstock **124BC:** Thinkstock **124BR:** Thinkstock **125:** CIRES **126:** Thinkstock **127:** Gerner Thomsen/ Alamy **128T:** ALMA **128B:** Thinkstock **129:** Shutterstock

Lesson 9

130: NASA/Science Source **133T:** Thinkstock **133TC:** Thinkstock **133BC:** Thinkstock **133B:** Getty Images **135T:** Arterra Picture Library/Alamy **136:** Shutterstock **137:** Thinkstock **139:** Gary Hincks/Science Source **140:** Shutterstock **142T:** Getty Images **142B:** Combre Stephane/Alamy **143T:** ITAR-TASS Photo Agency/ Alamy **143B:** Associated Press

Lesson 10

144: Thinkstock **146:** Thinkstock **147:** Thinkstock **149:** Shutterstock **150:** Wikimedia **151:** Norman Kuring, NASA/GSFC **152T:** Getty Images **152B:** Thinkstock **155:** Paul Moore/Dreamstime

Lesson 11

156: Getty Images **158TL:** Shutterstock **158TR:** Shutterstock **158BL:** Shutterstock **158BR:** Shutterstock **159:** Thinkstock **159L:** Thinkstock **159R:** Thinkstock **160:** Shutterstock **161T:** John Reddy/ Alamy **162:** Thinkstock **163:** Thinkstock **164:** Thinkstock **164:** Thinkstock **164:** Thinkstock **164:** Thinkstock **164:** Thinkstock **165:** Thinkstock **165TL:** Thinkstock **165TR:** Thinkstock **165C:** Michael Schmeling/Alamy **165BL:** Thinkstock **165BR:** Shutterstock **166:** amc/Alamy **167:** Shutterstock **168:** Shutterstock **169T:** Shutterstock **169B:** Shutterstock **170:** Library of Congress **171:** Aurora Photos/Alamy

Lesson 12

172: British Antarctic Survey/ Science Source **174L:** MasPix/ Alamy **174C:** Stocktrek Images, Inc./Alamy **174R:** dieKleinert/ Alamy **175L:** Lynette Cook/ Science Source **175C:** Richard Bizley/Science Source **175R:** Stefan Schiessl/Science Source **176T:** Thinkstock **176B:** Shutterstock **177T:** imageBROKER/Alamy **177C:** Thinkstock **177B:** Thinkstock **179:** Everett Collection Historical/Alamy **181R:** Thinkstock **182T:** Thinkstock **183:** Shutterstock **184:** Shutterstock **185:** Shutterstock **186:** David Hay Jones/Science Source **187T:** Melanie Conner/ National Science Foundation/ Science Source **187B:** British Antarctic Survey/Science Source

Lesson 13

188: Environmental Stock Images by Streeter Photography/Alamy **190:** Ashley Cooper pics/Alamy **191T:** NASA Goddard Space Flight Center **191B:** E. Valentin/Altitude/ Science Source **192T:** Rick & Nora Bowers/Alamy **192B:** Thinkstock **193:** NPS Photo **194:** USGS **195T:** NASA **195B:** Accent Alaska.com/ Alamy **196:** NatPar Collection/ Alamy **197T:** Thinkstock **197BL:** Thinkstock **197BLC:** Thinkstock **197BC:** ThinkstockWILDLIFE GmbH/Alamy **197BC:** Jane Gould/ Alamy **197BRC:** Thinkstock **197BR:** H. Mark Weidman Photography/Alamy **198:** IPCC **199T:** Thinkstock **199TC:** Thinkstock **199BC:** Thinkstock **199B:** Thinkstock **200:** Thinkstock **202B:** Wikimedia **203:** Thinkstock

Back Matter

204: Reto Stöckli, Nazmi El Saleous, and Marit Jentoft-Nilsen, NASA GSFC **206:** Corbis Premium RF/Alamy **207:** iStockphoto **208:** Image Source Plus/Alamy **209:** Thinkstock **211:** Shutterstock **213:** Shutterstock **214:** Shutterstock **215T:** Karin Hildebrand Lau/Alamy **215B:** A.J.D. Foto Ltd./Alamy **217:** Thinkstock **221:** Shutterstock **223:** Shutterstock **225:** Thinkstock **227:** Shutterstock **229:** Shutterstock **230T:** Wikimedia **231T:** Thinkstock **231C:** Thinkstock **235T:** Thinkstock **235C:** Thinkstock **236B:** iStockphoto **237T:** Thinkstock **237C:** Getty Images **237B:** NASA **238:** Thinkstock **239:** Borislav Toskov/ Dreamstime **240:** Image Source Plus/Alamy **241:** Hero Images Inc./Alamy **244:** Blend Images/ Alamy **245:** iStockphoto **246:** Thinkstock **247:** NASA/JPL **249:** Thinkstock **252:** Wikimedia **257:** Ted Foxx/Alamy **258:** iStockphoto